Double
Play

Double Play

The San Francisco City Hall Killings

Mike Weiss

▲▲ **Addison-Wesley Publishing Company**
Reading, Massachusetts   Menlo Park, California
London   Amsterdam   Don Mills, Ontario   Sydney

Excerpt from "Easter, 1916" (page 6) reprinted with permission of Macmillan Publishing Company, Inc., from *Collected Poems of William Butler Yeats.* Copyright 1924 by Macmillan Publishing Company, Inc., renewed 1952 by Bertha Georgie Yeats. Reprinted with permission of Michael Yeats, Macmillan London, Ltd.

Excerpt from "Letting Their Clowns Out" by Ira Kamin (page 173) reprinted with permission from *California Living* magazine. Copyright © 1978 San Francisco Examiner.

Excerpt from "Dan White, a Lexical Profile" (page 276) reprinted with permission of David Frankel, from *A David Frankel Sampler.* Copyright 1979, 1981 by David Frankel.

Library of Congress Cataloging in Publication Data

Weiss, Mike.
  Double play.

  1. Murder—California—San Francisco—Case studies.
2. White, Dan. 3. Crime and criminals—California—San Francisco—Biography. 4. Victims of crimes—California—San Francisco—Case studies. 5. Moscone, George, d. 1978.
6. Milk, Harvey. I. Title.

HV6534.S3W44 1984   364.1'523'0979461   83–22391
ISBN 0–201–09595–5

Jacket design by Mike Fender. Jacket photograph by Frank Wing/Stock, Boston. Set in 11-point Times Roman by Datapage Division, Western Publishing Company.

ISBN 0–201–09595–5

ABCDEFGHIJ-DO-87654

First printing, January 1984

For C.L.: mermaid, magician, metaphysician

Prologue
Perverse Acts

If the soaring dome and steeple of San Francisco's splendid City Hall speak of aspirations—of civilization's highest hopes—then the barren exterior of its Hall of Justice a mile distant on the south, or wrong, side of Market street tells a dreary tale of disappointment and failure. Work on the Hall of Justice was begun in 1956 in the midst of the Cold War; its bulky, shoeboxlike exterior faced with gray granite suggests the earliest aboveground work of a bomb shelter architect. Inside the Hall, as it is usually called, is an atmosphere swollen by boredom and frustration, acrid with greed and fright. The Hall gives concrete expression to the crushing, exasperating system of rules and regulations we call justice.

The top two floors of the Hall, the ones with bars on the windows, house the city jail; beneath them is police headquarters; on the third and second floors are state and municipal courts, and finally, the lobby level, where a blind woman makes change at the newsstand. The cafeteria in the basement has no windows. It is lit by many bulbs yet remains dim and timeless On the morning of November 27, 1978—a Monday— Police Inspector Frank Joseph Falzon was sitting by himself at a faded formica cafeteria table nursing a cup of black coffee and reading the *Chronicle.*

In everything he did it was Falzon's habit to leave the best for last. When he ate a meal he pushed the morsels he most cherished to the side of his plate until everything else was gone, and when it came to the *Chronicle* he saved the "Sporting Green" section to read last. A member of the elite homicide division and the most recent recipient of the Policeman of the Year award, Falzon had made himself wealthy by restoring and selling old homes. He liked to think of himself as a ballplayer, a star whose teams fought their way to championships. "I come from the lowest neighborhood but I've made myself a lucrative man," Falzon would say when asked about himself. "I'm in the forefront and I'll pat myself on the back if I'm doing a good job. I'm a Reggie Jackson—you either hate him or you love him, but even those who hate him love him, there's a lovable quality. Hey, he's Mr. October. And that's the way I like to think of myself."

At about eight o'clock Falzon pushed back his cafeteria chair and walked to the elevators to return to his desk on the fourth floor. He was thick-bodied and moved with a heavy determination. Clipped to his belt was a seven-sided star; at his right hip was a black leather holster from which protruded the butt of his police issue .357 Magnum. Falzon was handsome—people often told him he resembled the movie actor James Caan—with watery blue eyes and light-brown woolpad hair sprinkled with gray. The springiness of his hair made his leonine head appear even bigger than it actually was.

Falzon spent the next several hours at his desk, working the telephone, typing up reports, making lists. He began each case by making a list of clues to be followed up, tasks to be done, and questions to be answered, and as his investigation progressed he updated and revised the lists. This orderliness, he acknowledged to himself, was his way of keeping his distance from the sometimes tragic and often bestial acts it was his job to investigate until their perpetrators were brought to justice, or until some smart lawyer got them off. When he had caught up with his desk work he went downstairs to consult with an assistant D.A. named Jim Lassart about a pending case involving the murder of a radical ex-convict. At a moment or two after eleven o'clock the phone rang.

"Yeah, he's here," the D.A. said. "Frank, it's for you." He handed him the phone.

It was Falzon's commanding officer. "Frank," he said, "you better get up here right away. The mayor's been shot."

"Listen," Falzon replied, mildly irked, "this joke's been played on me before." A few years back his buddies from Homicide had wakened him with the news that a dinner guest of the mayor's had been stabbed to death. Falzon had stumbled out of bed and put on his clothes before they had called back to razz him.

"I'm not kidding," the lieutenant said. "Get up here."

Five frantic minutes later Falzon and his partner, Herman Clark, were running to their unmarked car and screeching out of the underground garage with their siren wailing. What information they had was fragmentary: at 10:56 the mayor's bodyguard had called an urgent request for assistance, and several moments later an officer who had arrived at City Hall had gasped into his walkie-talkie, "We've got a homicide here." At 11:02 a call for help had also been received from the City Hall offices of the Board of Supervisors. Every available police unit was scrambling toward City Hall.

On the radio a police dispatcher was asking with a tinny urgency: "Does any unit have any description at this time? Are we looking for anybody? Can anyone give us a 1013? Are we looking for anyone?" Clark, who was at the wheel and whose face was normally the color of café au lait, looked positively white. As Clark wheeled to the left to pass a slow-moving truck the truck driver inexplicably veered directly into their path and there was a jolt followed by the crunching, squealing sound of metal crushing metal. Other police units sped past the pileup with their sirens screaming. A moment later Falzon and Clark hurtled forward again. Falzon had already decided this would probably be the murder of the century in San Francisco when they crippled up to City Hall with their car belching black smoke from under its badly dented hood.

The detectives hurried up the broad stairs to the second floor where the cool, wide marble corridor was jammed with gawking civil servants. A few women were weeping. A police guard was barring the way into the mayor's suite of offices but Falzon and Clark were waved through the double oak doors into a reception room. From there they went back along a narrow, carpeted hallway into the airy, light-filled formal office of Mayor George Moscone, whose suit jacket was neatly hung on a clothes stand beside his desk. Behind that grand office was a smaller sitting room. There, sprawled face down in a puddle of his own blood, and guarded by a couple of frightened young cops with their guns drawn, was the body of the mayor. When he was shot, George Moscone had pitched full length between an easy chair and a couch where he lay now, his silver hair stained a deep purple by the thick, sticky clotted blood from a head wound. Falzon had seen an awful lot of dead people and had of necessity become inured to it, but seeing the mayor dead—assassinated—was something else again. The shocks, however, were just beginning.

"Harvey Milk's been shot too," one of the young cops blurted. Milk was a supervisor—a councilman, he would have been called in most cities. He was, in addition, a homosexual, the first avowed homosexual to be elected to public office in America.

"Suspect?" Falzon asked.

"Dan White, sir," said the cop. "Supervisor Dan White was the last person in here."

Dan White. Like stop-frame photographs, bits and pieces of memory came to Falzon: Dan sliding headfirst into home plate to win a big game for their championship team; Dan, his parted hair slicked down and his round Irish face serious and ardent, telling Falzon he was running for supervisor; Dan, his eyes blinking furiously on the evening newscast as he explained how the mayor had promised to return him to the supervisor's seat he had abruptly resigned, and now wanted back.

The detective backed away from George Moscone's body and went to the reception room where a police command post had been hastily set up. He approached the captain in charge.

"If Dan White is picked up," he said, "I want to be notified immediately."

As the on-call homicide team, it was the responsibility of Falzon and Clark to take charge of the investigation. But more than duty compelled Falzon to make that request of the captain. Dan White was his friend, and more; Falzon thought Dan was a man among men. During certain crises in White's life he had turned to Falzon for advice and approval, as one would to an older brother. Instinctively Falzon understood that if White would explain to anybody what had happened, it would be to him. Of course, that very intimacy also argued for Falzon to remove himself at once from principal responsibility for the case. But how could he do that? His professional pride and something deeper than that—a consuming need to know how a man like Dan White could commit such a perverse act—insisted that he not relinquish his duty.

As he stood there deep in thought a police radio crackled. "Attention all units." It was a man's voice. Earlier the dispatcher had been a woman; Falzon hadn't known it was Dan White's sister Patty. "Attention all units. Suspect on the 187 at City Hall, suspect named Dan White. White male adult. Thirty-two years. Six feet. One hundred eighty-five pounds. Wearing a three-piece brown suit. Considered armed and dangerous."

Falzon returned to the mayor's body and followed all the rote steps of examining the crime scene, taking care not to touch or move any object until the crime lab boys and the coroner had had time to complete their work. But his mind was overwhelmed by a question—why?

At 11:37 word arrived that White was in custody at Northern Police Station several blocks from City Hall.

Sitting on a bench in the assembly room at Northern Station, Dan White seemed detached but his eyes were bloodshot and large as watermelons and he looked old, very old. He had crossed an abyss. Nobody said much; White's savage revenge seemed something deeper and more resonant than mere criminality. This feeling was all the more acute because he was an old comrade; many of the cops in Northern had worked with him or played ball on the same teams. Bob Moore, the sergeant who booked him, had lived only three doors away from White's childhood home. And then, too, any misstatement could jeopardize this case, which was bound to come under microscopic scrutiny. So the station was quiet but you could feel the high-wrought tension.

Officer Paul Chignell searched White's pockets, finding some live and expended cartridges, and then put him on the bench to wait for the homicide inspectors who had been called when White turned himself in less than an hour after the killings. They waited in a room where White had sat often before when he had been a policeman assigned to Northern Station and then, later, when he had come by to visit. The room smelled of stale sweat and fright and disinfectant. Some of the policemen who spent a good part of their lives in that room and others like it turned inward and cynical after seeing so much pain and despair and corruption. You can tell which cops are like that because they use a certain phrase for the human garbage they are supposed to keep sweeping off the streets: "He needs killing," they say.

Again and again over the years White had listened to cops talking about how they had saved George Moscone from the consequences of his indiscretions, he had seen the drawing on station house bulletin boards of Moscone's man Police Chief Charles Gain in the crosshairs of a rifle, he had participated in endless grumbling about gays taking over the city, though not in language as polite as that. The talk in the station houses was the blunt, tough talk of the streets the cops were paid to keep safe and knew they couldn't. He had shared the bitter sentiments aroused by the feeling among old San Franciscans that they were a people colonized in their native land. Now cops drifted in to look at

White and nod in his direction, and some even came closer and touched him lightly on the arm or the shoulder. Their loose words had not seemed dangerous, but dangerous ideas sometimes find fatal expression and so now the cops held Dan White in a certain awe.

He had stepped over an invisible line, he had transgressed, and yet his transgression had accomplished something that many of them had said or thought they wanted, almost as if he had acted for the collective will. It was an awesome conundrum for these keepers of the law: as they looked at him or touched him it was as if he were their gravest considerations suddenly incarnate.

Once, looking up at Officer Chignell, who was vice president of the Police Officers Association, and whom he trusted, White said: "Is he dead, Paul?"

"They're both dead," Chignell said. He asked White if he wanted to make a statement.

"No." He shook his head. "Ah, make sure they keep that Irish poster that was in my coat." He meant the book jacket he had ripped off and taken with him along with his gun when he had gone down to City Hall. The title of the book—*Ireland: A Terrible Beauty*—had come from Yeats's poem "Easter, 1916," written about the Irish patriots' doomed uprising against the English troops occupying their homeland:

> He, too, has resigned his part
> In the casual comedy;
> He, too, has been changed in his turn,
> Transformed utterly:
> A terrible beauty is born.

The poem celebrated the redemption to be found in a single act of heroic martyrdom. It was the closest the prisoner came to offering an explanation.

Chignell said he would do what he could.

Leaving Clark to oversee the crime scene and question witnesses, Falzon drove to Northern Police Station, his car still spewing oily smoke. At the door of the station house he saw Thomas Norman hurrying out. Norman was the chief homicide prosecutor in the district attorney's office, the man who would probably prosecute Dan White.

"He's been removed to the Hall," Norman said, getting in beside

Falzon. "They've transported him to Homicide." The lawyer didn't use simple words like "taken."

The streets in the vicinity of City Hall were clogged with police cars, their red lights flashing and their radios rasping. Sawhorses obstructed the entrances to the building, but outside the police barricades, in the street and the spacious plaza where white geysers burbled above the reflecting pool, a crowd was gathering as mutely and certainly as grief is drawn to death. Policemen ran to and fro with the diligence of blueclad ants. Falzon pushed the accelerator. Neither he nor Norman spoke. Both men knew their jobs. There was nothing to say. As he drove, more images flickered through Falzon's mind: shoveling the ball to Dan as he cut across from shortstop, pivoted, and threw out a runner at first base to complete a double play; Dan, bitterly describing the deceitfulness of the other supervisors; a lazy afternoon in the playground where they had both hung out as boys, Falzon sprawled on the warm, worn grass with a hardroll sandwich in his hand. And always that same question—why? Fanning the deck of his memories for a clue.

Something else was on Falzon's mind too as he raced through and around traffic, something new. As a cop, even a former cop, Dan had been a brother. "Once a policeman," cops would say, "always a brother." For them there was an invisible line; on one side of it stood policemen, and on the other transgressors and potential transgressors. Two different worlds separated by a single set of rules. If you stepped over that invisible line then you chose a different world. White had crossed the line. Falzon's car, siren wailing, sped through a red light. However reluctantly, Falzon must pursue his friend, must know why.

On the fourth floor of the Hall of Justice Falzon and Norman turned a corner, opened a door with a frosted glass window on which was stenciled HOMICIDE, and encountered chaos. The little reception room was packed with reporters, television crews and their equipment, cops, the curious, assistant D.A.s, and the chief public defender who was demanding entry, shouting over the din that he had standing as Dan White's lawyer. Norman immediately decided to stay there and tie up the public defender in colloquy, while the inner door was opened by the uniformed policeman so Falzon could slip through. Inside was a startling quiet. Homicide was a bullpen-like room divided by pillars. There was a haphazard array of desks, metal file cabinets, and piles of lopsided packing cartons jammed with casework. On most of the desks were framed photographs of wives and children. A few detectives were in their chairs, jackets off and guns on. Inspector Eddie Erdelatz, a born-again Bible thumper with an altar boy's mien, was munching on a sandwich. Beyond the windows, noontime traffic moved sluggishly along the freeway.

"Where is he?" Falzon asked. Erdelatz, chewing, nodded toward a tiny interrogation room at the back of the bullpen. Falzon started toward the closed door.

Even at the best of times when he was smiling and happy there was worry in Falzon's watery eyes and in the cast of his face. This was hardly the best of times and Falzon looked as if he and he alone had been assigned to hold up the sky. Falzon had been born on Washington's birthday and his late father had always told him it meant he had to be especially honest. In those few seconds as he prepared to open the door to the interrogation room he felt himself to be most sorely tried; never before had his sense of duty and his personal loyalty been in such riotous conflict, never before had he stood so ambiguously astride that invisible line. He turned the knob and pushed the door open.

White's head was bent over the table, cradled in his arms. He looked up, his face gray and blotchy. The bone structure was visible to Falzon beneath the tightly drawn skin, like a death mask. White's eyes met his and misted over.

"Why?" Falzon erupted without thinking. "I feel like hittin' you in the fuckin' mouth. How could you be so stupid? How?"

Tears rolled down Dan White's pallid cheeks. "I, I want to tell you about it," he gasped. "I want to, to explain."

For the next twenty-five minutes White would answer questions with a spasmodic desperation while a tape recorder rolled, admitting that he had killed Mayor Moscone and Supervisor Milk, attempting tearfully to explain himself. White accounted for the proximate causes: how Moscone had promised to reinstate him and then reneged, how he had discovered that Milk was furtively working to deprive him of what he thought was by rights his. He accounted for all the proximate causes. But to understand what had happened required more than that, required knowing about three very different men and the city they all called their own. San Francisco, where Dan White had grown up a son of the forgotten Irish workingman; where another native son, George Moscone, had for forty-nine years cut a dashing figure; where an outsider named Harvey Milk had cast himself as the vehicle through which a hundred thousand homosexual emigres expressed their hopes and fears.

In the end Dan White's confession did not, *could* not, satisfy Falzon's question: Why?

Book One
THE ACT

I have not slept.
Between the acting of a dreadful
    thing
And the first motion, all the
    interim is
Like a phantasma, or a hideous dream.
The genius and the mortal instruments
Are then in council, and the
    state of a man,
Like to a little kingdom, suffers then
The nature of an insurrection.

> Brutus in *Julius Caesar* (II, i)

The miners came in '49
The whores in '51
Shortly they begat
Frisco's native son

> San Francisco ditty

1
Native Son

The San Francisco in which George Moscone came of age was a town emptied of its men by the war. There were, of course, the soldiers and sailors swarming through the self-contained and stable little city that in no time flat had become a port of embarkation for the Pacific theater, but though they whooped over the hills in their jeeps, whistling at the California girls, making the black marketeers rich, and keeping the practitioners of the world's weariest trade on the streets day and night, the boys in uniform were merely passing through.

George was a San Francisco guy, George and his best pal Cappy Lavin, riding the streetcars from one end of town to the other in search of the ultimate schoolyard basketball game. Anywhere they went they were at home; neighborhoods spilled one into the next, from Cow Hollow to Crocker Amazon the town was a compendium of villages. In this provincial cosmopolis everybody knew everybody else and where to find them.

The city had a unity and a sense of human scale set against the expansive vista of the Bay and the ocean and the great suspension bridges, still new enough to be novel. For Cappy life at that time had a bittersweet feeling, a fabulous glow doomed to fade as the city and its boys encountered the business of the world. But that was only a dimly sensed apprehension as Cappy and George bounced through the city on their rubber soles, two thin, handsome rascals with all the moves. George's hair was always cut short, he thought that made him look like Cary Grant. Ever since "Faultless Physique" McCoppin had been elected mayor in 1867 the Irish had controlled City Hall, the professions, the police and fire departments, and had condescended to the Italians, who were by and large merchants. So George always told his Italian barber to keep it short, that way he would look less Italian. Thirty years later Mayor George Moscone would present the key to *his* city to the same barber and when the button-down ids at the newspapers and his anal-retentive political enemies disapproved, George would smile his public smile, all teeth and smarmy sincerity, and say: "A man's got to take care of his barber."

Everywhere George and Cappy roamed they came to another hill and at its crest caught a glimpse between tall buildings of an open panorama of the fresh, salty water; blue under the midday sun, green in the dim light of dawn, a burnished copper at twilight, gray as the battleships under the winter fog. Cappy was so acutely self-conscious, almost visionary. It was he who would say of the water, "It's so close you could wrap it up, wrap it in your handkerchief and put it in your pocket."

"Wet your fuckin' pants, Cap," George would answer. But he got it, they both knew that; the attractive, compelling pony, the natural performer, George Moscone didn't miss much. At fifteen they had a freedom bestowed on them by time and place and circumstance. They were rogue princes of their city.

Who could say just where this feeling came from? Probably it had something to do with their both being the only sons of mothers alone, both of them bathed in womanly affection, both with few restraints at home or in the safe, familiar streets of San Francisco. George had been born during Thanksgiving week in 1929, the first and only child of Lena Marguerite Monge, whom everybody called Lee, and her husband, George Joseph Moscone, a milk wagon driver who was so devilishly good-looking it was said he was a dead ringer for Errol Flynn. The elder George Moscone's teenage bride was the daughter of a San Joaquin Valley winemaker; she was warm and pretty and full of life. By the time little George was eight his parents' marriage had reached the drowning point: his father delivered the milk but preferred the grape. Lee had swallowed too many bad-tempered hangovers and empty pay envelopes; she divorced her husband and after that it was just George and Lee, moving from apartment to apartment while she tried to find a job during the Great Depression.

Once, after the divorce, when George's father had a job as a guard at San Quentin, he took his son to see the electric chair at the fortress-like prison. His father described an execution, described it in such gory detail that for all the rest of his life George Moscone always opposed the taking of a life by the state. That first, humanitarian impulse was his father's legacy. The elder George Moscone eventually died in a state hospital where he had been committed for treatment. And he also passed on what surely was an unintended legacy: his son would become a man who had been raised and shaped by his pretty, flirtatious, kindly mother. Young George was fiercely jealous of Lee's attention, he even threatened to move out and never see her again when she was thinking of remarrying. All his life George Moscone would be a man who appreciated women.

The moves came on basketball courts and in the back seats of borrowed automobiles and in the thoughtful, fast-paced give and take with Cappy. It was in George Moscone's nature to get away with things that nobody else could. School was duck soup for him. No less than the pals he made so easily and the girls who adored him, teachers were drawn by his theatrical emotions—big gestures and balloon feelings and hands that were always in motion, always touching. He was vain and some of the money he picked up working at odd jobs always went for clothes. George was the first guy in his crowd to have the new shirts with the collar pins, which were coming back into vogue, and buck shoes. His head was cocked on a long swan neck, there was a magnetism in his scamp eyes.

By the time he entered college from Jesuit-run St. Ignatius High School on a basketball scholarship, the war was over and San Francisco was waking up to its own transformation, which was as profound if not as dramatic as the aftermath of the 1906 earthquake and fire. Nearly two hundred thousand new residents of a rainbow of hues and polyglot dialects had doubled the population, making vast demands upon the goodwill of the city and its housing, transportation, sanitation, and schools. But the war had been won and it seemed a time of hope, and of faith. At dawn on Easter 1949, fifty thousand people went up Mount Davidson to worship at the stone cross which was the highest point in the city of St. Francis.

At Hastings College of the Law, George found a vocation, if not a calling. His study of the law taught him that he had the persuasive power to talk anybody into or out of just about anything. He was hanging out with a crowd of young lawyers, politicians and cops in the cafes of North Beach, a neighborhood of sunny hilltops chockablock with delicatessens, bakeries, bars and clubs, a neighborhood where papas strolled out after dinner to smoke a cigar and drink espresso and argue the issues of the day with their paisans. George's North Beach crowd of young blades included Johnny Burton—"Shakey," they called him—who was tending bar at Bimbo's. And Willie Brown, a law school sidekick. Willie was a black guy out of Texas who, poor as he was, dressed sharper and talked faster than any man had a right to. They all knew they were better and smarter than the ordinary run and they planned to make it big in the world.

Way back in grade school, or so George told the story, he had seen Gina Bondanza in pigtails and a green gingham dress and he had been out to capture her ever since. The ambitious law student had a summer job as a playground director and he strutted around his bailiwick with a proud grin, his slim, dark, round-eyed girl on his arm.

The day of the wedding at St. Vincent's, George and Cappy were side by side at two urinals, wearing tails, and Gina was already in the church in her white gown, when Cappy decided that he had an obligation.

He turned to his friend. "You can still not do it," he said.

Gina never appreciated the gesture of male solidarity, no matter how many times George told the story over the years.

"But don'tcha see, Gina, for chrissake," George would say, tilting back in a kitchen chair, holding his cigarette like Cary Grant but trying to sound like Marlon Brando. "Don'tcha see? Just walk away, that's what a best man *should* do."

By the time George had passed the bar exam and gone to work in a small law firm where he was being paid $300 a month, Jennifer had been born. When he called people to give them the news he said, "Gina and I just became a real family."

After work George would head for North Beach as often as he did for home. The crowd gathered in the evenings at Bimbo's, or Mike's Pool Hall, or Enrico's, a sidewalk cafe that served as North Beach's neutral turf, the place where the hard cases and club owners and lawyers and cops and swells and poets all gathered on the outdoor patio to consider whatever needed consideration. Margo St. James fell in quite naturally with the gang at Enrico's.

Margo was the daughter of a Washington dairy farmer who had read a newspaper article about the best generation and with as little delay as possible boarded a train for San Francisco. She was freshfaced and frisky and before long her pad around the corner on Grant Avenue was known as St. James Infirmary, where bruised or hungry spirits could repair. A lot of guys passed through. One night in 1959 Margo was at home listening to "La Boheme," trying to improve her mind, and keeping company with another girl whose story was that she was on the lam from a drugstore holdup in Seattle when some scrawny little guy showed up at their door. He and the other girl had just bedded down when he produced a badge and signalled his compatriots, who were waiting nearby at Louis Friscia's Fresha Fish. Led by a vice cop named Joe Ryan, the constabulary thundered up the stairs to be confronted by a farmer's daughter who was loudly protesting that she gave it away for free. Margo's conviction was, after a time, thrown out on appeal, but her skirmish with the law decided her on becoming an attorney herself. She enrolled in law school but ran out of money and began to turn tricks after all. Eventually she gained an international reputation as the founder of a loose woman's organization, COYOTE. Eventually, too, George's association with Margo St. James and what she represented became part of what was held against him by guys like Joe Ryan, who seventeen years later would work in the campaign of a young man promising to return decency to the city of San Francisco, a young man named Dan White.

All across the land in 1961 and 1962 handsome young lawyers and businessmen were following Jack Kennedy by throwing back their heads, jabbing their fingers at cheering crowds, and exhorting them to find a better way. It was the Burton brothers, John and Phil, who steered George into politics. John was grateful to George, who had successfully represented him on a charge of bookmaking. John's older brother Phil was a state assemblyman. An imposing figure with a sagging face, quizzical bushy Irish eyebrows, and open shirt collars, Phil Burton breathed brimstone and fire; crossing him was said to be a very big mistake. His kid brother called Phil "God" when he wasn't in earshot. Phil Burton was beginning to build a liberal political organization that he said would someday take the city away from the entrenched Irish machine, and he was looking for somebody to run as a sacrificial lamb for an Assembly seat against a Republican who was conceded to be a shoo-in. When Phil asked John if any of his lawyer buddies wanted to work for a couple of months with no pay in order to get his ass kicked but in the process make some friends, John Burton suggested George Moscone.

That led to a meeting between George and John at a Mexican restaurant.

"Yeah," George said, "I'd be interested. But what's involved? I mean, what would I have to do?"

"Christ, how would I know?" said John, who someday would be a congressman himself. "I'll ask God and get back to you."

That first campaign in 1960 was a catch-as-catch can affair. What George knew about politics wouldn't have filled a ravioli. So he did what came naturally, went out into the city to meet as many people as he could. When he turned those Italian eyes on a potential voter he had a quality of attentiveness that was at once a source of his power and a servant of his ambition. Women sensed his coltish sensuality, were fascinated by the little downward puckers at the corners of his mouth, and decided that he would make a fine assemblyman. Men shook the hand of a guy who was everybody's pal, a manly man always quick to laugh at a joke or remember a good time, and thought that it wouldn't hurt to have somebody regular representing the city up there in Sacramento.

He was a pure actor, not that he conned a role so much as he followed his instincts. In the springtime of Camelot, George had the right church, the right spirit, and even the right teeth, prominent when he smiled like the President's, with narrow gaps between them. He was animated by the game of politics. But nobody expected him to win. George lost that first campaign, but he ran stronger in the district than had any Democrat in memory. As his party's Assembly candidate he got a seat on the city central committee and that made him a player.

In 1963 he ran again, this time for a seat on the Board of Supervisors. And he won. By then Gina Moscone had begun to wish that politics wasn't her husband's passion. She was proud of his victory but she was a private soul, content to be a wife, a mother—their second daughter, Rebecca, had been born—and a homemaker. In private Gina was witty, in public tongue-tied. The more embroiled George became in politics, the less time he had for her and the kids. Not that he didn't dote on Gina and the kids—before long Chris and John had been added to the family—it was just that he seemed to need the adrenaline hit of running and winning, of being recognized on the streets and of knowing that San Francisco really was *his* town. In his heart George was a good husband and father. But he didn't have the time and patience for it, and he knew he could rely on Gina while he scamped around town glowing in the favorable light cast by the adoration of strangers.

* * *

By day Fillmore Street was like any other bustling avenue, moving to the pace of commerce. By six every evening, though, it was as if the shift had changed. The retailers and the pawnbrokers and the second-hand clothes merchants rolled up their awnings and locked their doors and went home. Fillmore Street pulsated in the night.

Down at the corner of Ellis Street a kid named Flip Wilson was snapping his rags over gleaming, pointy-toed shoes in tones of high yellow and crimson you didn't find on bankers' feet, setting a rhythm for the street and cracking jokes that would someday put his name in lights. On the air the delectable smells of fried chicken and barbecue drifted into nostrils along with the sweetness of sweet potato pie, apple and peach cobbler and the odor of marijuana. There was music swinging out of the open doors of the Plantation Club and after hours the legends of the jazz world, through with their downtown gigs, jammed at Jack's on Sutter Street. Happy faces nodded in passing and stopped to talk, the tap tap tap of shoe leather seemed a kind of dance. If you knew the town and wanted a good time you just directed your feet to either side of Fillmore Street. Girls whose work it was to make you feel good stood in doorways with poses that were implicit promises.

It was a good place to be and a good place to walk and every night Rotea Guilford and Wendell Tyree walked Fillmore Street all the way from Broadway to Haight, such a long beat that there were nights when the two young black cops from Northern Station never completed it. Things came up to divert them.

On this particular night they saw a whore and her trick heading into the New Yorker Hotel, and because it was their job to enforce the laws against pleasure for hire, no matter how they felt about it themselves, they followed, waiting outside the room until the sounds from the bed told them it was time. They forced their way into the room and declared that both the whore and her trick were under arrest. It was their own policy, not the police department's, to arrest johns.

The woman took it in her stride. It was a bitch, but her pimp would have her back on the street by morning. The trick, a white man, was mortified, but Guilford and Tyree were accustomed to that, too. This one didn't bluster and threaten, though, and he didn't offer a bribe. Instead he got back into his clothes and said, "Look, man, I guess I better tell you. I'm George Moscone."

Once he said it both cops recognized him. And more than that. Guilford, like George, was a comer. A former pro football player, along with Willie Brown and a couple of other bright young black guys, he had been tapped by the black powerbrokers for big things. Guilford had been steered into police work because he had the mental stability and toughness to take all the hatred that would come his way, while giving the black leaders a man of their own inside the citadel from which so much power was exercised. The two cops knew *exactly* who George Moscone was—he was a white man who had gone to Mississippi to help register black voters, he was the liberal hope—and they knew as well what it would mean if they went ahead and busted him.

George stood there waiting for their reaction. "Jeez, man," he said.

"Let's cut him loose," Guilford said to his partner.

Tyree said, "No."

George's heart fluttered.

"No?" Guilford said, still talking to Tyree. "C'mon, man, let's cut 'em both loose. Let's forget it."

The woman had stopped freshening her makeup and was in front of the mirror over the wash basin, poised like the rest of them, her lipstick in her hand.

"Shit," Tyree said. "Okay."

It didn't take George more than three snaps of Flip Wilson's shoeshine rag to get himself out of the New Yorker Hotel and far away from there. But before he left he stopped to look at Guilford. Tyree had his eyes firmly fixed on nothing. "I won't forget this, man," said the city supervisor with the big future, and he was gone.

Just a few days later Guilford ran into Willie Brown, who was also practicing law and starting to make his own political moves. "I hear you made a friend for life," Willie said.

Guilford said, "It was nothing any cop wouldn't do for his brother." They laughed.

"But no, seriously, Gil, the man is grateful to you."

Not everybody would be. By doing his job, and then by doing what he felt he ought, Guilford had put himself at the eye of a storm that would blow hot and cold until the day George Moscone died. Over the years other cops would do as much for George; it was a secret that would become a kind of quasi-public knowledge in every quarter of town, stirring bitter passions the better known George became and the more power he accumulated.

In the early sixties the Board of Supervisors was facing several decisions necessitated by the boom economy downtown. Often enough Supervisor Moscone defined himself as he went along, weighing exigencies and calculating advantages, but where the little guy was in conflict with power and profits George usually didn't hesitate to take sides. The Yerba Buena project was like that.

The city redevelopment agency was proposing a clean sweep of several square blocks south of Market Street in order to build an exhibition hall, a convention facility and perhaps a sports arena. The plan was heavily backed by the big hotels and the satellite businesses that made their money off the hotel guests, by the tourist industry which was becoming the city's greatest source of jobs and revenue. They were pushing for a Yerba Buena Center because it would enable them to service an even greater volume of tourists and traveling businessmen. Undoubtedly it was pure happenstance that the land they zeroed in on would enhance the holdings of Pacific Telephone, Standard Oil, the biggest department store in town, United California Bank, and both major newspapers, which owned most of the property around the planned development. Coincidentally, as well, the newspapers touted the project. The issue, said the editorials, the single overriding issue, was that Yerba Buena represented progress; it was blight removal, it was good for the city.

All that stood in the way of the bulldozers were the four thousand or so people who lived there. The newspapers, with all the objectivity that money can buy, referred to the place as "skid row." But Jack London, who had been born there (by this time his birthplace was commemorated by a plaque outside a branch of a Wells Fargo bank), called the neighborhood "South of the Slot," a reference to the trolley car slots along Market Street, the city's bisecting boulevard. "Old San Francisco," London wrote, "was divided by the Slot. . . . North of the Slot were the theaters and hotels, the shopping district, the banks and the staid, respectable business houses. South of the Slot were the factories, slums, laundries, machine shops, boiler works and the abodes of the working class." Who remained South of Market in 1965 were mostly elderly men, retired seamen, miners or lumberjacks, men who had built railroads or cleared forests or hauled silver and gold or gone to sea. And those who had never worked, the hoboes; or men who did seasonal work in the orchards, or took whatever work was available. They were poor and for the most part aged. Their day was past and what most of them really were doing south of Market was waiting to die. Pensions, if they were lucky, or social security, paid their bills. If they were broke, the missions fed them. For entertainment there were the orators who would get up on soapboxes to harangue them.

Their neighborhood was a bleak place, warehouses and industrial businesses flanked by pawnshops and saloons and cafes with blueplate specials. It was nothing much to look at but it was cheap and decent. The streets were flat and the weather sunnier than on the west side of town. People who had been south of Market for a while knew each other, so that it was altogether a less lonely home than some newer, finer neighborhoods. Graybeards and sagging stockings filled their days with talk as circumscribed as their lives had become. They were expendable. They had no value in the profit-and-loss ledgers, they figured only as eyesores: you wouldn't want the tourists to see them.

These people whose homes were threatened pleaded their case before the Board of Supervisors, but the redevelopment planners had the facts and figures to refute any challenges. Their master plan even included what they called a "relocation component" for the displaced. Maybe they'd even rehabilitate a couple of the old residential hotels, they said. When the Yerba Buena Center came to a vote it was passed 9–2. George Moscone cast one of the two votes against it.

The Freeway Revolt was another such issue, and his identifying himself with it was what probably propelled George to a smashing victory in the election for a state senate seat in 1966. His opponent in the Democratic primary was the protégé of Senator Eugene McAteer, the Irish boss, and the contest took on the symbolic aura of a showdown over the future of the city.

George figured to run well in the poorer and polychromatic neighborhoods to the east of Twin Peaks. But more of the city's voting population lived in the miles of near-identical single family homes erected on landfill piled on top of sand dunes that stretched west to the ocean on both sides of Golden Gate Park. The Avenues these neighborhoods were called, and they were home to San Francisco's comfortable masses.

The highway lobby and the downtown business establishment wanted to lay a roadway that would link the consumers in the Avenues with the central business district. They proposed two alternative routes, one of which bent around the waterfront and never had much of a chance. The second proposed route would have run right up the east-west spine of the city, laying waste large chunks of black-occupied housing and biting off an edge of Golden Gate Park. This plan united poor blacks, neighborhood associations of white homeowners and lovers of the park. The freeway planners had forced an alliance among people who otherwise would have had little common ground, and George championed their cause. It was this nascent coalition which a few years later would become the core of the partisans for district elections, and district elections would bring Dan White and Harvey Milk to City Hall. When George won the election by ten thousand votes, a landslide, it was the first distant bugle call of the bitter political battles of the 1970s, the first substantial indication that a new majority was forming to replace the Irish machine that had run City Hall for a century.

The senator-elect from San Francisco stood on a platform in a hotel ballroom, his eyes damp and his voice nearly shot, hoarsely acknowledging the huzzahs of his delirious supporters, who were of every race, every nationality, every age and income bracket. He had one arm around Gina, who seemed so small next to him and so ill at ease, and with his other arm he was shepherding his kids in closer. On his mug was a big, toothy, exhausted grin. His tie was pulled loose of his open collar and there was a drink in his hand. George Moscone, the only child of an alcoholic milk wagon driver, a gregarious man with some secrets to keep, had arisen from the city's past to speak for its future.

2
I Left My Bucks
in San Francisco

If you observe San Francisco from as far north as the Stinson headlands in Marin County or from as far south as the coastal beaches at Devil's Slide, from the Oakland hills east of the Bay or the Farallones Islands west of the Golden Gate, from every point on the compass what you see on a hill high above the skyline is Sutro Telecommunications Tower. It stands above everything else and yet it is one of those structures you look at but somehow don't register. The white and international orange steel tower is little remarked upon and less considered. But it stands for all that changed in the city. The changes were economic, demographic, political; they had altered the look of the city and the feel of daily life. They had, as well, created a reaction, a liberal political force led by George Moscone that was competing to revise San Francisco's future. They were about to put Harvey Milk into a position of power.

One thousand feet of open girders and taut guy wires, the tower looks like a space age buccaneer ship, or in a gloomier view, an electronic praying mantis sucking up our stillborn dreams and beaming them back to us as soap salesmen with perfect teeth. Its ceaseless, silent chatter is part television transmissions, part ambulance band, part taxi, fire and police calls. The only audible noise is an eerie sound like a cosmic harp when the breezes whipping off the Pacific strum its wires; but its silence is clotted with the business and misery of the city beneath it.

Once it had been plugged in on July 4, 1973, nobody paid much attention any more to the tower where it rose from near the middle of town. On the nights when the moisture carried by the west winds breezed across the cold coastal waters and condensed into dense, cool fog, the slender tailor's dummy shape of the tower was enveloped in gray bunting until at last all that appeared was an occasional flicker of one of its beady red lights warning off low-flying planes.

Sutro Tower it was called, after old Adolph Heinrich Joseph Sutro, whose five-mile shaft driven into the Comstock Lode had mined enough silver ore to make him just about the wealthiest man in San Francisco, where he settled after selling his interest for five million 1859 dollars. Sutro bought up vast land holdings left intact from the days of the Spanish *ranchos,* including the twin peaks where the communications tower would someday be built. He called the hilltop Mount Parnassus but everybody else called it Mount Sutro; it was wealth, not knowledge, that the forty-niners hankered for.

Until the tower was put together like the grandest erector set west of Paris, the highest structure in the city had been the stone slab cross on Mount Davidson, where the faithful gathered on Easter Sundays. But in 1973 the cross was eclipsed by the new tower which pierced the heavens eighteen hundred feet above sea level, just as the Catholic Church and its adherents in the newspapers, the Port, the parish houses, the police and fire stations were also being inundated by a new breed of San Franciscan tumbling west as if the country were a vast funnel and California the final vessel.

Knowledge workers, that was what the President of Pacific Telephone called these new Californians. They came for the beauty and the climate but most importantly, like the forty-niners and the refugees from the dustbowl before them, they came west for the promise of jobs. The tower was the symbol of their triumph.

They found jobs, but not of the kind that had existed back when San Francisco had been a workingman's town and the Port was the anchor of its economy. The Bethlehem Steel yards and Marin shipyards were no longer turning out the fighting ships the navy had needed during the war. By the mid-seventies the Port and all the industries built up around it were in decline. Its piers, once bloated with coffee, newsprint, autos, heavy machinery, grains, steel and spices, were shabby and lean. Poor planning and bad guesses about the extent of the cargo container ship revolution had decimated many of the shipping concerns, and more than a few of the shipbuilding yards had fallen into disuse after the war. New ideas about the development of the waterfront were gaining the ascendancy. Move 'em in and move 'em out was still the order of business, but what was being moved now were tourists from Tokyo and Minneapolis, from Sydney and Hamburg.

By the late 1950s national prosperity and cheap air travel had presented a new opportunity to the city. Hundreds of thousands of GIs returning from the war in the Pacific had passed through and been smitten by the lovely town perched on a clutch of seaside hills. More than a few of them wanted to bring the wife and kids or the company convention to this little gem of the American West with its romantic history of shanghaied sailors and Barbary Coast bordellos, its Gold Rush and its earthquake, its quaint cable cars arduously but somehow daintily climbing and plunging up and down the steep hills, and its sybaritic appreciation of food, wine and abandon. San Francisco was what Europe would have been if it had been made in America.

The bankers, the big insurers, the wealthiest and most powerful of developers and financers—the quiet men sitting in board rooms and private clubs whose all but invisible designs on profit had more sway over the city's future than any politician or ballot proposition because their investments weighed heavily in political campaigns and planning decisions alike—they knew that for tourism to thrive, it must be encouraged by government policy, by aggressive promotion, and by attractions that can constitute a "tour package," the places to see if you want to be amused without learning anything much about where you're visiting. By the early 1960s the city's Board of Supervisors had enacted a three-percent hotel room occupancy tax with the proceeds going toward financing a Convention and Visitors Bureau. It was the job of the Bureau to sell outsiders on the allure of the city. Mayor George Christopher and his successors took it on themselves to sell San Franciscans on the benefits of this self-transformation. The Bureau, at least, did its job. By the 1970s nearly three million out-of-towners a year were spending a billion dollars in the city whose motto was *Oro en paz, fierro en guerra*—Gold in peace, iron in war.

The tourism business included hotels, stores, transportation and tour interests, banks, restaurants, professional baseball and football teams, hotel and exhibit suppliers, liquor wholesalers (the foremost among whom soon became the town's most influential checkbook Democrat), clubs and saloons, as well as the unions of all the people employed by the many enterprises. Public relations and advertising firms were hired to be sure that all Iowa City knew about the splendors of Chinese New Year, Columbus Day, and the Japanese Cherry Blossom Festival. Construction firms were doing just fine building two new hotel rooms for every one that had existed in 1959. Based as it was on glitter and image, this marketing of the ephemeral was bound in the long run to sap the city of of its distinctive vitality. Over the years its skyline would become all but indistinguishable from Houston's and Philadelphia's.

Nowhere was the frenzy of development more evident than along the northern waterfront. Fisherman's Wharf had been built in the 1850s by an entrepreneur named Meiggs. Meiggs hired five hundred ablebodied men to cut down forests in Contra Costa County, haul the timber across the Bay to a sawmill he had built, and construct a promenade and boat dock. At first, in the 1880s and 1890s, Fisherman's Wharf was the place for Sunday afternoon family strolls. By the 1920s Italian immigrants were fishing in the waters offshore and living near the Wharf. Their homes sprawled all the way from the bayfront to the hills of North Beach. Automobiles had not yet come into common use and climbing the hills was hard; if you were well off you lived at the base of a hill. The men went to sea (or opened stores and markets, or built homes) while their wives and children hauled huge iron cauldrons onto the Wharf where they steamed the succulent crabs their husbands caught and sold them to the promenaders. Thursdays were fish market days, when the inland housewives came down to the Wharf to stock up their iceboxes with supper for meatless Fridays. In the 1930s some prosperous fishermen invested their profits in restaurants. The gradual evolution of the Wharf from the time when its uses were determined by public habit and shrewd individual investment picked up steam in the postwar boom, and with the coming of the Convention and Visitors Bureau in the early 1960s capital needs and bureaucratic agendas were deciding how this valuable waterfront land would be employed.

Ghirardelli Square, a cluster of abandoned red brick factory buildings on a steep rise just above the northern end of the Wharf, had originally been a woolens mill that manufactured uniforms and blankets for the army. After that it became a spice, coffee and chocolate factory, its sweet and pungent effluences mingling with the scents of crabs cooking in the salt sea air. The gulls grew fat and sassy. In 1962 a family of shipping magnates, noting which way the trade winds were blowing, invested five million dollars to convert the old factory into an architecturally stunning arcade of shops, restaurants and cafes catering primarily to tourists. Ghirardelli Square was a great success; soon enough other investors bought the rundown Del Monte fruit cannery one block south and poured enough money into refurbishing it to feel that it warranted an upper-case existence as The Cannery. Up and down the northern waterfront investors kept a ready watch not for storm clouds or troubled seas but for the main chance.

By the early 1970s, how people were employed in San Francisco was changing as rapidly as a sunny September afternoon was transformed by the fog ripping in off the Pacific and east across Sutro Tower toward Fisherman's Wharf into one of those bracing, late summer nights which caught the shivering tourists unprepared but delighted San Franciscans, who carried sweaters and confided in each other that the damp mist was good for the complexion. Longshoremen and teamsters, who had fought the bloody battles of the 1930s that made San Francisco a union label town, by this time no longer had the biggest or the most influential unions. Restaurant, hotel and bar employees organized into several locals that were soon to merge, outnumbering the longshoremen and every other union.

Dramatic as these changes were, what was happening inland of the near northern waterfront, along lower Market Street and Montgomery Street—which the knowledge workers liked to call the Wall Street of the West—was even more profound. "Once celebrated as a quaint city of relaxed and sophisticated attitudes, San Francisco has now emerged as a financial launching pad of significant proportions," a government report noted in 1973. "Corporate giants have consolidated and grown there, and have constructed monumental office towers to house their developing concerns. Oriental trade and Western American business have boomed." A weekly newspaper whose editor hoped to be a burr in the flesh of the powerful called the process "Manhattanization," and the interests behind it "downtown," and his phrases became coin of the realm among politicians and planners, as well as other journalists. Standard Oil of California, Southern Pacific, Transamerica Corporation (which constructed a remarkable office tower shaped like a pyramid), Crown Zellerbach, Utah International, Del Monte, Foremost-McKesson, the Bechtel Corporation, Pacific Telephone, Pacific Gas and Electric, Wells Fargo, Crocker National Bank and Bank of America, the world's largest banking house, all located their headquarters in San Francisco.

In 1964 manufacturing had been the second largest employer in the city, but by 1974 it had been surpassed by finance, insurance, real estate, transportation and utilities. As in virtually every other American city, services, not goods, were becoming the mainstay of the economy;

paper shuffling, not labor, was what was needed and wanted by the major employers downtown. Clerks, technicians and professionals were replacing craftsmen and foremen as the urban working class. Just as the Spaniards had routed the Indians and in turn been routed by the forty-niners and their descendants who had paved the way for the Irish, Germans, Scandinavians and Italians, the knowledge workers were now driving out the teamsters, butchers, fishermen, plumbers, printers and brewery workers. A big town had become a small city and the squeeze was on those large families whose daily bread was guaranteed by union contracts. Their attitudes toward the knowledge workers was ambivalent, part scorn and part envy.

Not just the knowledge workers but immigrants from South Asia, Mexico and Central America were taking up residence in their neighborhoods. Slowly the older white working class was squeezed out of the north and central parts of town as housing was demolished to make room for new office towers or condominium complexes, and as decay and fear of differences hastened their departure. The advancing legions of knowledge workers, of the Spanish-speaking and of Asians, backed the Irish and German blue-collar families right up against the black housing projects at the southeastern rim of the city. These predominatly Catholic families, and most especially their children as they came of age, began in the 1960s to leapfrog in increasing numbers over the blacks into the tract home suburbs south of the city.

Each generation thinks it is the terminal station but the truth is that history is a moving train: when it rounds a corner everybody who isn't holding on tight enough falls off. This new gold rush in which not ore but favorable interest rates and good views were the source of wealth was doing remarkable things for the real estate market, as more and more young professionals could afford to pay top dollar. Despite the steady influx of new arrivals, the census takers noted that the population was slowly declining. The people who were leaving were more often than not large families, while the arriving knowledge workers were for the most part young, single, childless. For fifty years San Francisco had built its economy on the bedrock of Catholic family life, and now, gradually, that was shifting just as the earth beneath the feet of oldtimers and newcomers alike was shifting imperceptibly along the San Andreas fault. This new San Francisco earthquake was making rubble not out of buildings but of the expectation that the existing social contracts were endlessly renewable.

The new working class, which did not labor, wanted things from their adopted city that had previously been offered only to the truly prosperous. They wanted the amenities that went with their softer hands and laundered shirts, with their disposable incomes and their single lives. They wanted restaurants, attractive bars, nice furniture, flowers, fancy foods, stylish clothing. If they earned enough they wanted their homes decorated and perhaps their parties catered. Their idea of style derived from the portrayal of the good life on the television commercials that were beamed from the tower high above the city to the flickering icons in each of their homes.

Because most of the young professionals had come from the East and the Midwest and so felt somewhat uprooted here in the raw and spacious West, they wanted antiques to give their lives a touch of continuity. And because San Francisco did not have the ample lawns, the old oaks, maples and dogwoods they had known back home, they wanted gardens and indoor plants. All these desires created still more economic opportunities, opportunities well suited to the sensibilities and talents of a good number of middle-class homosexuals. Meanwhile, tourism had created jobs for waiters, busboys, desk clerks, salespeople, bartenders—jobs toward which less well-educated or less upwardly mobile gay men had often enough gravitated. There were jobs here for them and so homosexuals came to San Francisco. There was no way of knowing how many. The Chamber of Commerce guessed 100,000 by the late 1970s, and gay politicians guessed as many as 200,000 in a city of about 700,000. A lot.

Jobs alone would not have been enough, of course. A certain degree of tolerance also has to exist to lure 100,000-plus stigmatized outcasts to a certain place at a certain time in history. For all that gays were harassed and picked on by the local constabulary for public and private acts the law prohibited—as late as 1971 there were 2800 arrests of homosexuals on sex-related charges—it was also true that ever since the days of the Barbary Coast, when certain restaurants were known to hire all-male staffs and provide private booths to their male patrons, homosexuality had been a part of the San Francisco underground. World War II, when millions of men passed through and tens of thousands more were dishonorably discharged for being gay, their blue termination papers stamped with a block *H,* had brought a lot of homosexuals to San Francisco. A certain number, shamed by the circumstances of their discharges, chose to stay on rather than to return to their hometowns. There were a very few gay bars the police allowed to operate. The first national organization of lesbians, Daughters of

Bilitis, was founded in San Francisco in 1955. And in 1966 two liberal assemblymen, George Moscone's good friends Willie Brown and John Burton, won the backing of a low-key but aboveboard homosexual organization called SIR (Society for Individual Responsibility) in exchange for a promise that they would try to expunge an 1872 law concerning "crimes against nature" which prohibited consenting adults from behaving as they wished in private. Homosexuality was condemned and it was persecuted but everybody knew it was there and as long as it was kept in the closet, so what?

Harvey Milk arrived in San Francisco as a part of the mass migrations, yet another New Yorker with experience in finance and an artistic flair. He first came in 1969 on the heels of a lover named Jack McKinley. McKinley was neither stable nor happy and one of his suicide attempts involved jumping off Fisherman's Wharf. The tide was out, however, and he landed in a few feet of water and walked away coated in ooze from the muddy bottom of the Bay. But San Francisco held other attractions for Harvey besides McKinley. Always in tune with his times, in 1969 Harvey's hair fell to his shoulders, his jeans were faded, and he wore a long string of love beads. Haight Ashbury was the unofficial world capital of hippies, and Harvey hung out with the road company of "Hair" that was performing here; he had known many of the same people in New York.

The apparent hippie, however, found a job on Montgomery Street as a market researcher, until he quit during a protest of Nixon's Cambodian policy on the steps of the Pacific Stock Exchange. Harvey embodied a berserk composite of the kinds of people migrating to San Francisco: young, single, gay, anti-establishment, and with skills he could sell in the financial center. It was as if he were a bad cubist painting of what he would later become, the pieces all there but a certain coherence missing. But he was positive it would all come out right before he was through. As McKinley said of him, "She didn't know what she'd do next but she knew she'd do something."

Harvey returned to New York in the summer of 1970, only to come back to San Francisco again two years later, this time with the idea that he would stay. Oodles of gays with the same thought were also arriving in the early 1970s. They were coming to stay. "Where else can we go?" they asked, "Oakland?"

Harvey had decided that he loved San Francisco, the ease of living more than anything else, and the beautiful men. The second time he came, he packed all his belongings in shipping crates and urged his New York lover, Scott Smith, to follow Horace Greeley's advice and join him. Harvey bombarded Smith with passionate postcards and letters extolling his new home, and in March 1972 Scott followed along. Like most of Harvey's many lovers Scott was younger and smaller. He was a trim man with the build of a handball player, muscular and bouncy. His reddish-brown hair fell across a well-shaped head and when he spoke you could hear the molasses melodiousness of the Mississippi town where he had been raised. Scott fancied himself to be Harvey's wife. At first they lived with some friends in a large apartment in a section of North Beach that was a domain of artists and writers, on a street of secondhand clothes shops, inexpensive restaurants and cafes with patios that a North Beach poet described as the closest thing to the Left Bank in America. The apartment had a panoramic view of Alcatraz Island in mid-Bay and of the Golden Gate Bridge. They stayed there for seven months and every evening when they were home they would sit at the window smoking a joint or drinking wine and watching the sun setting over the Pacific. Like so many of the newcomers to California in those days, Harvey and Scott lived well but inexpensively off their combined unemployment checks. It was the twilight of the sixties, a time when a lot of young men and women who had worked hard before and would work hard again relaxed and enjoyed life and considered questions without answers. The patois of the age was saturated with phrases to describe their attitude: dropped out, laid back, going with the flow, not pushing the river. In the mornings they would stroll out about eleven, when the fog lifted and the sun dappled the sidewalk, and have coffee at the Savoy Tivoli. Afterward they might amble over to Cuneo's bakery and buy fresh bread, or cross the few blocks to Chinatown for the Chinese smorgasbord lunch of *dim sum.* Even when he was laid back, Harvey was peripatetic, always on the move.

Harvey decided that he simply had to have an account at the Chinatown branch of Wells Fargo Bank when he noticed that the tellers' counters had miniature Bacchuses sculpted into them. Their account was lean but it was enough for what Harvey wanted, which was to show Scott San Francisco and California so he would fall in love with it, as Harvey had. They bought a well-seasoned green Dodge Charger with a black vinyl roof and spent the better part of 1972 exploring California, when they weren't lazing about the city. Together they would throw their sleeping bags into the back seat and drive up to see the redwood forests, or down six hundred miles to San Diego to catch a dolphin show at Sea World. Along the way they stopped in Big Sur and sat on the grand deck of the Nepenthe Inn sipping wine and looking out over the expanse of cliffs and sea. But they were hippies and Nepenthe was too slick for their tastes so before long they pushed on, continuing along the tortuous spine of Highway One clinging to the coastal range, which was none too easy for Harvey, who had a dreadful fear of heights. Wherever they went they played classical music on the radio. They were in love. At Yosemite in April the waterfalls were gushing.

By the end of summer it was time to move out of their friends' apartment and find a place of their own. They had several times gone to join the line of people that stood, day and night, in the sunshine and in the rain, outside of an ice cream parlor called Bud's, and on their way there they passed through a section of town known both as the Castro and Eureka Valley, a neighborhood of dowdy Queen Anne Victorians at the southeastern slope of Mount Sutro. Harvey and Scott liked the area, it had a real village feel. It was the kind of neighborhood where the merchants learned their customers' names and where you could shop for dinner at the butcher, the fresh produce shop, the bakery, without ever having to set foot inside a supermarket. You could buy fresh cut flowers and get your newspaper from a man in a corner stand instead of from the yellow vending machines where most *Chronicles* were sold. The Castro was also gaining a certain popularity among gays, especially hip gays. When a bar they had been frequenting in North Beach closed its doors, Harvey and Scott began to spend some evenings at the Midnight Sun on Castro Street where longhairs, both straight and gay, danced and drank. Finally they found a small apartment right on the main drag with a tiny wedge of Bay view from which they could watch the clouds scudding across the sky.

Within two years the corner of Eighteenth and Castro would become the crossroads of the homosexual world; within four years Harvey would become the best-known gay politician in America, a man with such a strong sense of being an outcast that he would find the courage and the conviction to give voice to the hopes and fears of his fellow outcasts, thereby finding his place in the world. But in the autumn of 1973 it would have been hard to find a rational man to take a bet on either coming to pass.

Harvey's talent for getting things done, which he had demonstrated on Wall Street and in the Broadway theater, was finally getting the better of his prolonged idleness. He was older than most of the people who had withdrawn from the workaday world, and the workaday world was now sending him a message: his unemployment checks were running out, it was time to support himself again. When some photographs that he and Scott had taken on their travels came back from a neighborhood pharmacy blurred and distorted, Harvey decided it was a great idea to open a camera store that would also provide photographic services. Never mind that all he knew about a camera was to point it in the right direction and depress the little plunger.

The storefront that he and Scott rented for their new business with their last thousand dollars was poorly located on the slow side of the slow block of Castro above Eighteenth. The only other businesses on their block were a real estate broker, an insurance agent and a dry cleaners, not the kinds of establishments that drew much pedestrian traffic. But the rent was cheap.

Business was slow at first. Maybe four customers a day would wander into Castro Cameras. Scott and Harvey had a television in the store and during the summer they stayed glued to the Watergate hearings. Harvey would pace around the store talking back to the witnesses and the senators on the Ervin committee. Basset-faced John Mitchell in particular irked him. Mitchell's pipesmoking complacency about lying would send Harvey into paroxysms of public-spirited outrage. "You goddamn lying cocksuckah," he would shout at the image of the Attorney General of the United States on his television screen. Harvey had always loved theater, opera, the drama of the stage. But this was a higher drama than any stage production, the stakes were real. It stirred the patriotism of this grandson of a Russian immigrant, of this former high school football player and Navy sailor, and made him want to *do* something. Those evil Nixon bastards were trying to steal the country, wrap up two hundred years of democracy in the constitution like yesterday's fish dinner and toss it on the garbage heap of history. Right there on national television the good guys were clobbering the goddamn *gonifs*. Democracy worked, flourish of trumpets. Suddenly politics seemed like a true opportunity, a stage on which his principles and his talents could be brought to bear. For the first time in his life Harvey Bernard Milk, a forty-two-year-old Jewish homosexual with a ponytail and a small business, who had migrated to California full of inchoate convictions about his future, began to talk with Scott about running for public office.

What was happening in the Castro was a phenomenon never before experienced by any city in the course of modern western civilization— an entire neighborhood was being resettled piecemeal by openly homosexual men and women. They could double and triple up to offer prices for the Victorian homes and flats that the older Catholic families of Most Holy Redeemer parish could neither match nor resist. These men and women with no children to feed, clothe or school, no future but their own to lay away for, had little trouble finding jobs in the new economy of San Francisco. Even the banks and the corporations would hire them so long as they kept their sexual orientation low-key. They began to constitute a new bourgeoisie, a conservative economic force with a special concern for civil rights. The migration of gays and knowledge workers was fostering a real estate boom and more than a few gays became brokers or agents themselves. The second gold rush was creating a neighborhood and a constituency on which a talented opportunist like Harvey might, conceivably, build a political base.

While Harvey would offer himself to voters as a gay man seeking gay support, which in itself took a certain courage, he never let his homosexuality limit his concerns. Small things tipped him toward running for a seat on the citywide Board of Supervisors in the 1973 election, trivial things which he took to heart. One day, for instance, a school teacher came into Castro Cameras wanting to know if they rented slide projectors. She explained that there was a slide show she wanted to screen for her class at the Douglass Elementary School but if she requisitioned a projector through school channels it would take months to arrive and by then it would be too late for the lesson she was teaching. Harvey was incensed at the ponderous bureaucratic inefficiency. San Francisco children deserved better than that.

Another thing was that Harvey and Scott, who were sliding by on the seats of their trousers, had neglected to pay the hundred dollars required of all businesses for a sales tax stamp. One afternoon a chubby bureaucrat came by to dun them for the money, threatening to close down the store if they didn't pay up. Besides bemoaning the absence of a decent corned beef sandwich and being aghast when restaurants served a simple American hamburger smothered in raw alfalfa sprouts, Harvey had a problem a lot of transplanted New Yorkers did in San Francisco. When he didn't like something he shouted and fumed. Harvey began to yell at the bureaucrat, who became alarmed and made some rather rude suggestions of his own. A couple of customers who had been in the store left hastily. "I'm paying your fuckin' salary and you're chasing my business away," Harvey ranted. "You mean to tell me if I'm poor I can't open a business in California? I don't have a hundred lousy dollars so I can't go into business? What you're doing smacks of everything that's wrong with capitalism."

Not satisfied when the man retreated, Harvey went down to the state office building to fight the system. He could be indignant with the best of them. To begin with, he really felt indignant, but on top of that he loved the chance to give it the full theatrical treatment with all the appropriate flourishes. It was an act, and then again it wasn't an act at all. A feeling that an injustice was done (especially when it meant money out of his all but empty pocket) really bothered him; the belief that he could do something to remedy it, just like Senator Sam Ervin, excited him. In the end he haggled his way into a partial payment of thirty dollars. Harvey had won his first political skirmish. He would run for Supervisor.

The campaign was a lark but it was serious, too. Harvey stood on a box with the word SOAP painted on it to announce his candidacy. He backed an early attempt to substitute district elections for citywide election of supervisors, declared that he didn't want a city "trying to become a great bank book, a major money center" but rather a "city that breathes, one that is alive and where people are more important than highways." He was reflective in the few interviews that were requested of him. "I'm forty-three years old," he said in one. "I can concentrate on making a lot of money while I enjoy perhaps ten more years of active gay life. Then I can just coast, call the whole thing good. Or I can get involved and do something about the things that are wrong in society. I've got to fight not just for me but for my lover and his next lover eventually. It's got to be better for them than it was for me."

He had very little money for his campaign and was shunned by the more established gay leaders, who found him alarmingly radical and spontaneous, but he finished a respectable tenth. It was enough to encourage him.

After the campaign, Harvey made some vows and some changes. He cut his hair: nobody was going to elect a supervisor with a ponytail. He decided he would never again smoke marijuana. And he made a concession as well to the sensibilities of people who were alarmed or repelled by homosexuality: he would no longer go to bathhouses. The biggest and best known of the gay bathhouses was called Sutro Baths, a play on the cavernous, enclosed swimming pool that old Adolph Heinrich had built on a cliff above the ocean and which had finally been razed. Some of the gay bathhouses had contraptions called glory holes, which were boards with knotholes drilled in them. One man stuck his member through and other men, never seen by him, performed fellatio on the other side. It was this kind of thing which alarmed people who felt that tolerance of gays would lead to the moral decay of all San Francisco. After dark, Eighteenth and Castro turned from a quiet, village-like shopping area into a cruiser's bacchanal. There were still a lot of old-timers living nearby and they carried stories of what was happening to their relatives and friends in other parts of the city.

People like Joe Ryan, the vice cop who had busted Margo St. James, found the gay scene hateful and frightening. "We had one fruit place in the city for many years, the Black Cat," Ryan said, "and we controlled the streets, the police did. We used to get the homosexuals in the men's room in the Emporium and Macy's, we'd look through the air vents and catch 'em. Then the Supreme Court ruled all that was unconstitutional. San Francisco, we always felt we could take care of our own town. The mobsters, the Mafia never got in. Then we were overwhelmed, it was unbelievable. Over in Eureka Valley, Holy Redeemer parish, we used to have forty-one straight bars. Now we got forty fruit bars and one straight bar.

"What they did, it didn't have anything to do with family. The condoning, that's what upsets a lot of people. The family takes a pounding," said Ryan, who has five kids and four grandchildren. "It's a singles scene, schools are closed. They don't bring children into the world, it's a dead lifestyle in that sense, it's a selfish lifestyle."

It didn't matter to people who felt the way Ryan did that Harvey himself always cared about kids, that as a supervisor he would fight and beat the Board of Education when it threatened to close down Douglass Elementary School. They never knew that Harvey was the kind of man who would give an hour-long interview to a junior high school kid while an aide impatiently tried to pry him loose to attend to other business. What mattered to them was that Harvey was the spokesman for homosexuality, that he wouldn't apologize for it or urge gays to cool it.

Harvey's own style was frumpy, there was something of Buster Keaton in his long face and sad eyes and plastic, comic expression. But Harvey was not typical. Nor was it typical for two homosexuals dressed in matching outfits of black leather vests, no shirts, tight leather chaps and black cowboy hats to sashay down the street, one shrieking at the other, "Oh, you silly girl, you!" But it happened, and that was what people remembered and talked about, even people who didn't have any moral qualms about homosexuality. Such scenes were in and of themselves amusing, but experienced again and again in one form or another, they were disquieting. The kind of reasonable, liberal people who had always supported civil rights and women's rights found themselves discomfitted by homosexual assertiveness. It seemed that street gays, at least, combined effeminacy with posturing machismo, to concoct a subculture out of the least appealing aspects of both femininity and masculinity that was neither here nor there, inherently false.

The mockery of gay attitudes toward simple, traditional values of the culture annoyed many other San Franciscans because they suggested class distinctions. Their archness was understood as a form of condescension, and little thought was given to the idea that it might be a defense against prejudice. And even the word *gay* itself. What's so gay, people asked themselves, about guys who socialized in bars with names like the Boot Camp and the Trench?

When you combined it all—the moral objections rooted in Catholic doctrine, the class objections based on posturing and posing, the economic objections based on the relative freedom of homosexuals to be unconcerned about the future because they would not have children —what you had was a kind of sexual integration crisis, made worse by the stampede of politicians falling all over each other in their haste to befriend a large and growing group of voters.

That was what Harvey was confronting when he decided that sooner or later he would win elected office in San Francisco, a gay man running as a champion of his own kind but wanting to represent everybody—from school kids to old ladies on fixed pensions whose rents were threatened by the landlord's market (created, at least in part, by the number of homosexuals willing to pay top dollar). A lesser man would have blanched and retreated into the quietude that characterized the gay leaders with whom City Hall usually did business. But Harvey never lost his heart or his humor. "Milk Has Something for Everybody," that was his first campaign slogan.

3
Unite and Fight

On a fine spring day in 1977 Dan White of Engine Company 43 and Father Tom Lacey of Our Lady of Visitacion parish were taking a stroll along Leland Avenue. The four blocks of neighborhood storefronts still looked like a stage set for a grainy black-and-white movie made in the 1950s, when Dan had been growing up nearby. Back then Visitacion Valley, as the neighborhood was called, had been a green place of truck farms, dairies and flower nurseries irrigated by underground streams. Though much had changed in Vis Valley since Dan had been born in 1946, some things had remained exactly as they were then; in 1977 you still would have had to search diligently to find a registered Republican, a college graduate or somebody who earned more than $20,000 a year.

Dan was a head taller than the priest and he walked with a muscularity not entirely devoid of vanity. His large face gave the impression of purposefulness, especially his chin, which was bisected by a deep cleft. He had deepset, level green eyes that narrowed when he smiled. There was a web of smile lines radiating from the corners of his eyes, but none around his thin lips. His cheeks were round and prominent. A cowlick fell above his right eye and his straight, dark-brown hair was worn short although his sideburns were nearly muttonchops, wide and furry in a style that suggested tintypes of old-time firemen. His clear skin was thick. The overall impression was of vigor and control; it was a face that gave hint of bursts of glee rather than a sustained humor, a pleasant, earnest face, not ascetic and certainly not sensual.

Father Lacey could never look at the young fireman without thinking that, jeez, he was a handsome devil. And tough. When a black kid from the Sunnydale projects made some remark as he strutted past, Dan tensed up and half turned after him, as if he were still the boy who had built a reputation on these streets with his fists, or still a policeman. But Father Lacey put a hand on Dan's arm to restrain him.

"We've got to get people to the point," Lacey said in a voice that was deep and bigger than his compact little body, "where if one of these black kids is roughing somebody up then he's just got to get the shit knocked out of him, I mean he has to be physically beaten to a pulp. I mean, sweep the little bastard into the gutter and say, 'C'mon boys, the next guy who wants some of this, c'mon into our neighborhood.'"

"It's the only thing they understand, some of 'em," Dan agreed, as they continued to walk. He was as angry as Father Lacey about what had happened to his old neighborhood.

Dan and his eight brothers and sisters had been raised just a few blocks further up Leland Avenue in a stucco bungalow facing an undeveloped expanse of urban park. The bungalow was one of dozens that ringed the block, built on narrow bowling alley lots and painted pastel shades that faded in the summer sun and the winter rain so that after a while you wouldn't notice the color of one from the other: pink, salmon, sky blue, lime green, white, buff, mustard, wheat or yellow, it hardly mattered. The three-bedroom bungalows with their closet-sized Mexican-style vestibules outside their front doors had the tiniest of lawns, but their narrow backyards formed a hollow where vegetables and flowers grew and the laundry was hung out to dry. It was a placid place.

That idyllic little village within the city so well remembered by Dan, a place perhaps softened by the affectionate light of nostalgia, no longer existed. Cheap wine, reds, Eli Lilly bullets and glue had by this spring day in 1977 become many a young person's communion. Black and white youngsters alike hung out on their separate streetcorners, high and idle. The worst of them were burglars or muggers or even rapists. The police seemed powerless to prevent their marauding. The streets weren't clean anymore, nor were the postage-stamp lawns uniformly tended, but most shocking of all were the wrought iron bars protecting the doors and windows of nearly every home in the Valley. The good people hid in their flimsy fortresses feeling angry and helpless, while the streets outside their doors turned dirty and frightening. As the city's economy had turned away from the work that thickened their fingers and tested their backs and toward white collar industries and tourism, these Irish and Italian families found that their sons were no longer sure of a decent wage and a place in dad's union. Church attendance was in decline, as Father Lacey knew only too well, and the number of savings accounts at the Leland branch of the Bank of America was diminishing: faith in the future was all but exhausted.

Their health clinic had been closed by the city, their branch library was in jeopardy, they had to wait longer between buses than people elsewhere in the city, even though Vis Valley had more homeowners than any other area of town who paid the property taxes that kept the city government running. In more ways than just geographically, their neighborhood down in the southeast corner of town just north of the county line was as far away from City Hall as you could get.

"We've got to stick all together," Father Lacey was saying to Dan as they strolled past the pharmacy where Dan's godmother waved from behind the counter. "I mean, I told the same things to Charlie Gain and you know what he said? He said, 'You're bordering on vigilantism.' And you know what I told him? I told him, 'I don't care.' "

Dan laughed. He had heard about the faceoff between the pitbull priest with so much moxie and Police Chief Gain, who was solemn-faced and aloof. When Lacey had asked for a stop sign on the corner where a teacher at the parish school had been killed by a hit-and-run driver, he had gotten a runaround. So he had called a neighborhood protest meeting; fifteen hundred people had filled the pews and Chief Gain had come out to listen to their grievances after all.

"So I told him, 'Look, you can do what you want about this thing but the next time somebody gets killed we're going to march right down the freeway with a casket on our backs.' You know what he said?"

"You told him that?" Dan smiled.

"Damn right. So he says, 'You've got to be kidding.' I told him, 'There's only one way to show you guys and that's to be civilly disobedient or whatever you call that.' And he's a clever cookie, don't think he isn't. He called me back to say okay, you'll get your stop sign, and by then he knew everything about me." The priest had upset the parish by announcing from the pulpit that he was an alcoholic, that he belonged to Alcoholics Anonymous.

The two men had reached the foot of Leland Avenue, down by Schlage Lock, which piled up over several blocks. Wing after wing had been added as the business expanded, each in the style of its decade, so that from the classic original factory with its small-pane windows to the aqua-faced fifties addition to the sleek modern office wing it represented a microcosm of the architecture of mid-century. Beyond Schlage Lock was the freeway, and beyond that the ghettoes of Bayview and Hunter's Point and as far east as you could go were the shipyards down by the Bay, where Dan's father had worked at Engine Company 16.

Father Lacey had been taking Dan around to meet the people at SAFE—Safety Awareness for Everyone—but when they arrived they found that nobody was in the storefront today. SAFE, Lacey explained, was based on the principles of mass-base organizing taught by Saul Alinsky. Alinsky's idea was to identify the problems in a neighborhood and then give people a sense of power by organizing them behind their own natural leaders. Power, that's what it was all about, power for people who didn't have any.

"You've got to ring doorbells," Father Lacey explained. "You got to sit down with 'em and say, 'Look, I'm gonna help you protect what you got. And if you want to hear how to do it, c'mon over to a meeting next Tuesday.' "

Dan nodded. After a while the two men shook hands—for a big, muscular man Dan's hand was surprisingly small, but his grip was energetic—and went their separate ways. But the padre had given Dan something to think about.

Power, political power, was up for grabs in San Francisco. For the first time in half a century the city had been divided into districts, eleven in all, with each of them to elect a supervisor. Nobody deserved more credit, or blame, for the new district election system than a tall, lean community organizer from Haight Ashbury named Calvin Welch. Welch was an unlikely-looking power broker, with his ponytail and his Vandyke beard and the sleeves of his flannel shirts rolled up over his sinewy forearms. But he was tireless and magnetic and hard and he had a vision of changing the system which had sent supervisors to City Hall who somehow always seemed to live in the same few prosperous neighborhoods. His vision made him stronger in the long run than men and women who only wanted to protect what they had.

Welch had been instrumental in bringing about a confederation calling itself Citizens for Representative Government, which had tried but failed to enact district elections on several occasions before they had finally won. Their victory in November 1976 was in large part due to the bitter aftermath of a municipal workers' strike earlier that same year. When the unions of municipal workers had been bucked and beaten by the conservative majority on the incumbent citywide Board of Supervisors, they had vowed to get even. The Police Officers Association, for instance, and the city's firefighters, had recognized in district elections a way of taking their revenge by turning out all eleven supervisors. Welch and his allies had assiduously cultivated the resentments of the uniformed employees.

It had posed quite a problem for the Chamber of Commerce and the more conservative politicians to convincingly portray district elections as a radical coup when cops and firemen were pounding the pavement with pro-district election literature. Yet the departure was radical. At-large elections helped the invisible power brokers—"downtown"—maintain their control over the future of the city and thus over who would profit. First, because running a citywide campaign required a goodly sum of money, their contributions were essential; most supervisors took office beholden to the financial barons. Second, since no supervisor spoke for any one area or constituency, responsibility was diffused. Things happened but nobody in particular was accountable. Elections-at-large produced a form of civic management more like a corporate structure. District elections would bring with them a more adversarial, political style of governance, and thus more public clashes of policy and ideology.

In the battle for jobs and better services, most cops and firemen and machinists and other white union members resisted the demands of the various minorities and tried to ignore the existence of the growing number of homosexuals altogether. And those underenfranchised groups believed that no matter how fairminded an individual cop on the street might be, the Police Department and the POA would never willingly treat them fairly as a class, especially not when it came to hiring. So the unlikely alliance of the left and elements of the entrenched working class to pass district elections was like a confluence of two rivers that for one brief stretch had flowed together, becoming deeper, wider, and more powerful than either was alone, and then diverged again. That confluence came in November 1976, when fifty-two percent of the votes cast were in favor of the new system of electing supervisors by individual districts.

In the area around Leland Avenue—what would become District 8—the margin was even greater, fifty-six percent. The new district was bounded on the east and west by two freeways; its neighborhoods—Vis Valley, Crocker Amazon, the Portola and the Excelsior—were places that people who lived downtown drove *around* on their way to the airport or the ballpark. All of a sudden they had become a political entity that would choose a supervisor to speak for them. But whom?

In Dan's firehouse on Moscow Street there had been much talk of district elections; firefighting involved more waiting than anything else. The talk had set Dan to thinking: he had always felt destined to leave his mark on the world, now here was a chance. What Father Lacey had said about power, the power to make them pay attention downtown, had impressed him. There was hardly a block in the new District 8 where he or his wife Mary Ann didn't know someone. There were plenty of firefighters and his old cop pals and the guys he had played ball with in and out of school who would be ready to back him up if he made a run for it. He was well known and almost universally liked. Of course he didn't know anything, not a thing, about politics, in fact it had been years and years since he had even registered to vote. But he had the issues—all you had to do was look at the bars and gates on the homes in District 8 to see what was wrong—and he was sincere, gung-ho, and a natural leader. All his life other boys and men had been drawn and inspired by him.

So one day that spring Dan drove down to City Hall and declared his intention to run. The only thing was, he and Mary Ann were living in an apartment out near Ocean Beach, an address that was in District 10, where incumbent supervisor Quentin Kopp was as sure a bet to be re-elected as the fog was to creep off the Pacific and up the streets with their otherworldly names: Ulloa, Taraval, Wawona, Judah. Procedure had always made Dan impatient. His address might have been in District 10 but he was a Vis Valley guy, everybody understood that, didn't they?

Goldie Judge had a plump finger in all the political pies that were baked in Vis Valley. Her headquarters, if you could call it that, was a sweets shop on Leland run by her good friend Roland Percival. If she wasn't there, or at Andy's Cafe, she was at home in her mustard-colored, peeling bungalow with a wounded window in the garage door.

Though Goldie wasn't Jewish she was certainly a *yenta,* a busy-body who often enough had a big cauldron of chicken soup on the stove; there were those who thought she was white pretending to be black and those who thought that she was black passing for white; though she had never been to Brooklyn the stream of words that gushed from her wet, mobile mouth like fizzing seltzer sounded like a streetcorner monologue in Flatbush. When it came to politics she was an emotional pragmatist, somebody who knew it was a cutthroat business and knew also that in every person there were forces and spirits that were as real and immutable as good and evil.

The phone in her kitchen rang all day and night and the caller was as likely to be the mayor or a supervisor checking up on the latest gossip as anybody else, and every time the phone rang Goldie poured herself another cup of coffee and lit another cigarette and settled down to swap tales. Goldie was to Vis Valley what Walter Winchell had been to all the ships at sea.

One day in May 1977 a friend introduced her to Dan White out in front of Cinti's barbershop, and Dan told her he had been looking for her.

"Why?" Goldie asked. Everything Goldie says comes out melodrama.

"I'm running for supervisor and I was recommended to see you." In all that happened afterward Goldie never felt that she got a straight answer out of Dan about who had recommended her. At any rate they agreed to have lunch the next day at Andy's Cafe.

Dan showed up with his wife Mary Ann and immediately his stock rose in Goldie's estimation. Goldie liked schoolteachers, which Mary Ann was, and besides that Mary Ann seemed a nice combination of well bred, educated, and the Irish mother type. They took a booth and ordered coffee and started to talk. Goldie snapped questions and she noticed when Dan didn't have the answers Mary Ann would help him out. Ah-ha, Goldie thought.

She liked the respectful way they treated each other. Like when Mary Ann said, "Can we have some more coffee?" and Dan answered, "Coming right up." He went and fetched the pot and refilled the cups himself, even remembering to tell the waitress to add another cup all around. That was another point in his favor. As was his familiarity with the neighborhood.

Then there were his clean-cut good looks and his superhero personality. She thought he had sharp, clean lines and that cleanliness appealed to her. The guy was saleable. Goldie was trying to decide whether she wanted to work with him; he had already asked her to manage his campaign, something she had never done but always wanted to. Still, it would be a big commitment and Goldie wanted a second opinion besides her own and some more time to think. She could also see that they were judging her, too, and needed a chance to talk it over. She had already decided that Mary Ann was the wiser of the two.

"Why don't you guys come over to my house for pizza next week, I make a damn good pizza," Goldie said. "There's a lot of factors to be considered on how we could win. There's no use getting involved in this if we can't win."

His eyes got darker and his manner earnest and his big jaw worked and Dan said, "I have every intention of winning."

About Mary Ann Burns it had often been said that she would make some lucky man a perfect wife.

Tall and broad-boned without being heavy, at thirty-four she wore clothes in the same style as when she had been a schoolgirl: pleated skirts, demure blouses, blazers, sensible shoes. She was a trifle shy but more than that, self-contained. There was nothing flamboyant or exuberant about the way she looked or acted, and so while her features were attractive and regular she was not attention-catching. She looked cool and clean and stately in a parochial way. There was a lot of sympathy but no nonsense in her brown eyes, which were set wide in a narrow face. Her pug nose wrinkled with pleasure or disapproval. Her hair, a brownish blond in color, was worn straight with a soft wave at the collar. Her hands were large, well cared for and womanly; they were capable hands. At her age in 1974 popular wisdom would have had her married but she was a woman who knew her own mind. She was waiting for Mr. Right.

Mary Ann's father, Leo, who was the lieutenant in command of the firehouse where Dan was stationed, and her mother, Isabelle, who had been a Sheehan before her marriage, gave their daughter a good Catholic upbringing and the proper sort of education. They were a solid, middle-class Irish family and in Mary Ann both the religion and the values took. For many girls of her sort and background, barely breathing seemed a sin during adolescence, and a woman seemed an almost shameful thing to have become.

At St. Rose's Academy and Sacred Heart High School she was a good student and she finished up with a teaching degree at Lone Mountain College. At college she was a quiet, placid girl, well enough liked but not very well known except to a very few other girls. After she graduated, Mary Ann taught grade school at army bases in Germany and Japan. When she came back home to San Francisco she worked at a school in Hunter's Point where children from some of the roughest projects in town were her students. She was always cool and poised but there was a pinched quality around her eyes as if the waiting had perhaps taken a toll.

By 1975 she was living in an apartment in a modern two-unit home at the edge of the Castro district, in Most Holy Redeemer parish. The apartment was at the brink of a hilltop cul-de-sac and from the long windows in her neat living room she looked out over her alma mater, Lone Mountain College, down past St. Mary's Cathedral and the dome of City Hall. The irreverent joked that the white spire of St. Mary's, with its peculiar three-sided design, looked like a washing machine agitator, but Mary Ann saw in it the crowning achievment of her culture in San Francisco.

She met Dan White when a fireman pal of his set up a tennis match with Mary Ann and a girlfriend. Danny kept everybody laughing, he was such a terrible player, yet somehow he made the others want to play their very best, keeping up a running patter of blarney. Mary Ann was drawn to the life in him.

Dan liked Mary Ann Burns as well. She was intelligent and pretty and she smiled at him in a way that was both demure and welcoming. She was lovely and gave every indication of being steadfast. It didn't bother him that she was nearly five years older than he was; he liked older women, his steady lover at that time was even older than Mary Ann. It never entered Dan's mind how much like his own mother Mary Ann was. What he knew was that he was smitten.

From the beginning they found it easy to talk and to laugh. They had a great deal in common. As children the nuns had taught both of them that they would go forth into the world as the custodians of western civilization, the frontline resistance to barbarism and paganism. To the rules the nuns had taught—respect, honesty, service to others—Dan had added what his father had shown him about the value of uncomplaining hard work, courage and self-reliance. Dan paid all the proper obeisance to the rules but his principal sin was pride: he was reckless and sometimes acted as if he were not just the arbiter but the very rules themselves, as if he were morality incarnate.

As they got to know each other, Dan told Mary Ann how his dad had died in 1963, when Dan had been seventeen. Charlie White had been that kind of Irishman whose truest feelings were buried with him in the grave. In a way, Dan had felt as if he never had known his dad. Charlie had worked weekends and off-days running a one-man contracting business; with ten mouths to feed at home he couldn't ever stop working. Love had been spread thin in the crowded household in Visitacion Valley.

If Charlie had labored, so had Dan's mother, Nora Twomey's girl Eileen Sterling. When Dan spoke to Mary Ann about his mother, his tone changed; none of the respect but some of the warmth dropped away. Eileen White was the very embodiment of Dylan Thomas's characterization of the Irish sentiment: "Oh, isn't life a terrible thing, thank God." Eileen's strength was no less than her husband's had been; she was a rock to her children, seeing to it that they were properly raised and fed and that their clothes were clean and mended. Dan's mother had expected her children to stand on their own feet and was quick to let them know when they were disappointing her.

From what Dan was telling Mary Ann Burns, sometimes by what he said but more often by what he didn't say, Mary Ann understood that Charlie had been not only the parent whom Dan had admired but also the one he adored.

Charlie White had been an uncomplaining man whose strength was as unmistakable in his wide sloping shoulders and deep chest as his appetite for food and drink had been in his bulging banana belly. He had that fatalistic joy the Irish seem to take in hardship. After the fifth of his children was born Charlie took up his hammer and saw to build an extension onto the rear of their home, but even with the extra rooms and the big family den in the basement where the kids did their homework, the little ones had had to double and triple up in the bedrooms and wear the older kids' hand-me-downs. "I've got nine children," Charlie White used to boast when he took a ribbing from his mates at the firehouse about the size of his brood, "and no one of them is any worse than any other."

An old Irish harp Charlie White had been, singing the praises of the homeland and lamenting British rule. He was a man of strong opinions and no hesitation in stating them, a bullhead. His convictions were so firm and vociferous that he had a kind of persuasiveness. His fireman-mates had found that you couldn't argue with Charlie White, he was too stubborn to admit any other opinions into his closed system. Consciously and unconsciously the son had patterned himself after the father.

In a poor neighborhood like Vis Valley a boy had to make it on the streets, whether by cleverness or combativeness. It was his father who had seen to it that Dan learned this lesson. Some toughs who hung out on Dan's streetcorner had settled on him—a skinny ten-year-old with a crewcut and a round face as Irish as Paddy's pig—as their patsy. They would push him around until the fright and shame rose in him and he would run home crying. One afternoon Charlie was waiting when his boy burst in seeking refuge. Large, menacing, uncompromising, he had cuffed his son and laid down the law: Dan had to stand up to the boys who were picking on him. The next afternoon Dan fought back against his tormentors, fought them wildly until they backed off. When he told his father what he had done Charlie beamed and tousled his hair and Dan blushed with pride. It was a moment in his life that had taken on an inconographic value: a man must never back down, humiliation was worse than a thrashing. From then on, whenever Dan stood up for himself he felt idealistic.

It had been a financial hardship for his parents to send their children to parochial schools, but they made the sacrifice willingly. At St. Elizabeth's Grammar School and Riordan High School Dan had been known as a boy who was handy with his fists. He wasn't anybody to take on unless you were willing to see things through to the end. His fights distressed his mother, whom he hated to disappoint, but it had a special meaning to him that he could take care of himself, it was his response to the pressures to do well and prepare himself for manhood.

Mary Ann understood the intimate nature of these confidences. Charlie White had died young of cancer, but not before he became a hero by carrying out a daring rescue, and Dan talked with great, reluctant feeling about how he had let his dad down by making so much trouble and then been cheated out of a chance to make it up. Mary Ann could see how Dan's determination to be strong and handle everything was a way of living up to his father's legacy and paying off a debt of conscience. She understood what it signified that he would talk to her about these things, it drew her closer to him. It had taken very little time for Mary Ann Burns to fall in love with Danny White.

The flush of romance was upon them; they would be married. Whatever else life as Mrs. Daniel James White would be like, Danny promised her, it would never be dull. Dan's life seemed to have been one great adventure. Some nights they would sit holding hands in Mary Ann's neat, homey living room looking out over the romantic city. The understanding grew between them that they would raise a family.

When he left Mary Ann, Dan sometimes drove across the Castro district. The street scene there had a pulsating urban energy; no corner in town was more crowded with the restless vagaries of San Francisco life than Eighteenth and Castro. When the rest of the city was going to bed for the night the Castro was lighting up. But Dan didn't notice the vitality, anymore than he noticed the election posters with Harvey Milk's name on them. What he saw was the mockery directed toward his kind in the construction workers' costumes, with their pre-ripped tee shirts, that were the latest gay style; or the boy with stumps for arms and a leather shirt open to his navel leaning against a building offering himself. He saw men who his church and his own inclination told him were living in sin.

"They're screwing around right out in the streets," Dan steamed to Father Tom Lacey. Lacey liked Dan's tough, square morality. He was an ordinary gum chewer.

"What the hell are those guys doing?" Father Lacey responded. He flushed at the collar and jabbed the air with a finger. "Are they living together just because they like to cook and they like to be friends, or are they screwing around with some sort of sodomistic behavior?" From the cold way Dan returned his look Tom Lacey knew that he shared the priest's opinion that the gay community was a cancer growing in San Francisco.

Father Lacey approved of Dan's choice of a wife without reservation. In his opinion Mary Ann was a queen, a girl with a double-double Catholic background and Jesuit professor-priests on the faculty of the University of San Francisco in her family. No question about it, Dan was marrying up and getting a really feminine, demure bride. The new Mrs. White was an iron moth.

The tough-guy priest, though, knew nothing of Dan's deepest anxieties about the impending marriage, how he had hesitated on the brink and even backed off once. But in the end Dan did what was expected of him, and what he expected of himself. The marriage was performed the week before Christmas by a cousin of Mary Ann's father, Leo, who gave away the bride. Mary Ann had chosen the chapel at Carmel-by-the-Sea because she adored the old mission of the Franciscan fathers overlooking some of the most ruggedly beautiful coastline in the world. It was a picture-book setting.

The sacrament itself meant much more to the bride than it did to the groom. Dan had long since rejected the mumbojumbo of church doctrine. He still prayed in an offhand way to St. Patrick, whom he had taken as his patron. But the Church had left indelible impressions on his way of looking at the world: sin and salvation were at war for his soul, and judgment came naturally to him.

Family and friends drove down the coast to fill the little side chapel to bursting. Dan's little sisters were the flower girls. The ceremony was simple and followed the book. The bride and groom exchanged gold wedding bands.

All along Danny had told Mary Ann of his love for Ireland, and it had always been agreed between them that they would go there for their honeymoon. When Danny talked of Ireland he always made it sound so peaceful and friendly, like heaven on earth; he had visited there before and found it to be a sanctuary of the sort he had always dreamed about. Mary Ann was excited about the honeymoon; they had planned it for months, talking and looking at books and brochures. But nearly from the moment they arrived Danny withdrew, turned cold and aloof and wouldn't talk to Mary Ann about what was wrong. His world was a black place, a lightless tunnel through which he was condemned to walk for all eternity. The deeper he sank into his doubts the more contemptible he found himself. He had been cheated out of a chance to put his father in an adult perspective and so was left with a giant against whom to measure himself, and left as well with all the bedeviling sexual conflicts of an adolescent boy. He went out and left his bride in their hotel room crying and asking herself what she had done. For the first two weeks their marriage bed was a cold and grief-torn place. Dan was on edge; the slightest thing would set him off. He tried to assure Mary Ann it was just him, it had nothing to do with her. But she blamed herself and was miserable. Whatever was troubling her *husband*—the word was a palpitation—she wanted to help him with it. But he wouldn't allow that, he was too much of a wretch in his own eyes to deserve help. Finally the mood broke.

Their marriage since then had by and large been a happy one. They both had good jobs and didn't want for anything. They were thrifty and were saving to buy a home. But Mary Ann couldn't forget what had happened on their honeymoon, nor could she stop blaming herself. So when Dan announced to her, full of glee and determination, that he was going to run for supervisor, she told him she was all for it. Whatever kept him happy pleased and relieved her.

Before Goldie Judge had a chance to get together again with the Whites, a flyer came around the neighborhood from Dan announcing a public meeting. Goldie was stunned to find three hundred people in the auditorium. This was six months before the election, nobody else had even begun to actively campaign, and Dan got a turnout like this. The people seemed to love him. She thought the speech was good. It came down hard on crime, but there were other things in it Goldie knew would have to be toned down and refined. Dan handed around a mimeographed sheet that was pretty much the same as the speech and Goldie followed along, reading as he spoke.

"For years," it said, "we have witnessed an exodus from San Francisco by many of our family members, friends and neighbors. Alarmed by the enormous increase in crime, poor educational facilities and a deteriorating social structure, they have fled to temporary havens.

"In a few short years these malignancies of society will erupt from our city and engulf the tree-lined, sunbathed communities that chide us for daring to live in San Francisco. That is, unless we who have remained can transcend the apathy which has caused us to lock our doors while the tumult rages unchecked through our streets.

"Individually we are helpless. Yet you must realize there are thousands and thousands of frustrated, angry people such as yourselves waiting to unleash a fury that can and will eradicate the malignancies which blight our beautiful city.

"A recent headline proclaimed San Francisco a 'Cesspool of Perversion.'" Goldie remembered that one, it came from that kook Senator Briggs who was on some kind of crusade against the gays. What the hell, she thought, there were no gays in District 8. "Should we continue to be maligned and shamed throughout the nation? I say NO! Only by banding together and taking positive action can we repudiate these charges.

"I am not going to be forced out of San Francisco by splinter groups of radicals, social deviates and incorrigibles," Dan said, winding down. "Believe me, there are tens of thousands who are just as determined to legally fight to protect and defend our conservative values."

Dan and Mary Ann came for pizza a few days later. The evening was quite pleasant. Dan was sweet and played with Goldie's children and tried his best to answer all the questions she had prepared. Dan talked a lot about crime, about how it made everybody scared, and he knew from experience how the hands of the police were tied by politicians; only ordinary people like themselves could prevent it continuing by taking back control of their own neighborhoods. At one point Goldie's boyfriend, Roland Percival, asked Dan, "What were you thinking about when you gave that speech the other night?" Listening to the speech, Roland had sensed something dangerous in the man.

Dan said, "Oh, nothing, I was just trying, you know, to appeal to the people so I could get their support."

"Those people are your friends," Roland spoke with a faint European accent. "They're your friends already. So what was your message?"

"Well," Dan said, concentrating and scrunching up his forehead, "My message is we've got to unite, the good people like us, we've got to unite in order to fight the criminal elements that have taken over."

In her mind Goldie put it together: Unite and Fight with Dan White. They had a slogan. Later on, when she was working up a campaign brochure, she used it. She took his speech—naturally she edited out "malignancies of society" and "cesspool of perversion"—and made a brochure out of it in three tones: white, brown, and Irish kelly green.

But that night in Goldie's living room there was still more to talk about. "If I'm going to manage your campaign I wouldn't like to see you sell your soul in order to get on that board, Dan. You can go in there clean and establish yourself. Then you can play ball with the big boys, because they play rough, politics is rough. Why in hell do you want to be a politician anyway?"

"It's just my duty," Dan said. "Somebody's got to do it."

"Is it the fame? There's a lot of fame and honor coming with this, is that it?"

Humbly, sweetly, he smiled and said, "No, it's like I said, it's just my duty."

They talked a long time and finally sometime past midnight Goldie said, "Okay, I'm gonna do it."

"Oh, Goldie, good," Mary Ann said.

"Now we got a lot of work to do," Goldie said. "We got to have a campaign office, and . . ."

"I've already rented the campaign headquarters," Dan interrupted. "Down on San Bruno."

4

Black and White

By mid-June thirteen candidates had stepped forward to offer themselves to the voters of District 8. Every one of them had done the same arithmetic. About sixty thousand people lived in the four neighborhoods of the district where the population had been declining for a decade, as it had everywhere in the city. Sixty thousand people, but only 28,000 registered to vote. Maybe half of those would go to the polls. With so many candidates, that meant you could win with as few as three thousand votes, and five thousand would be a landslide. An awful lot of people figured they could round up three thousand votes. One of them was Len Heinz, who had been Dan's English teacher at Riordan High School and was big in the affairs of Epiphany parish.

Heinz was a high school English teacher and dry as chalk dust. Through his work at Epiphany parish he knew Dan's mother and had, in fact, enlisted her in his campaign. In late May, though, she approached him, much abashed. Although her face was heavily lined with wear from all the years and all the children, her eyes still flashed. She was self-effacing but proud as she explained that she would have to withdraw because Dan was also running. Heinz was startled. "Hasn't he been living out near Park Merced? That's not even in our area."

The issue soon became one of those things the other candidates threw in Dan's face. As soon as Goldie heard about it she made Dan and Mary Ann file a change of address. Dan told her not to worry, he and Mary Ann were going to buy a home in the district, and for the time being they moved into his mother's place, which had an in-law apartment. Heinz kept hammering at Dan for being a carpetbagger but the message fell on deaf ears.

And for good reason. There are no picture-postcard views in District 8. The only real hill to speak of is a spine called Portola Heights that runs east and west just a half mile above the county line. From the Heights, looking north and east, the monotonous flatlands of the district are spread below. The striking thing is how faded it all is: the modest cottages, the patchy lawns, even the tomato plants tied to backyard stakes are a dull orange breed called San Francisco Foggies. The jeans worn by the younger men are faded, as are the plain dresses of the women, as faded as the ideals of stewardship of civilization and service to others taught in St. Elizabeth's School and Epiphany and Visitation parishes by nuns who watched three and sometimes four generations of the same families pass through their classrooms.

Standing on Portola Heights and looking out over the flatlands it seemed that perhaps all that ever changed were the cars in the driveways, their hoods up and the bodies of teenage boys bent over their motors. The cars were the only shiny things in all the flatlands.

Carpetbagger? Dan didn't have to tell these people who he was and where he came from because most of them already knew: knew him because they or their children had been in school together, where Dan had been a baseball and football star, or had a cousin or an uncle who had been with Dan on the police force or in the fire department, or knew one of his brothers and sisters, or knew Mary Ann or her family, or knew Dan's mother, Eileen, through the mother's club or parish work. Every night Dan and Mary Ann visited five homes and introduced themselves. Dan came to them as one of their own. With a lifetime of service behind him in war and in peace, he came as a success, a clean, good-looking boy. He had filed in the wrong district because he had no experience with politics, but that naiveté, that freshness, only gave him more appeal. Because in the flatlands politicians were *them:* fast-talking strangers who were as unreal as movie stars, just other faces from the television screen. *They* drove up and shook hands and asked a few questions and whispered with the priest and the president of the block club and then they were gone back to wherever they came from, which sure as hell wasn't the flatlands. But he was their own, he spoke their language and gave a voice to their fears and their frustrations and their faded dreams. He was stepping off the shelf of history to which they had been consigned and riding forth, his white banner snapping as crisply as the worn sheets and pillowcases strung out to dry on a thousand backyard clotheslines from one end of the flatlands to the other.

"By choosing to run for supervisor," he told his audiences at the end of his campaign speeches, "I have committed myself to the confrontation which can no longer be avoided by those who care."

"What confrontation, Dan?" If Goldie had asked him once, she had asked him a hundred times, "What the hell are you talking about? Are you worried the gays are comin' in here and are gonna screw our good all-American daughters?"

But Goldie couldn't get anything out of Dan except his sweet, earnest, slightly wounded smile.

"What? What are you all about?" Goldie would sometimes scream. "Tell me!"

As the campaign continued, Goldie Judge remained not suspicious exactly, but irksomely paranoiac. She was sure that something was being kept from her, that there was more to Dan White and who backed him than she was being told. She kept encountering secrets, half-revealed problems. Dan's stepfather, Frank McHugh, told her, "I'm not going to sign up to support Dan yet. I'll tell you what I decide in a couple of weeks." When Goldie pressed McHugh about what the problem was—God, it would look awful if it got out—the retired fireman would only say, "I've got my reasons." Eventually he came around and put his name on the list of sponsors but that wasn't until August, after Dan's mother had worked on him.

Even the contributions that were arriving every day, more than one thousand dollars in fifty-dollar chunks from individual firemen, a couple of hundred from cops, another thousand dollars from Dan's family and close friends, seemed to her a sign that something was wrong. Goldie had never heard of so much money flowing effortlessly into a supervisorial campaign so early in the summer. It should have pleased her but instead it made her wary: who was this guy, what were his connections? There was no mistaking Dan's desire to win, though. He and Mary Ann loaned the campaign three thousand dollars out of their savings.

Between Goldie and Mary Ann a certain understanding had come about; they were behind the same man. Mary Ann seemed more familiar with the political issues than her husband was, and it was she who wrote down the lists of answers that Goldie demanded so that she could manage the campaign. Goldie could tell because Mary Ann's handwriting was round and open, the kind that got an *A* in sixth-grade penmanship, while Dan's hand was cramped and slanty and tightly controlled, almost painful to look at.

Once, when the two women were in the headquarters alone, having a girl talk Goldie mentioned something that she had noticed and didn't like. Going into a meeting, Dan had rushed ahead of Mary Ann, not holding the door open for her, leaving her to fend for herself. He didn't show his wife any tenderness in public, never touched her or held her hand. Those kinds of things didn't look right. When Goldie had remonstrated with Dan about it he had smiled and replied, "Okay, boss, anything you say, boss."

But now, discussing it with Mary Ann, Goldie remarked that most problems with today's marriages are in the bedroom.

Mary Ann sighed, "Oh, I know what you mean, Goldie," she said, and confided to her what had happened on their honeymoon.

A few days later Goldie asked Dan, "Dan, do you like sex?"

"Yep," he said.

"Do you have it often?" She pronounced the *t.*

"I'm not gonna tell you that."

"Well, you just told me," Goldie shot back. "You know, the best thing for a candidate is to have a lot of sex."

Dan laughed and took it in good humor, but he was also red in the face and hung his head like a little boy.

Most of all Goldie wanted to educate Dan, to prepare him for what he would find at City Hall. She dispatched him down there to watch committee meetings, and set up appointments for him. One night they were sitting in a car in front of her house, it was late, they had been at a community meeting.

"Goldie," Dan said, "What do you want out of all this? What can I do for you?" It was the first time he had asked.

"What do *you* want?" Goldie said.

"All I want is to be a supervisor."

"Okay, we'll make you a supervisor. What I want in return is you to let me be your guide through your first year in City Hall."

"What do you mean?" Dan asked.

Goldie explained as if she were talking to a child. If he confided in her, she said, she could show him how to make the deals, get the things he wanted done. "Harvey Milk's gonna win in five," she said. "Are you ready to deal with him?" Even then she had figured out that since they voted in alphabetical order on the Board there was a pretty good chance that White would be voting last. He would be the one who could break ties, they'd have to come courting him. "That means you can play some hard politics, okay?"

For an instant Dan's high, pale forehead was scrunched up. He looked out the windshield toward the empty street. "You want to be my aide?" he asked. There was just a hint of the street tough lurking behind his guarded way of speaking, the faintest suggestion of "dese" and "dose," like a buried archeological layer of speech.

Each supervisor could hire two aides. "I don't care, I don't need no title," Goldie said. She felt sad and frustrated, it was as if he hadn't understood a word she had said.

"I'll have to think about it," Dan told her.

Now that was a hell of a note. She had worked for two months, night and day, without ever asking for or being offered a nickel, and she hadn't even asked to be a paid aide, only to help him. And what does he say? "I'll have to think about it." He dodged her the same way he had dodged the question the day they had first met about who had recommended Goldie to him, dodged whatever he didn't want to talk about the way only trained policemen could, saying what he wanted and no more. Just like a goddamn cop, Goldie thought.

On the last day of 1967, when he had been twenty-one years old, Dan had come home from a three-year Army hitch, including a year in Vietnam. He had returned without any clear sense of direction. He passed a few months collecting unemployment insurance and delivering pizzas. He hitchhiked to New Orleans, impressing his buddies by doing something they all dreamed about. But there was an emptiness in him, a yearning.

Insofar as he had a plan, it was to become a writer. But he had to earn a living and so he drifted into becoming a cop, the way a lot of guys from his neighborhood did. There were enough reasons for him to find the idea attractive. His religion and his parochial education had encouraged his zealousness and left him with the notion that service was the greatest good. He wanted to do the right thing and he could see that the deterioration of the old neighborhood made cops more important than ever. The pay was pretty good. And there was still another appeal. The police department was a brotherhood, they were the last protectors of the old values, the difference between law and anarchy. As a rule they were condescending to all but their own kind. Dan's kind.

Ever since James Curtis had become the first police chief back in 1856, when the cops who patrolled the waterfront alleys wore long coats and carried Bowie knives as their only weapons, the list of chiefs had read like a roster of the Ancient Order of Hibernians: there were Cockrill, Quinn, Crowley and Ahearn, Burke, Healy, Dinan and Dullea. Dan had every reason to believe he'd fit in and he badly wanted to feel that he belonged somewhere. Although for the first twenty years of his life he had always been a part of some family or fraternity— whether it was the White family, or the Church, or his high school teams, or the army—and though he had strong loyalties, within himself he had always stood alone because secretly he felt different. He believed that he was far from commonplace; his sense of destiny, which was vaguely mixed up with his being Irish, told him he belonged to some design of history.

He wanted to pattern his life after Jack London, whose books he carried with him. Dan thought that if he could write, then he would be able to give expression to his own feverish, inchoate impression that life's task was to live rationally, distinguishing between right and wrong. At the deepest level he was unambiguous, life was black and white. If he belonged anywhere while he worked out his fate it was in a prowl car.

When his training was completed, Dan was assigned to Northern Station, just a few blocks from City Hall. Cops considered Northern a battle station. Its men patrolled high crime and corruption areas from the Tenderloin with its tawdry streets and bars to the restlessly crowded housing projects of Hayes Valley and the Fillmore. Dan was assigned to work undercover as a narcotics officer, but before long he asked for a transfer. He wanted too much to be liked; he wasn't cut out for befriending dealers only to turn around and bust them. The deceitfulness offended him.

But routine patrol didn't appeal to him either. He found himself reluctant to make arrests for minor crimes and petty offenses and got a reputation as somebody who might have been more suited to be a social worker. Cops who weren't charmed by his blarney, or whom he didn't respect himself, thought he was smug and condescending. Pretty much all that did appeal to him about police work was the camaraderie; the games of five-card pedro in the station house, or the easy talk at the Doggie Diner.

His reputation for being different was assured when Dan quit the department after only twenty months, grew a beard, and took off for Alaska the way Jack London had. Nothing worked out in Alaska, though, and before long he had returned to San Francisco and signed up to rejoin the police department, for lack of anything better to do.

The day he got back from Alaska he went looking for a buddy he owed some money to, and found him at a restaurant and bar that was popular with cops, the La Barca Room, where Alma de LaPantera was a waitress. Alma spotted the young man with the bushy red beard the minute he walked in and something in her moved. She went to the bartender, and nodding her head toward the stranger who was pumping hands and slamming backs with a couple of cops, she said, "If this guy he asks for my name, you tell him I am single woman."

After a ten-year struggle to get the papers that allowed her to escape Colombia, Alma had come to San Francisco only to find that her man, who had preceded her, had set up another woman in an apartment across town. Not even that could depress her naturally buoyant spirits, though. Even motionless she seemed bouncy. She took the infidelity for what it was, a disappointment that left her free to do as she pleased. And something about this stranger pleased her.

Dan noticed Alma too, as she put herself in his path. She was just barely five feet tall with a soft, sensuous body. Long reddish-brown curls fell around a valentine-shaped face with small, slightly sharp features. Her eyes slanted exotically and there was a pretty dimple in her cheek. When she smiled, which she did often enough for some cops who didn't know her name to refer to her as "that gal at La Barca with the million-dollar smile," she lit up.

"Hey, Dan," one of his buddies said, after Alma had flirted with him while serving them drinks, "she likes you."

The next time Alma returned to their table he asked her name. When she told him he gave her his own winning smile. "What's such a short person doing with such a big name?" he asked.

Dan hung around until Alma's shift ended at eleven and that very first night they went together to his friend's house. Alma found Dan to be inexperienced but not shy. He was considerate and tender with her. A few days later they saw each other again and went to a motel. Dan had rented an apartment but he was ashamed to bring Alma there because he had no furniture, just a mattress on the floor. And Alma couldn't bring him home because of her man, whom she hadn't told Dan about.

Somehow Dan found out where she lived and one morning he showed up. He rang the bell and was standing there with a goofy, happy, Surprise! sort of grin when the door was opened by a man. Dan recovered quickly. He asked for Alma, explaining that he was a customer at La Barca and he owed her some money. The man wasn't fooled but he didn't care anyway. That evening Dan came looking for her at the restaurant. He asked her why she hadn't told him the truth, and she explained that she liked to be with him, it was a good thing, they both needed someone and wanted each other.

"Let's always tell each other the truth," Dan said. He began the truth-telling by admitting why he had never asked her back to his apartment. But he was about to start a second hitch in the police department and he was renting a new place; she could visit him there.

Alma told him there would be no ties between them, that was the way it should be. In bed it was good for them, and they were becoming friends. "Whenever you find a somebody else you like better, you tell me, yes?" She said.

Dan agreed that would be their understanding. No ties, lots of lovemaking, consideration, and a promise to tell the truth.

"You like my new dress?" Alma asked.

He reached out for her. "No," he said, "I like what's underneath."

In Alaska, Dan had come to the conclusion that a man who works for a living is a fool, that being a wage slave the way his father had been wasn't for him. Although he had to be a cop again to keep body and soul together, he was determined to save every penny he could. He figured that with enough operating capital he could make himself rich. In the grip of his plans for the future he would pace obsessively and say to Alma, "I've got to get some money, that's all it takes, getting some money to start up." He boasted to her that he was a man who always got what he wanted, too. At twenty-five he had drifted away from the Church but not from its turn of mind: his actions he tried to ground in reason but they were launched upon a leap of faith. No way was Dan White going to wind up among the ranks of Thoreau's quietly desperate.

Dan had rented a small apartment on Visitacion Avenue. In exchange for looking after the yard and maintaining the property he was allowed to live nearly rent-free. He kept the place as clean as a barrack and just as cold and unadorned. He had one knife, one fork, one spoon, a cup, a bowl and a platter. That way he didn't have to waste time washing dishes. His few possessions included some books, a sleeping bag and mattress, and a typewriter. From time to time, in a frenzy, he would hunch over the typewriter and pound the keys for hours and hours. Alma would usually watch the soaps on TV while Danny was being a writer, she didn't care much for books. When he was finished he read her what he had written. She was glad he had written a story, it seemed to make him happy, but her mind wandered as he read it to her. She was an uncritical audience, the story was about somebody's life, that was all she understood of it.

By now they were seeing each other most days. Alma was six years older than he was, he called her "old lady" and when he did there was a light in his eyes; they turned greener. Afterward he would shower. Danny was very strong, with rippling muscles he kept up by playing ball and lifting weights. He was proud of his body and Alma adored it. When he was naked she never took her eyes off him. As far as she knew Dan had always been faithful to her.

In August 1972, when Dan went up to Lake Tahoe with a police softball team, Alma was already in his bed waiting for him when he came home late Sunday night. He got out of his clothes and into bed beside her, chattering all the while about how his team had won the tournament and he had been given an award. Alma came into his arms. Danny went cold and resistant. It was the first time in the two years they had been together he hadn't wanted to make love when she offered herself.

"You don't want me?" she said.

"I'm tired, that's all."

"You always want me before, Danny."

"It's nothing. Let's go to sleep." He turned his back to her.

"It's something. Tell me what. You promise you will tell always the truth."

"I'm just tired."

"You promise."

Dan gave a long sigh and rolled over. Even in the dark she could see he was blushing. "Well, uh, we, you know, we won, we won the championship. So there was a celebration, and, uh . . ."

"There was a woman?"

"Uh huh. She, uh, well, uh. I mean, some of the guys bought girls."

"You don't want me?"

"No, it's not that. I'm just worried you might, I mean, I might have, you know, a disease or something. I want to get a doctor to check me out."

"Okay, Danny. I'm just glad you tell the truth."

This second tour of duty on the police force he found, if anything, even less pleasant than the first. He was tightly self-disciplined on the street, and especially effective at calming domestic quarrels. But he seemed shy of using force except as a last resort. Around Ingleside Station they told the story of how Danny White had tried to reason with a blind-drunk, fighting-mad three-hundred-pound Samoan and got knocked on his keister. He simply couldn't make sense out of the reality of police work when it clashed with his ideal. When it suited him, when the rules seemed illogical to the point of becoming cruel, he broke them.

Take the night when Dan knew Alma's man was away and he stopped by her house. He was in uniform and on duty.

"What is this about, Danny?" she asked.

"Hows about a cup of coffee?" he said. Over the coffee he explained that he was assigned that night to drive a paddy wagon and he had two boys, little more than children, in his custody. They had been picked up for some petty vandalism, nothing worse than his hijinks when he was a kid. If he took them to Ingleside they'd be booked and printed and have the beginning of a police record.

"The wagon's unlocked," he explained, and grinned conspiratorially. "When I'm finished with my coffee they'll be far away."

Dan was a floater, a cop without a regular shift or partner. Quite often, though, he was teamed up on the four-to-midnight with another floater, Ed Fortner. In the locker room at Ingleside was a chinup bar and one afternoon when they were changing into their uniforms Dan challenged Fortner to a chinup contest.

"No," Fortner said, "I don't think so."

"Hey, c'mon, Ed, you can probably lick me."

"What the hell," Fortner said, "Okay."

They flipped a coin to see who would go first, which was a disadvantage, and Dan lost. He set himself under the bar, wiped his palms on his pants, seized hold of the bar with his small, strong hands, and began to hoist and lower himself. Fortner followed the count idly.

"Twenty-two," Dan grunted, dropping to the ground. "You're up."

At his fifteenth chinup Fortner began to tire, but he pushed himself, aiming for twenty-three. His eyes were bulging even more than usual. Twenty-one and twenty-two were a struggle, but giving it everything he had, Fortner hoisted himself one last time.

"Twenty-three," he gasped. "I win."

"Unh-unh, I did twenty-four." Dan was gleeful.

"The hell you say. You did twenty-two."

"I did twenty-four. I knew I couldn't beat you so I had to con you." He was tickled pink with himself.

Fortner was a clever man, another would-be writer, his oblong face usually set in an intelligent scowl. He found Dan White to be an interesting study. In his estimation Dan was trying to lead an examined life, and though Dan's conclusions might have been jejune, Fortner believed his partner's thinking might mature as he learned more about life.

Hour after hour, day after day Dan and Ed Fortner rode the Outer Mission in their prowl car, grousing about the irrational way they were making a living. They saw all the mean senselessness of the streets, they grew familiar with violent death. First as a soldier and now as a cop Dan had tacitly signaled his willingness to kill when duty or justice demanded it; one way or another he had seen a good number of live people become dead people. The general awe with which death, even violent death, was regarded, as if it were some thundering event, came to seem rather silly. Dan remarked that he had lost his sense of astonishment. Fortner said: "You could ask any farmer, the transformation of something live into dead meat is trivial, mechanical."

Fortner was more stoic about it, but Dan didn't think police work was a life for a rational man. He worried that if he stuck with it he'd become jaded, that the sharp edge of his righteousness would grow dull and he'd become like all the others. He could see all around him how years and years of wearing the badge had made older cops close themselves off; they had to discipline themselves to look the other way when that was prudent, and worse, to be unaffected by people. There was something embittering about being a cop. It was the final Station of the Cross of police brotherhood, this attitude which shielded them and excluded all outsiders.

Dan seemed forever poised on the threshold of moving on again. He struck Fortner as a moral man, but somebody much given to being born again—for all his talk of the family and the old neighborhood, somebody without sure roots. Usually his system of values and goals was internally coherent and predicated on some idea of right conduct.

Yet during their long nighttime talks, spasmodically interrupted by episodes of violence or terror or frustration, Fortner decided he saw in Dan White a man who might wake up one morning, and reasoning that some course of action—*any* course of action—was his duty, would do what he believed he must.

Despite the apparent conventionality of much of his life, Fortner thought that Dan didn't feel himself bound by the social contract. He had extraordinary self-discipline; he was, after all, banking nearly his entire paycheck, and that discipline, grounded in his devout faith in himself, had bestowed on him a rare Nietzschean independence. Where duty compelled him he passed beyond the pity and sway of other men and became remorseless.

So Ed Fortner mused about his handsome young partner and, musing, sometimes found that he was scared, though he could not say for whom or of what.

Dan had one foot out the door when the incident at the Shy Fox slammed it closed behind him, and he quit the department for the second and final time. It was a Friday night about 11 P.M., only an hour to go on the shift when the dispatcher called a 418, a bar fight, in a neighborhood place called the Shy Fox just a few blocks from where Dan and his partner were cruising. They were the first to respond to the scene. When they got there the fight had spilled onto the sidewalk.

Within moments several other cars arrived and as it turned out everybody was needed. As Dan pulled up, there were two guys getting pummeled and kicked on the pavement. Some women from the bar were throwing drink glasses—when the cops arrived several were aimed toward them—and the fighters were rolling around in broken glass. There was a lot of screaming and shouting, the sounds of glass shattering and crunching, some blood. It was your run-of-the-mill Friday night bar beef.

What made this one a little different, though, was that the guys on the sidewalk who were getting the worst of the fight were brothers in blue, off-duty cops from Mission Station. It had all begun because a gang of Mission District bikers were having a bachelor party for one of their men who was getting married. The groom-to-be was large and nasty. By coincidence, some cops from Mission Station were having a night out and they, too, ended up at the Shy Fox. Among the policemen was one who had had the pleasure of busting the groom-to-be on a narcotics rap. At first the two knots of men drank separately, but everybody was pretty loaded and it was palpable that it would come to a fight, there was no way either side was going to walk away from it. One knot of men was law and the other was outlaw and certain points of honor were demanded by both their codes.

Fists began to fly, landing with the sickening thud of bone smashing bone, and then bottles and heavy-toed boots. The Mission Station cops were taking their lumps when Dan and then the other on-duty cops arrived to lay waste to the bikers and send the boys from Mission home to lick their wounds. The bikers were hustled into prowl cars and driven to Ingleside.

By this time it was nearly midnight and there was the usual chaos of a shift change underway in the station house. Cops in and out of uniform were milling around when the sullen bikers were wheeled in, and just a moment later the cops from Mission who had been sent packing showed up too. The atmosphere was about what could be expected, a lot of sweet nothings back and forth about one man's ancestry and another's body scent. A lot of these men had known each other for years. They had attended school together, or dated each other's sisters, or simply were familiar with the streets they both patrolled, the cops in their well-pressed blues and the bikers in their outlaw colors.

One of the cops reporting to work for the midnight shift was Officer Jay Wallace, a small man known to his brothers for having a small man's complex in a tough man's world. Wallace had a reputation for mixing it up with prisoners, and that rubbed some of the other cops the wrong way, among them Dan. Dan had had some previous run-ins with Wallace; neither had much use for the other. Wallace came upon the scene in the station house at its most chaotic. The groom-to-be, faced with the bleak prospect of spending the eve of his nuptials in a jail cell, was prowling around in handcuffs aching to rearrange some cop noses.

"Sit down," Wallace ordered.

"Sit on my face, midget," said the groom-to-be.

In the stack of police reports on what ensued, stories differed but several officers seemed to think that Wallace shouted, "You want me, you can have me," and took the handcuffs off the prisoner. Others contended the cuffs remained on, most vehemently Officer Dan White. It was an important legal point because a policeman is entitled to subdue without restraint an unhandcuffed prisoner who is resisting, which is what Wallace began to do to the groom-to-be.

As the first officer on the scene at the Shy Fox, Dan was responsible for the prisoner. Though he had seen such things happen before, Dan had a burn on about Wallace: just because he was a cop didn't mean he could beat up whoever rubbed him the wrong way. Dan wouldn't countenance it.

When peace was finally restored Dan decided to write a report accusing Jay Wallace of brutality. A lot of cops treated blacks, *all* blacks, disrespectfully and sometimes brutally, but for one cop to blow the whistle on another was a violation of the police code of brotherly solidarity tantamount to treason, an attack on the sanctity of the department by one of its own. But Dan was in the grip of self-righteous indignation; he wasn't considering the consequences.

Most everybody else wanted to minimize the incident, but Dan went ahead and wrote up a scratch and once he did there was no turning back. Reports had to be filed with Internal Affairs and every cop who had been around had to write up a report, which did not endear Dan. By the time all the typewriters stopped clattering there was a file more than an inch thick. The station commander, Captain Laherty, tried to talk sense to Officer White about it. Laherty was of the old school and he tried to explain that what had happened wasn't the kind of thing that would shock a sensible policeman. After all, the captain explained, one stubborn Irishman to another, the prisoner was bigger than Officer Wallace, and a man who could handle himself. If Officer White had been a conscientious cop he would have helped to restore order by lending a hand in subduing the suspect, not by writing up a fellow officer.

There were cops at Ingleside who respected what Dan had done. But even the policemen closest to him couldn't understand why he felt he had to do it, why he was subjecting them all to a test of loyalty. Out of the blue they had to choose between the cop's code or Dan White. Breaking the code was damn serious business—Dan's life was threatened and for quite a while afterward, even after he quit the department, he carried his gun with him.

So it didn't come as a surprise to Alma when Dan called her at home one day in 1973 and said, "I finally quit. Call your boss and tell him you're taking two days off. We're going up to Vegas and getting rich." For months he had been carrying a pair of dice with him, on duty and off, rolling them again and again and counting how often double sixes came up. The casinos in Nevada paid off at 36–1 on double sixes, or boxcars, and Dan was obsessed with mastering the percentages.

On the plane he told Alma that he would join the Fire Department in January, but first he was going to break the house in Las Vegas and then go to Ireland for a holiday. He was frantically excited and showed Alma a two-thousand-dollar check that was his gambling stake. The episode didn't really seem out of character to her, even though it was crazy for somebody to have scrimped the way he had, only to risk gambling away so much money. She had long since decided that Danny was unstable, that he always wanted to be somebody else, that contentment was not possible for him.

In Vegas he rented a car and they checked into Caesar's Palace. Danny wanted to go right down to the casino. Alma thought he'd start in to bet immediately but instead he bought a stack of chips and stood at the table for a long time watching the action without making any bets himself. Hostesses in scanty costumes and mesh stockings were serving free drinks and Alma got quickly and quietly drunk on champagne.

"Hey, Danny, when you bet?"

"I'm checking it out, I've got a system." He kept his eyes on the felt table. "It's the probabilities."

"You bet, go ahead."

He shook his head. "Not yet. You'll see. We're waiting for boxcars to make us rich."

Alma didn't know what he was talking about. Then all of a sudden he pushed a stack of chips onto the betting surface and lost. When the croupier swept his chips away Dan smiled as if it was just what he had hoped for. It seemed to Alma that he was mad. On the next roll he bet again. And again on a third roll. Each bet was bigger than the one before it. With the fourth roll his stake was lost. Danny was absolutely crestfallen, his system had failed him. They spent most of the next two days riding around town in the rented car, eating in the hotels and watching stage shows. Alma managed to stay drunk for forty-eight straight hours.

Dan took a vacation alone in Ireland, but was back home by January 1974 to begin two months of training as a fireman. He had been looking forward to the training, but as things turned out the next eight weeks were among the most trying he had known. The cause of the turmoil was a lawsuit that had been filed against the Fire Department, accusing it of racial discrimination. Just before Dan's training began the suit was settled out of court and a federal judge imposed a minority hiring quota.

There were at the time only four black firemen in San Francisco, so it was a real departure when nine black men were included among the forty-eight trainees, or probies as they were called, in Dan's class. Black men with lower scores than some white applicants had been admitted to comply with the court order. Dan himself had excelled, finishing thirteenth among 463 candidates. On the physical agility test he had come close to a perfect score. He was in strikingly good condition. He held himself with a peasant-like stiffness that suggested endurance and stubbornness. Men who had served with his father recognized him at once as Charlie's son. Even at twenty-seven, though, there was something more finished about Dan than there had been about his father. The son was clean, impeccable, diffident at first, with less booze and brawl and good times in his face and bearing.

Not surprisingly, the court order, which had to be complied with, was also resisted. Chief Keith Calden and many of his men did not take kindly to the idea of a judge requiring them to lower their standards, in their view, and thus perhaps to endanger their lives. These rationalizations substituted for acknowledging the prejudice felt by many white firefighters: when there had been only one black firefighter in San Francisco he had had to carry his own mattress from firehouse to firehouse since none of his fellows would lay themselves down where he had rested. The firefighters were men who had to rely on each other in situations where a mistake or a mishap could mean the end. Without total mutual confidence they were in deep trouble, and it wasn't unusual for them to believe that blacks were lazy, shiftless and unreliable. Though they complied with the letter of the court order they did what they could to circumvent its spirit by instituting, for the first time, ongoing evaluations throughout the training period. In the past, once a man was admitted to the Fire College he was assured of a job. For hopeless cases there had always been desk work, but no longer. It was pretty much up to the Fire College staff to decide who would make it all the way through and who would not. The probies were under enormous pressure to perform.

The pressure drove the probies closer to each other, a spirit of cooperation prevailed, and nobody worked with more fervor nor had a more inspirational effect than Dan, who stood at the top of the class. Often he stayed late to tutor men who were having trouble. Just before the training was completed it was announced that three blacks and one white had flunked out and wouldn't be hired. Dan took a leading role in circulating a petition asking for their reinstatement, but the department turned a deaf ear.

Meanwhile Dan was spending every evening in front of his old typewriter pecking out his valedictory address. He had been chosen to speak for his class and the honor meant a great deal to him, though he took pains not to show how pleased he was. By joining the Fire Department, and by excelling, he was living up to what he knew his dad would have expected from him; in a sense he was going home to his father's other family, to where as a boy he had been initiated into the all-male world of polished brass, sudden alarms and short-sheeted bunks, of regimented lives and practical jokes and dangerous work stoically accepted. The honor bestowed on him was, in addition, the most important recognition the world had shown him. It would be his first public speech and he typed and retyped until he got it right.

When the big day arrived there was a winter breeze ruffling his hair and blowing it in his face as he faced his expectant audience. He began by politely thanking Chief Calden, the Fire College staff, the families and friends who were present. Then, his boyish voice cracking with emotion, Dan said what had to be said.

"We, the members of the forty-eighth training class, haven't any doubts concerning our ability to become proficient firemen. Not only in performing the physical act of fire service but also as"—he paused for emphasis— "exceptional representatives of what a San Francisco fireman should be.

"Any such doubts a man may have harbored ceased to exist upon the culmination of his training. For this training subjected each and every one of us to the most terrifying experience a man can know— psychological fear." In his written address he had typed it out as Psychological Fear!!

"Fear," he exhorted his audience to understand, "that he might lose the means of providing for himself and his loved ones. A fear so insidious, so devastating that it caused men to doubt their own abilities. We desired to strike out and destroy this thing, this invader . . . but we could not. For fear is not tangible. We could only endure; persevering until the day we would once again know peace of mind."

And probably it was pride rather than modesty which made him say "we," not "I": he spoke movingly and with a fine vocabulary, feeling himself to be a vessel through which the experiences of his fellows were being expressed. "We were tried under the most adverse circumstances . . . and we emphatically state that our graduation here today is testimony to the fact that we defeated that fear, that insidious threat to our wellbeing. Yes, we defeated it as individuals, and more importantly, we defeated it as *brothers* striving toward a common goal.

"Thank you," he said.

The applause was as warm and heartfelt as the speech. One by one members of his audience rose to their feet until they were all standing, smashing their hands together and shouting approval. He had spoken his mind and his brothers and sisters, by blood and sentiment, were giving him a hero's welcome.

Dan had come home.

During the years that Dan and Alma had been lovers their lives had taken on a certain routine familiarity. When Alma stayed with him she ate what he did; tunafish on Ritz crackers was his staple meal. Sometimes they went out to MacDonald's where Danny could put away double orders of french fries and two cokes with his Big Mac. Afterward he took her to his favorite ice cream parlor for chocolate cones. For the most part he subsisted on junk food.

He no longer spoke of sailing around the world, as he once had. That had become just another dream: there had been the flying lessons when he decided to become a pilot, and the delicatessen he had wanted to open, and plans to move to Ireland, and the novel he was going to write. Alma now saw that he always wanted something other than what he had, he was never content to be himself. Deep down inside he was like a man squirming to get off a stake on which he was impaled, flopping all about. One day when Alma came by his new place he stripped off his shirt to show her a new tattoo—a green shamrock on his left shoulder. Danny handed her a camera and had her take a picture of him in a musclebuilder's pose, showing off the tattoo and his terrific build. He was deliriously happy.

Alma knew he would never marry her, even if she left her man. In Dan's black-and-white world women were either whores or madonnas, and Alma was no madonna. They were good friends and she was a safe bet for him: old enough to know herself and make her own decisions, sensual and undemanding, still unsure enough of herself in America to admire and depend upon his superior wisdom.

Marriage was a subject that Dan had always skirted in his own mind. On the one hand, he wanted all that a wife and children symbolized. On the other hand, he was willful and solitary and his parents' life had taught him that marriage was a serious business that left very little time for doing what you wanted to do. He respected his mother for her discipline in running the family, but she had provided him with no hope that a wife could be soft and sweet or a marriage romantic. In the year before he had met Mary Ann, Dan had changed the way he lived, as if preparing for the domestic hunt. He had moved into the tiny cabin of a sailboat where he couldn't stand upright and didn't own a car. Then all of a sudden, he bought himself a new metallic-blue Porsche (he had to ask a friend where to put the oil in), and rented a modern apartment in a subdivision out near Ocean Beach that he filled with new furniture. All at once he had gone from living like an ascetic to living like a comfortable bachelor. It was one more indication of the black-and-white contrasts that constituted his inner life: ascetic/indulgent, moral/licentious, solitary/gregarious, superior/wretched. He was twenty-eight and his mother and his sisters were pressing him to find a wife and settle down, when he met Mary Ann.

The time had come to honor his promise to Alma. For the only time in the four years he had known her he cooked dinner for them at his apartment, wild rice and chicken in white sauce. He even lit candles and poured white wine for both of them. Alma was feeling coddled and romantic, and when Danny was called out to the firehouse she washed the dishes and waited for him to come back. While he was gone, his resolve stiffened to say what had to be said. When he came home she rushed into his arms and kissed him. He stepped back from her and began, haltingly, to remind Alma of their agreement. She could sense that something had changed.

"Is something wrong?" she asked him.

"No," Danny said. "Well, I met this lady." It hurt him to tell her and it hurt Alma to hear it but she was glad he had told her the truth. She left him that night without his ever having told her who the other woman was.

Once, a year later, she bumped into Dan and Mary Ann in a supermarket and Danny turned all red and purple. But he said hello and introduced her to his wife. Alma didn't think Mary Ann had noticed Danny's discomfort, he always said hello to everybody. Mary Ann didn't give any sign that she knew who Alma was. The thing that struck Alma was how much alike the two of them were, almost as if they were brother and sister.

The first week in July, 1977, Dan opened his campaign headquarters by throwing a big party. They rented a sound system to play the campaign song he had chosen, the theme music from *Rocky*. Dan could really identify with the story of the prizefighter who had seized his one great opportunity to rise from a nobody to heavyweight champion. The music fired him up.

It was a banner week for Dan and Mary Ann because they had also taken title to a new home, a simple three-bedroom bungalow in Epiphany parish that had been built in 1939 and on which they had taken a $55,000 mortgage. It didn't seem more of a burden than they could handle; their combined income approached $40,000 a year.

The new house was perhaps roomier than what they required but they wanted that extra bedroom because they planned to have kids. There was a finished den in the basement, very much like the room that Charlie White had built for his family, and that became Dan's study. Dan and Mary Ann were too busy to set the house up right all at once, and for quite a while a lot of their belongings remained packed in crates. But Dan did put some books on the shelves in his study, including his entire set of Will and Ariel Durant's *Story of Civilization.* He had always been a voracious reader, an autodidact. He was quite well educated from his reading but not fluent about what he knew: ideas fit him like a suit that was too tight in the shoulders. In one corner of his new study, right beside his desk, which wasn't much bigger than a school child's, he taped to the wall the story that had run in the newspaper that had declared his father a hero, about how he had rescued a suicidal minister's son from a tower on Twin Peaks.

And in the closet at the opposite corner of the room, on a shelf at the back out of harm's way, he put his gun and his ammo. The Smith and Wesson .38 revolver with a two-inch barrel that he had bought for eighty-five dollars was all he had left from his years as a policeman. Unlike the badge, it hadn't gone back to the department when he had resigned. It was his. The gun stayed with him.

5
Pauper's Pension

The eight years that George Moscone spent in Sacramento after being elected to the state senate were important ones for him: he arrived a talented beginner and departed a mature politician.

Ronald Reagan was governor. In his second year in the senate George was chosen as floor leader by the Democratic majority, and thus became a spokesman for their opposition to Reagan's policies. He sponsored laws to require public agencies to hold open meetings, to establish a consumer protection agency, to restrict the scope of injunctions against striking workers, to reduce the penalties for possession of small amounts of marijuana to the severity of a traffic violation. His proudest victory was a school lunch program for poor children, which he shepherded into place over five years and despite a string of Reagan vetoes. In the senate he had found a sanctum where he could exercise his singular abilities.

His success derived in part from his instinct for accommodating all varieties of political concerns, from knowing what a colleague could do and what he couldn't, how far he could bend without hurting himself back home. Within the meaning of the term to politicians, he was honest: he wasn't on the take and he said the same thing—albeit a little differently—to everybody. He loved debate, thrived on it, and because he was passionate, clever, articulate and invariably well prepared, he was effective. He was flexible and subtle enough in his appreciations so that while he personally would have abhorred his wife or daughters having an abortion, he was able to support a woman's right to one.

When it came to the arcane art of drawing a bill, he was a craftsman; he could make a law do what he wanted it to.

Yet for all his skill at dealing with tens of millions of dollars and the sensitive egos of other politicians, he was unable to balance his own checkbook. The whole time he was in Sacramento he never wrote a personal check. His secretary took care of that, deciding from month to month whether to pay the priests who were educating the four Moscone children or the butcher who was feeding them. George never seemed to have enough money and fretted about it constantly. By 1974 not only his financial straits but the sameness of Sacramento had begun to get him down. The challenge had been met and was no longer a challenge. Ambition was nipping at his heels again. That year he made an ill-planned attempt at winning the Democratic nomination for governor, dropping out months before the primary that was eventually won by Jerry Brown.

All the time he had been away George had sung a torch song for his hometown. The year 1975 was to be the last of Joseph Alioto's two terms as mayor, and would-be successors were already elbowing each other for position. It looked like a wide-open opportunity. As majority leader, George had done a lot of fund-raising and he knew he could finance a mayoral campaign. He had around him, as well, a young staff of political pros which could comprise the nucleus of a campaign organization. He thought he could win and he wanted to be closer to his kids, who were growing up with a weekend father. Being mayor paid better, too, and would present fresh challenges. No matter how he looked at it, being top dog among all the San Francisco guys made sense. If he had owned a hat he would have thrown it into the ring.

Waste of a perfectly good hat, John Barbegelata would have sneered. Look at that bare head, naked ambition. Then he would have ground the hat under his heel. City Supervisor Barbegelata (whose name translated as "frozen beard") was a well-to-do realtor who saw George Moscone as a Trojan horse for the radical elements that in his view were trying to take over San Francisco. Barbegelata seemed to believe that his opinions represented a divine hold on the truth, and it was an article of his faith that Moscone was a scoundrel.

At first George and his campaign staff didn't take Barbegelata quite seriously; after all, he was to the right of Attila the Hun. Among George's four rivals Dianne Feinstein, the young President of the Board of Supervisors, seemed the most substantial contender. Feinstein, a wealthy surgeon's wife associated with those "good government" organizations that had attached themselves like pilot fish to the shark of Manhattanization, spoke for technocratic decision-making. Her vision of San Francisco was a rhetorical idealization of what was being espoused by the redevelopment bureaucrats and the big investors who were the real powers behind the transformation of the city. She spoke not of profits but of jobs; not of destruction of neighborhoods but of proper planning, of harmonious reconciliation and not of the difficult resolution of painful conflicts. But as election day drew nearer Moscone's own private polls showed Barbegelata to be his closest competitor.

George presented himself as the candidate of the people without money or power or voice strong enough to be heard on their own: the people in the neighborhoods south of Market and east of Twin Peaks, the poor, the people of color, renters, gays, the rank and file of labor, the decent and the humane. He pledged that he would give them a place in city government. He said that he was against the soulless "ripoffs" represented by the Manhattanization of the skyline, and refused to accept campaign contributions from organizations which did business with the city. He refused, as well, all contributions greater than one hundred dollars.

The toughest problem was getting the people to whom he was appealing out to vote on election day. Calvin Welch and his allies in the district elections movement had organizers in all the kinds of neighborhoods George needed to reach, so he struck a deal with them. George would finance a voter registration drive if Welch and his group would provide the streetcorner registrars. That was the above-board agreement but there was a secret codicil as well. Some of the money would be funneled toward running a campaign for district elections in 1976, the year after George was elected mayor, and with his full backing. Welch understood George's game and didn't really trust him. At times he thought that Moscone was a pathological liar. But the organizer also saw their mutuality of interests. Forty thousand new voters were registered in under a year.

George's law school pal Willie Brown was by now a state assemblyman and he took front-and-center role in the mayoral campaign. In the minds of the Barbegelata forces, Willie and George were a tandem and it was open to question which of them was the cart and which the pony. And Willie Brown, a black man as smooth as his silk ties and gorgeous pocket handkerchiefs, as sharp as the creases in his thousand-dollar suits, as highly polished as his Gucci loafers, was even more suspected and feared than George was. On election day George finished first but with less than an outright majority. He faced a runoff against Barbegelata.

Things reached such a bitter pass that Barbegelata refused to shake George's hand at the beginning of their debates on public television. It was George's style to get even rather than to get angry and he maintained a civil forbearance; he had known Johnny B for many, many years, their children attended the same schools, he could never quite believe that the venom was entirely real, and certainly it was unnecessary. Ugly innuendos about George's sexual exploits and drug use were floated to the press, hinted at in debates. George was going hoarse, talking ten times a day, chainsmoking, driving himself. He was even forced to proclaim his own faith. "I'm a devout Catholic," he said. "By devout I mean that I do not let the socioeconomic pressures of neighborhood Catholicism tell me what my Church is all about."

On the night of the runoff it was close, very close. George ran up big margins in the black precincts of Hunter's Point, the Fillmore, the Western Addition; in the Spanish-speaking neighborhoods of the Mission; in the brown rice belt of Noe Valley and Haight Ashbury; among the predominantly gay voters of the Castro. He edged past Barbegelata by the narrowest of margins in the Outer Mission where Dan White had grown up. But west of Twin Peaks, where voter turnout was highest, among the homeowning middle class, Barbegelata accumulated substantial margins. When they finished counting, George was the mayor-elect, but by only 4,443 votes.

The new mayor spoke for the future; but because he had been raised and shaped in the city's past, because in the view of many a parishioner and policeman and executive he had broken ranks and gone over to the side of the enemy, his victory had cost him an enmity that was marrow deep. For every San Franciscan who adored George's rascal charm and his commitment, there was another who called him an apostate, a hypocrite, a whoremonger.

On the night of his inaugural celebration the triumphant and tipsy public man was walking to his car when a passerby stopped and stared at him. "Say," he asked, "aren't you George Moscone?"

"I was," the mayor said.

He was the mayor but he didn't have a desk. Under what might properly have been called the reign of Joseph Alioto, the mayor had ruled from a high-back carved antique chair behind a Louis XIV treaty table with a pair of gold candelabra. When Alioto departed so did the regal trappings. George arrived for his first day on the job in a driving winter rainstorm with the collar of his topcoat turned up and his hands thrust into his pockets to find that his office furnishings, thrown together by city workmen, consisted of a plain oak work table, a rug faded and wrinkled from years in the basement of City Hall, and a couple of motel-green armchairs. Every mayor is entitled to a desk; before long George had a desk he could call his own.

George loved his desk, loved it with the passion that a boy who grew up poor has for the trappings of power. It was made from a long slice of walnut shaped like a surfboard sliced down the middle. Facing the mayor but hidden from his visitors by a low console was a Captain Video array of gadgets. There was a pencil sharpener, and a calculator with a color-coded biorhythm indicator, but George lost the key card and so couldn't rely on his desk to tell him how he was feeling. There was a radio and a tiny television screen on which he could watch ballgames while conducting the city's business. Paul Zell, who designed the desk and presented it as a gift, must have been a student of Watergate because the desk not only had a built-in tape recorder (which whirred so loudly a deaf man could hear it) but also a paper shredder which dropped its confetti directly onto the new carpet. The desk had a speaker phone built into it and George would entertain delegations of schoolchildren by sending his press secretary, Corey Busch, into an adjoining room and telling the kids, "Hey, you know this desk talks."

"Suuure it does," a kid would invariably say.

"Try it, ask it a question." He hit a button.

"Okay. Desk, who plays first base for the Giants?"

"Willie McCovey, of course," the desk would say in a voice much like Corey Busch's.

It was a Rube Goldberg desk, but very handsome at that. George had hardly got the seat warm when the first municipal crisis arrived: the Giants baseball club was going to be moved to Toronto.

George's only chance to save the team was to find new local ownership. A wealthy real estate man, Bob Lurie, immediately agreed to put up half the $8 million purchase price. But a second buyer couldn't be found and time was running out. Finally on the day that the sale to the Toronto group was to go through, Corey Busch's phone rang with an offer from an Arizona businessman neither he nor George had ever heard of. With literally an hour to go before the deadline, a deal was closed and the Giants were saved. George went before the cameras to announce his triumph. "Bobby Thompson lives," he declared. If this was what it was like to be mayor, George figured he'd like the job.

The second week in July 1977 the word was out on San Bruno Avenue, which everybody called the Road, that Mayor Moscone was due out there to do some politicking. John Barbegelata, who couldn't stop trying to bring George down, had gathered enough signatures to force a special midsummer election that would not only repeal district elections before they had even been implemented but recall Mayor Moscone and several other liberal city officeholders as well. So just about noontime here came George, shaking hands all the way up the block, drawing stares and smiles, and accompanied by a couple of young men in suits.

When George came into Dan White's headquarters Dan was in the back room on the telephone but Goldie Judge heard the commotion and came right out. Mary Ann was standing there shyly, not introducing herself to the mayor. Goldie and George had a big, wet kiss.

"My paisano," Goldie gushed. George gave her a nice little pinch on the ass, the way a politician was supposed to. She wished Dan wouldn't shine off the ladies so coldly when they swooned for him.

"Goldie!" George said, with his great big toothy mayor's grin. "What are you doing here?"

Dan had come out of the back room, so Goldie pointed at him and said, "I'm going to put this man in City Hall, right next to you." Pure seltzer.

"You're kidding," George said, laughing. "I love it, I love it."

Goldie made the introductions and Mary Ann and Dan each shook hands with the Mayor. Dan was abashed, Goldie thought, as if he were meeting a god or something, but George was casual and friendly as always.

"You know," he said, looking around at the prints Mary Ann had hung on the walls of the spacious headquarters, "you know, I can remember when I first started out, my first campaign headquarters. This is a palace compared to that, you're really doing a job here. Gina and I didn't have anything, it was just a little hole in the wall." After George had reminisced for a while and heaped praise on them for what they were doing, Goldie made her play.

"George, paisano, would you give me a picture with Dan and Mary Ann?" She had a camera all ready. They walked out into the noontime sunshine and George got in the middle, one arm around Dan and the other around Mary Ann, and the picture was snapped.

"Okay," George said, "Good luck. See you in City Hall."

They shook hands again and he was gone.

Not long after the rollback of district elections and the recall of Mayor Moscone were decisively defeated in the first week in August, Dan went by the homicide division on the fourth floor of the Hall of Justice to let Frank Falzon know he was becoming a politician. For Dan, nobody's imprimatur was valued more highly than Falzon's.

Dan had been in the sixth grade when he first became aware of Frank Falzon. Sometimes after school Dan would walk the three blocks from St. Elizabeth's to Portola playground to play baseball. The local star was a husky half-Irish, half-Maltese boy with kinky hair and an earnest, gabby manner. Like Dan, Falzon had lost his father at an early age. When Frank was eleven, his father died, and the boy was told he was the head of the Falzon family. Frank had been a tough guy, decked out in blue suede jacket and matching shoes. But tough or not, at eleven he hadn't been prepared to be a man, and from time to time he would feel flashes of anger at his dad for having left him in the lurch, an adolescent yearning to prove himself to the father who was no longer there. By the time he was sixteen, Falzon was a star in three sports and had already decided that if he wasn't good enough to turn professional he would become a law enforcement officer. On sunny afternoons in Portola playground Danny White would shag the balls that Falzon could hit so far and so hard, and then hang back shyly while the big boys sprawled on the warm grass swapping boasts and jokes. Falzon had never noticed Dan; he was just another hero-worshipping squirt. But Dan never forgot Frank Falzon.

The next time their paths had crossed was when Dan joined the police department. On the ballfield, as nowhere else, Dan was able to relax the constraints he imposed on himself and give his drive and his emotions free rein. Falzon had become a cop in 1964 and requested assignment to Northern Station because he hoped to become a detective, and there were only two ways to accomplish that: either you played politics downtown or you built a reputation on the street as a supercop. Falzon had put himself in the thick of the battle and set out to make a name for himself.

With Falzon as its manager, the Northern Police Station softball team had begun to click, falling just a little short of winning the law enforcement league title. Falzon was maturing into a man with the dogged confidence of somebody who had come up a long way to achieve success as an athlete and a cop, a man on the rise. He was hitting infield practice before the opening game of the new season when a young guy in jeans and a tee shirt with a glove in one hand and his spikes slung over his shoulder walked up to him. It was a moment that became a freeze-frame in Falzon's memory, vivid and unforgettable.

"Frank," he said, "I'm Dan White. I don't know if you remember me but I grew up in Vis Valley. I used to shag flies for you in Portola playground."

Falzon didn't remember, there had been a lot of kids like Dan White hanging around the playground. "You've gotta be a cop to play for us," he said, stroking another ball to his infielders. He was really hurting for a shortstop; the guy he had out there wasn't much.

"I am," Dan said, and now Falzon looked at him more carefully. He saw a clean-cut, handsome kid with strong, sloping shoulders and long arms. His worn spikes and seasoned glove looked as much a part of him as his hands and feet. "I am, I'm a rookie at Northern and I want to play on your team." When he finished he stood there eagerly, waiting.

That Dan had played at Portola playground mattered to Falzon. Anybody who had learned his baseball there, as he had, knew the game. He figured he was only one infielder shy of putting together a championship season and had nothing to lose, so he told Dan to go out to third base and he'd hit him a few. Dan sat down to lace up his spikes and trotted out to third. Falzon waited until he was set and hit him a two-hopper that Dan gobbled up and fired over to the first baseman so hard you could hear the satisfying smack of the ball embedding itself in the leather mitt all over the field. Falzon hit him a harder chance in the hole, and moving to his left Dan cut it off and fired another bullet to first. After each play he banged his fist into his worn glove and made loud, enthusiastic sounds in his chirpy voice. Falzon could see written all over Dan White that extra something which distinguishes the star from the journeyman. There was an ebullience, an intensity in this kid that was inspiring.

Falzon penciled him into the starting lineup at third base. Dan had a couple of line-drive hits and scored a couple of runs, playing full-out and sliding hard as Northern won the game by a single run. To himself, Falzon said, "Holy cow, I've got myself another Pete Rose."

It didn't take long for the two men to become tight friends, although they were both reticent about their personal lives. They had their backgrounds in common, their love of playing and winning, that indefinable star quality, their code. They talked the same language and understood the same things. After games they'd often drink a few beers and reminisce about the old San Francisco Seals, whom they'd both followed as boys. There was a feeling between them, a kinship, as if Frank were an older brother. Dan's only older brother, Mike, hadn't let him tag along when they were growing up, so Frank Falzon's friendship provided Dan with something he had missed.

During the 1971 season, with Dan batting leadoff and Falzon batting third, they won the league championship. They dropped only one game, to the firemen, who came up with a couple of runs in the last inning. Afterward, Frank and Dan were alone in the men's room, and Dan was still steaming. When he came out of the stall he slammed the door so hard it almost came off its hinges.

"What the hell you do that for?" Falzon asked.

Dan's dark eyes were blazing, you couldn't see into them at all. He was tense and crotchety. "I hate losing," he said, raw with emotion.

"Jeez," Frank said, "Forget it, the game's over. Let's go get a beer." It was the first time he had seen Dan's temper, usually it was under control. But every once in a while, when Dan lost or felt he had been wronged, he was suffused with a rage all out of proportion to what he had suffered.

Dan unwound as they drank their beers, but he wasn't saying much. Falzon did most of the talking; he liked to talk, especially about his own exploits, but Dan kept things inside where they ate at him. The deeper something cut, the deeper Dan buried the wound. Sometimes it seemed to catch up with him. There were a few times when Falzon had known Dan to drop out of sight. It was something he seemed to plan because he'd tell Falzon, "If you want me you can reach me at this number. But let it ring once and I'll call you back. I'm not gonna answer the phone for a while, I'm gonna get away and get some rest." Black Irish depression was not unknown to Falzon. But these short furloughs from life taken by a man who had such an intensity and a will to win puzzled the older policeman; yet he never inquired about them, he accepted Dan on his own terms. Though Falzon was a superior investigator, his curiosity didn't usually extend beyond the facts; complex psychological motivations made him gun-shy.

Later on, Frank gave Dan a lift home. Dan, over his temper tantrum, was feeling contemplative, thinking out loud about what he was doing with his life and where he was headed. He had been a cop for more than a year. He didn't know how long he'd last, he said. There was something more he wanted for himself. He wasn't sure what to do.

"Why ask me?" Falzon wanted to know. For a moment he took his watery blue eyes off the road and looked across at his friend.

Dan smiled. "Everybody knows you're gonna be chief someday."

The compliment filled Falzon with a pious humility. "Hey. Anyway, you're a good cop too."

"No," Dan said. "My head isn't really into police work."

By January 1974, Dan had quit the force and joined the Fire Department.

In the summer of 1972 Falzon had taken a police all-star team up to Lake Tahoe for a statewide championship tournament. Dan at shortstop and Falzon at second base were the double-play combination. Together they turned an eye-opening number of twin killings, breaking the back of their opponents' rallies. But on the Saturday night before the championship game Falzon had found his star shortstop feeling no pain: Dan was in his motel bed wrapped around a nearly empty fifth of vodka with a *déshabillé* blonde wrapped around him.

"Hey, Frank, we're in the championship," Dan had cried happily.

It was two in the morning. *"Today's* the championship," Falzon said.

"Hey, Frank, don't worry none about me, I'll be fine."

And he was. The San Francisco team swept a doubleheader from Los Angeles and Dan was awarded a trophy for being the most valuable defensive player in the tournament.

The summer of 1977, for Falzon as for Dan, had been memorable. On his way to a night class Falzon was driving past a grocery store when he saw a robbery in progress. A gun flashed. He got out of his car and called after a man leaving the store to stop, but instead the thief ran up to within ten feet of him and began to fire a gun, getting off four rounds. Falzon drew his own gun and shot twice. The man dropped. Cautiously, Falzon approached, holding his revolver in both hands, circling the crumpled figure and shouting, "Please mister, please, just drop your gun, please." The man couldn't hear him. One of Falzon's bullets had entered his brain through the right eye.

For his courage Falzon was awarded the gold medal as Policeman of the Year by Mayor Moscone. But killing that man had had a profound effect on his way of looking at the world. Falzon had gone to the coroner's lab and seen the man laid out on a slab. "But for the grace of God, there lay I," he had thought. Not long afterward he was the investigator on a terribly sad case: the teenage son of another cop had accidentally killed his younger brother with their dad's revolver. That night Falzon went home and took out all his own guns and stared at them. Before he became a cop he had never owned a gun but now he had a couple of larger automatics, a pair of .38s, and from his days on the vice squad a little .25 automatic. Falzon stared at his guns and thought about his own children. He asked himself, what the hell does a gun do? It kills. That's all. As a policeman he had to have a service revolver, but these other guns, why did he keep them? He gathered them all up and sold them for enough money to buy a table saw, with which he planned to design and build his family a new home in Marin County.

When Dan came by in August, Falzon could see there was something on his mind. Ever since Dan had joined the Fire Department Falzon thought some spirit was gone out of him; no cop, he told himself, could have a true love for being a fireman. Falzon drew Dan aside and found out he was running for supervisor. He could see how excited his old double-play sidekick was, how spirit and desire were back in his face. He wished him all the best and gave him the names of the people he still kept up with out in the old neighborhood.

When Dan had gone, Falzon's partner, a big, florid Irishman named Cleary, who was something of a politician himself, said: "Danny's a good boy but he doesn't stand a chance in politics."

"I wouldn't put anything past him," Falzon answered, the bond he felt with Dan adding a special emphasis to the way he said it. "Hey—if Dan White's got the desire, I bet he wins."

Early on the morning of August 4, Dan was asleep at the firehouse on Moscow, working his twenty-four hours out of every seventy-two, when the alarm bells began to clang. There was a fire at Geneva Towers. When construction of the Towers began in 1963 the developer had intended them to be racially integrated, lower- and middle-income housing. When he went bankrupt, however, the federal government took over and the tenants turned out to be almost exclusively poor blacks, many of whom moved into the neighborhood from the crumbling World War II housing in Hunter's Point. In Visitacion Valley they thought of Geneva Towers as the beginning of their neighborhood's ruination. Ultimately, the Towers may have been the very symbol of everything that compelled Dan to run, but that had nothing to do with the task at hand.

Dan was on the first truck to arrive at the scene and when he looked up he saw a woman on a balcony way up high screaming, and dark, oily smoke pouring out of the apartment behind her. Dan and another fireman, carrying a coil of hose and a sledgehammer, rode the elevator to the seventeenth floor. There was a puddle of gasoline that seemed to have been poured under the door and set ablaze and the double bolt was set. They battered down the door with their sledgehammers and hooked up the hose and subdued the fire enough to move into the smoke-filled apartment with a flashlight shining. They crawled out to the balcony after the distraught woman and when they got closer they could see she had a baby in her arms. Everything was happening fast. They swaddled the baby in a blanket and led the mother and child to safety.

When Dan got back to the firehouse he was covered by the oily residue of the smoky flames and swampy wet and as happy as he had been in his entire life. There would be a medal coming to him for the rescue, but that wasn't what made him ecstatic. This was it! The zenith. He was a hero like his dad, and a winner. This was it! He was going to win.

Goldie's phone rang at five in the morning.

"Goldie?" Dan said.

"Whaaa?"

Dan told her what had happened. Goldie could hear that he was high as a kite. "Don'tcha know somebody at the *Chronicle*?" Dan asked. "I bet we could get it in the paper, I want it in the paper!"

"Want what in the paper? Dammit to hell, Dan, it's five o'clock in the morning. The paper's out already. It's not right anyway."

"I gotta have it in the paper," Dan shouted. "I gotta have it."

"You want me to make you a hero, huh?" Goldie said. She was trying to be calm, but it was hard.

"Yes." It was a wail.

"Okay, we'll talk about it tomorrow," Goldie said. "Goodnight."

The next day there were flyers on phone poles and lamp posts all over the neighborhood, telling the story of what had happened, just like a newspaper account. Goldie asked Dan if he had done that, but he said he hadn't. Naturally she didn't believe him. Somebody had called down to the *Chronicle* and a reporter came out and interviewed Dan and the next day, Friday, the story ran on page six, right at the top of the page: CANDIDATE FOR SUPERVISOR SAVES TWO LIVES.

Dan had a closeup picture of himself with his story. But his dad had made page one.

Charlie White may have had no use for politicians, may have thought they were bullshit pure and simple showing up at firehouses in election years and then never coming back after they won, but naturally he was as proud as the next Irishman when Jack Kennedy became the first Catholic ever elected President in 1960. It inspired Charlie to improve his own lot and he began to study for the lieutenant's exam. The exam was given every four years and even if you passed you might have to wait years more for a vacancy to open up. But Charlie had lots of time, he was only forty-one and in the prime of his life.

On April 1, 1961, a distraught young man—the son of a Tecumseh, Nebraska, hardshell minister—took a bus to San Francisco, called a newspaper to dictate a suicide note, and then climbed a 150-foot-high radio tower on Christmas Tree Point near the geographical center of the city. He hung on there, just a few inches short of the high-power voltage lines, threatening to jump. Charlie happened to be in the vicinity, and while other firemen and policemen set up safety nets and tried to talk the man down with a bullhorn, Charlie started up the needlethin tower. There were spotlights focused on him as he climbed up into the swirling fog, and a hard wind was blowing off the ocean. As Charlie climbed, a priest was called and a ladder set up with a second fireman waiting on it about fifty feet below the top of the tower.

For almost an hour Charlie hung on, talking to the young man before finally persuading him to go on living. The man climbed onto Charlie's big shoulders and Charlie started down, the wild wind buffeting him and only one hand free to hold onto the spikelike grips. Just as Charlie and his burden reached the top of the fire ladder the young man passed out, and if Charlie hadn't somehow held onto him as he swooned one hundred feet above the ground the man would have died after all, and perhaps Charlie as well. Somehow, though, he maintained his balance and refused to let go. Charlie and the other fireman got a rope around the minister's unconscious son and returned him safely to the ground.

Charlie was awarded the department's highest medal for valor, and Mayor George Christopher insisted on presenting it himself. Charlie put on his blue serge coat and shined his silver buttons. He slicked down his wavy hair with pomade and went to City Hall, where photographers snapped pictures as the mayor pinned on the medal and handed him the check that went with it. It was the proudest moment of Charlie White's life; he was beaming, looking ruddy and invincible and in the pink of good health.

Danny had always looked up to his dad as someone very big and special, and now, more than ever, Charlie was the giant of his teenage son's world. When, just a few months later, Charlie's appendix burst, it didn't seem too very serious. He was taken to the hospital and the appendix was removed. But when the doctors cut him open they found that Charlie White had cancer.

It didn't daunt him. When one of his mates from Engine 16 came by to visit him in the hospital Charlie looked him right in the eye and said, "I'm gonna lick it." He believed it too, believed it so hard that he convinced Eileen, who was as spirited as he was. Before long, though, it was hard to maintain the belief. That big round face that was a map of Ireland began to resemble the great famine. It was a long and agonizing illness. Although Charlie's body was as strong as cast iron and his will just as inflexible, in time the cancer proved stronger. He gradually lost the use of his legs but he never gave up fighting and even went on studying for the lieutenant's exam. "Jeez," Charlie said to his pal George Grimesey, "I wish I could hurry up and get better so I could take that test."

What was as bad as the illness itself, what was in fact even more excruciating to the people who loved and cared about him, was the matter of Charlie's pension. He was ten years short of automatically qualifying for a full pension. He could, however, apply for a reduced pension that would insure some provision, no matter how meager, for Eileen and their kids. To get the pension, Charlie would have to ask for it; it wasn't automatically his. At first he resisted filling out the forms because to put pen to paper was to admit that he might not lick the cancer. And he went on resisting for another reason too. Whatever fancy name they gave to the pension downtown at fire headquarters it was known in the firehouses as a pauper's pension. Charlie had held two jobs, shouldered every burden, and fathered nine children without ever complaining, he had done everything a man was supposed to do, but in the end he had to declare himself a pauper, a man not otherwise able to provide. The humiliation was a pain of another kind; if he had allowed it to, it could have made a mockery of his whole life. He resisted as long as he could hold out against the blandishments of his friends and family but of course in the end he relented, he had to relent, it was his final responsibility.

The doctors sent Charlie home to Hahn Street and the hush of death entered the house that was once so full of life, the home that he had made large enough for all that life with his own hands. A young priest new to the parish, Father Rasmussen, attended to Charlie and was impressed with the strength and character he brought to his last days. Just before the end came, George Grimesey stopped by to visit and Eileen let him in.

"He's asleep now," she said.

George shuffled his feet. "It's okay, I'll come back some other time then."

"No, stay," Eileen insisted. "He'll wake up soon and I know he'd like to see you. He just lapses off into these naps and then he wakes up. Stay, George."

Together they tiptoed into the bedroom and were standing at the foot of the bed when Charlie opened his eyes.

"Hey," he said when he saw George. "What's doin'? How's everything at work?"

"Fine, just fine, Charlie. All the boys have been missin' you."

"Ei," Charlie said to his wife, "Ei, give George a beer." When she went off into the kitchen Charlie whispered hoarsely to George, "God, I sure wish I could have a beer but the doctors won't let me."

It nearly broke Grimesey's heart to stand there sucking his cold bottle of beer while his dying friend watched. It had been Charlie's job to make up the daily work details and he'd always tossed Grimesey the sweet-cream assignments, like inspecting the downtown theaters. At the President Follies, which Grimesey always saved for last, he'd stand backstage watching the girlies flounce around, and when he'd get home his wife would ask how it went at work and he could always say, "Oh, I didn't find it too hard." A true-blue friend Charlie had been and he'd have gladly given him a whole truckload of Hamm's all beaded with icy perspiration if he could. Charlie was all doped up to kill the pain and soon he nodded off again and George left.

Just three weeks after Dan turned seventeen Charlie White died at home early one morning. In his grief Dan felt he had caused his dad a lot of trouble and now had been cheated out of a chance to make it up to him. His dad's death, his humiliation in applying for a pauper's pension, left Dan with an inchoate resolve. An element of franticness invaded him that never would relax—a desperate desire to prove his manliness. The family buried Charlie in Golden Gate National Cemetery. And Nora Twomey's girl Eileen, forty years old and a widow with nine children to support on a pauper's pension of $148.59 a month, took a job as a bank clerk.

The episode after Dan's rescue made Goldie so irrationally mad that talking to Dan about it she purposely blew smoke in his face, because she knew her smoking annoyed him. She told him that the whole thing wasn't right, using other people's misfortunes that way, and stomped out of the headquarters.

Monday morning when Goldie returned Dan was already there. He had loud music playing on the radio—he always played loud music when he was feeling celebratory and determined—and he was in the back shaving with an electric razor. Nobody else was around. Goldie locked the door behind her and put out the sign that said "Closed."

She walked back to where Dan could hear her over the din of the radio and the shaver and said, "Get your ass out here and sit down, I wanna talk to you."

"Goldie!" Dan said. He came out with the shaver still in his hand, his dress shirt open a couple of buttons, looking exultant. "Have you had coffee, Goldie?" he asked her.

"Yeah, I had coffee," Goldie said, but he fetched her a cup anyway. She looked at him a long time, right in the eyes.

"Is anything wrong, Goldie?" Dan asked.

"You tell me."

"I feel good, Goldie, I'm happy. Nothing's wrong, the campaign's going good."

"Dan," she began, "Dan, what are you all about? Who's behind you?"

"No one's behind me," Dan insisted. "I'm my own man, just like you said I should be."

"You are a liar," Goldie shouted. "Who's putting you up to this? Who's programming you?"

"Why're you so excited?" Dan asked her. He still seemed happy but his eyes had clouded over, there was something deadly there that Goldie sensed. Maybe he was just using the tricks he had learned as a cop to calm somebody down.

"And all the cops hanging around, I hate it. I hate it! Get them out of here, get them to give out leaflets or something, we can use women to stuff envelopes and answer the phones. I want them cops out of here!"

"Those are my *friends,* Goldie," he said. He was staying calm, much calmer than she was, but still giving her that evil eye.

"You don't have any friends in politics, this is a cutthroat business. Don't you understand?" Goldie got up and grabbed hold of his shoulders and began to shake him. "Tell me! Tell me!" Suddenly she noticed that there were tears in Dan's eyes.

"Oh, save your goddamn tears for yourself."

"I don't want to hurt you, Goldie," Dan said, the tears still brimming in his eyes. "I like you, you're a good lady, you've done a lot for me, Mary Ann likes you, Mama likes you . . ."

Goldie heard his words but she felt something else. Something so cold. Contempt, she decided, that's what it was. A chill went through her. "You got a wall around you, Dan," Goldie said, walking toward the door. "You take your campaign and shove it."

By Saturday Goldie had lost hope and decided to quit. Her reasons were muddled and overwrought, but she had concluded that Mr. All-American Hero really didn't believe in anything but himself. He was a cold, selfish bastard.

Goldie sat down alone with Dan and Mary Ann in a back room. Dan told her he was sorry if he had hurt her feelings, there was some warmth in it too, when he said it. "You'll see, Goldie, I'm my own man, I can play hardball down there with them, the hardest ball of any of them."

Mary Ann was crying. From her Goldie sensed a true compassion, as though Mary Ann were Dan's heart. "I hope we can always be friends, Goldie," Mary Ann said.

Goldie assured her it had nothing to do with friendship. She promised them that she wouldn't work against Dan. Dan never asked her to stay on. The last thing Goldie remembered him saying to her before she left was:

"You're wrong, Goldie. I've got no problem. I've had a lot of training and I can handle 'em, I can handle any one of 'em."

6

The Honorable
Daniel James White

There is something furtive about Ray Sloan. He's built slight with a
long angular face like an axe blade, a perpetual five-o'clock shadow and
eyes that are black and opaque. He'll stare intently at somebody talking
to him but if their eyes meet his, his gaze skitters away. He's got a long,
craggy nose that seems too big for his face and tilts crookedly, giving
him a slightly lopsided appearance. His hands, which are bony and
unkempt, are surprisingly quiet.

Yet Sloan's ferocious fast-talking self-salesmanship had a certain
appeal. He and his best pal Ray Shine had grown up in the suburbs on
the east side of the Bay with romantic schemes about San Francisco,
that cool and beckoning glitter beyond the water where it seemed to
them a young man must head if he wanted to make his name and his
fortune. Shine came to town and became a cop. Sloan stayed in the East
Bay where he started up a printing business, made a bundle when he
sold out, and took some of the profit to invest in a restaurant and rock
n' roll club that flopped. He had a passion for politics and had worked
in state legislative campaigns. He and Shine were still buddies so it
didn't surprise Sloan when Shine asked him in the spring of 1977 if he
remembered Dan White.

Sloan had to smile. Shine and Dan had worked together as cops
at Ingleside Station back in 1973, and Shine had talked up Dan White
to his old pal Sloan as if the guy were the greatest thing since sliced
bread: Dan had saved his life when he went overboard while they were
sailing in the rough waters of "The Potato Patch" outside the Golden

Gate Bridge, Dan had a dream of just taking off and sailing around the world, Dan had singlehandedly collared a wanted murderer in a tavern full of black hoodlums. Shine had finally arranged for the three of them to spend an evening together, but Sloan hadn't been impressed, he hadn't understood what the hell Shine had been raving about. Dan White had seemed like a polite, well-spoken young man, nothing more than that.

"Yeah," Ray said. "I remember him."

"Well, he's running for supervisor," Shine said. "You should talk to him."

Sloan met with Dan in May and turned down an offer to manage the campaign. He had been left cold by Dan's naiveté. Then, in August, Sloan read how Dan had saved a mother and child from a burning building and all of a sudden the polite young fireman had risen in the political manager's estimation. A story like that, Sloan thought, was worth maybe ten grand to a campaign. More. You couldn't buy that kind of publicity. A guy who could manuever a story like that, sucker a newspaper into it, was a shrewder guy than he had ever given Dan White credit for being.

Sloan was due to leave on a motorcycle trip up to Oregon with Ray Shine that afternoon, but before he left he had his assistant call Dan at the firehouse. Dan wasn't there—he was out campaigning—so Ray left a message and fixed it up with his assistant to arrange for him and Dan to have dinner when he got back.

Grison's Steak House had an air of carnivorous rectitude to suit Ray Sloan's mood. He arrived first for the meeting and had a drink at the bar. Shine showed up a few minutes later. When they finished their drinks, Dan and Mary Ann still hadn't arrived, so they ordered a second round. There was time, in fact, for Ray to order a third drink and it loosened his resentment at being made to wait. Shine kept assuring him there had to be some good reason why they were so late, but Ray didn't care. Who did they think they were to keep Ray Sloan waiting for an hour?

When the Whites finally did come they apologized. Dan explained that the Reverend Mark Coonradt was dropping out of the race and had asked for a spur-of-the-moment meeting to endorse Dan. That didn't mollify Ray's wounded feelings. A Protestant minister, he thought, that's great, maybe he could swing thirteen votes in the district. But when Dan said it wasn't Coonradt's votes which were important but his access to the Pepsi Cola fortune, Ray's mood rounded the curve: nothing cheered him up faster than the mixture of whiskey and money. Now *that* showed Dan was serious about winning, Ray thought, to go see a well-connected money guy even if it meant being late.

Once again Dan had risen in Ray's estimation, and it hit him that this thing could be won. Sitting there in the solid steak house working on a fresh drink, Ray understood, fully understood, that Dan White's straight-ahead drive, his unlimited energy, his hatred of losing, might finally carry Ray across the gray arc of the Bay Bridge into the city of his private romance.

Mary Ann and Shine were talking with each other, not taking much interest in the political discussion, and Ray calculated that Mary Ann wasn't going to be worth much to the campaign. Except, of course, that she was pretty and a devoted wife. Ray sensed as well that she didn't like him. But he quickly forgot all about Mary Ann when her husband looked him in the eye and said some of the sweetest words the campaign manager ever had heard.

"I need you," Dan told him. "Not because I know you but because I can win with you." Ray kept that pastiche of mismatched parts that was his face poker solemn because they were going to have to settle on his fee. Pretty soon they shook hands. They had a deal.

Dan was relieved; he knew winning was within his grasp, but with Goldie gone he didn't know how to tie up the loose ends, how to translate the support he knew he had into votes on election day.

"Okay," Ray said. "Now what you have to understand is this is real life, *you* want to be a supervisor, not me. Well, get out there and win it. Get ready to do things you don't like to do, and if you don't want to do 'em forget it, if you don't want to do 'em you can't win and the whole thing's off."

The reality of the campaign was one part of what set Ray's motor to racing, and the other was that there was only a finite amount of time. Here it was mid-August, and on the first Tuesday after the first Monday in November they would be out of business, win or lose. There were no grace periods, no extensions of the contract, no overtimes, no favors, no quarter, you just had to go out there and win the thing like it was a dogfight.

Soon the billboard at Silver and San Bruno, at the foot of the Road, had an enormous likeness of Dan on it. It was the only billboard of its kind in the district; none of the other candidates had thought to lease a billboard, but none of them had Ray Sloan to run them.

Ray had sized up the assets and liabilities of this campaign. The assets began with the candidate himself. Dan had that marvelous, boyish, winning Irish personality, he could charm a voter into pulling the lever beside his name. Secondly, the district was small enough to be controllable. You could identify your supporters and the other candidates' and pretty much do a head count. Lastly, they had the troops to do the job. It didn't take Ray long to realize that if you gave them one day's notice the firemen alone could canvass or leaflet every home in the district. That meant he would be able to identify and turn out all their voters come November 8.

The liability, the only liability, was that the campaign was a shambles. Ray junked the old brochure: the photograph had made Dan look like a twenty-year-old mick. Ray got a good professional photographer to snap Dan at a dais with a microphone in front of him and a big American flag in the background. It made Dan look ten years older, youthful yet mature, and a great deal more handsome. There was a certain glint in his eye that, ambiguous as Mona Lisa's smile, could be determination or something darker. Remorselessness perhaps. The cleft in his chin was front and center. Ray was proud of that photograph.

He saw that the volunteers weren't being properly used; they'd come by the headquarters and collect literature and then go stand on streetcorners handing it out. Ray went to City Hall, and using voter and census tracts identified different voting groups within the district. Union members, teachers, city employees, firemen, policemen—for each group he drafted a different letter. Then he dispatched the volunteers to particular precincts supplied with the appropriate pieces.

Meanwhile he scheduled Dan and Mary Ann to begin walking a few precincts a day, and he had them bring back specific information about who they had visited and whether each potential voter was committed to Dan, leaning toward him, undecided, or favored some other candidate. Dan and Mary Ann brought back their reports and Ray followed them up with a letter over Dan's signature to each of the homes they visited. By using the volunteers, the candidate, and the follow-up letters to the maximum advantage, he would be able to hit every house in the district three times before election day itself.

Officially, according to the lines on the maps kept by the Registrar of Voters, Sunnydale was a part of Vis Valley, but of course that was a fact that in no way reflected the truth. The Sunnydale projects were their own world, a world into which the other candidates seldom, if ever, ventured.

It had been a long, long time since Dan had lived across the street from Sunnydale. Back then Sunnydale families who didn't keep up their lawns were fined. Over the years, though, Sunnydale had become a picture of neglect and decay; some of the apartments that were piled two floors high in barracks-like rows had been burned out or abandoned and savaged. At the corner of Sunnydale and Hahn—the same corner where Dan had once been picked on by tougher kids and forced to stand up to them by Charlie—young black men slouched against the wall of a corner market in a congregation of many years' standing. Some of them had grown up to inherit that corner; their big brothers had held up the same wall before them. They called themselves the Sons of Sunnydale.

Ray Sloan liked to tell the story of how Dan had gone up there and rolled up his sleeves and got into a football game, playing hard, impressing the Sons and winning their allegiance. The story is plausible. Dan was playing tackle football without equipment in Sunnydale when the current generation of Sons had been toddlers. The turf was as familiar to him as his own front yard because once it had been just that.

The candidates opposing Dan, on the other hand, would have it that Dan had won over the Sons by buying them beer and promising them jobs, preying upon their weakness and their poverty, and that, too, was probably true. The leader of the Sons was Glen Porter, who was twenty-two and seemed to be a little slow on the pickup but in fact didn't miss much of what was going on around him. His lieutenant was a young man named Randy. Late in August Glen and Randy began coming around the headquarters on the Road. The friendship, or patronage, of a big man like Dan White whose picture was on the billboard, enhanced their standing on the streetcorner and gave them something to hope for. When they said they wanted to help out, Ray asked them what they wanted in return.

"Jobs, man," Glen Porter said. "We want jobs, we want out of this situation."

Ray passed the information on to Dan and when Dan went up to Sunnydale to speak, law and order never got mentioned. Dan talked about jobs, and about making the city provide better maintenance and security, and about skills centers. He told the people of Sunnydale that they were great, they could rely on themselves, they could take control of their lives into their own hands and he would help them.

Perhaps as a down payment on the jobs they had been promised if Dan were elected, Glen Porter was put on the campaign payroll. A small piece of change was tossed his way from time to time, once $115 and another time $300. The Sons were won over but they were skeptical too. Dan was, after all, a honky cop. But between the chance, however slim, of getting something better and the hopelessness of holding up that wall, the Sons chose Dan, who was the only candidate who had come courting. Sometimes they escorted him to candidate's nights. Their presence was frightening, Dan knew it was, and his opponents knew that he knew. When a phalanx of the Sons hooted and jeered the other candidates they complained to Dan that he was responsible, that he was practicing scare tactics and encouraging hooliganism. Dan told them to kiss off, the Sons were his supporters.

As election day drew nearer Ray printed up thousands of special campaign pieces for Sunnydale, and Glen and the Sons took them up the hill and told everybody that Dan was their man.

There were seven precincts in and around the projects and as it turned out Dan would get 474 votes out of them, very near to an outright majority in a field of thirteen candidates; more votes, in fact, from Sunnydale alone than eight of his opponents would get altogether.

In October Dan and Ray found the issue they had been hoping for in the Portola, which had the nicest homes and the highest voter turnouts among the neighborhoods of District 8.

The Sisters of the Good Shepherd had been sheltering wayward girls since 1932 at the University Mounds school on their convent grounds in Portola Heights. Truants, runaways, purse snatchers and the like were housed in a dormitory with a red tile roof behind stone fences and hedgerows. Pine and cypress trees swayed in the hilltop breezes and on Sunday mornings, when the bells in the turret were caroling and the sun was shining on the red tile roof you might have thought you were in a village in southern Italy, so complete was the peace of the sabbath. Every time a real estate agent looked at the eleven undeveloped acres, dollar signs danced in his eyes.

But Sister Mary Columba, the Mother Superior, had put too much of herself into her good works to ever allow them to be replaced by tract homes and Burger Kings. She was a spunky little woman of a certain age who wore the earpieces of her thick eyeglasses outside her black veil. She seemed always to be smiling. By 1977, however, her smile was wearing thin; it appeared the time had come to close the school. The courts had begun to refer harder cases to the sisters, felony offenders, and more girls were coming too. More and more of the nuns' time was being spent raising money, which was not their calling.

Just when it appeared as if the end had come, the sisters were approached by a group of mental health professionals and city agencies with a plan that would allow their work to be carried on. The professionals and the bureaucrats wanted to buy the convent and make it into an ideal, progressive facility. But their concept of what was ideal and the notions of the people who lived nearby were of quite a different order.

From the Heights to the flatlands, as word of the plan passed over backyard fences and telephone lines, in churches and in markets, panic set in. An organizer working against the Youth Campus got hold of the plan, and mimeographed copies describing the juvenile offenders were distributed door to door:

> Youngsters whose behavior is so chronically disruptive as to require long-term treatment . . . their behavior includes serious self-destructive and aggressive behavior, firesetting, severe impulse breakthrough . . . with psychotic or borderline symptoms.

That was who would be coming to Portola Heights.

It was a dilemma for many of the convent's neighbors, who were afraid of the arsonists and psychotics, but were also for the most part obedient Catholics little accustomed to defying nuns engaged in good works. Neighbor was bitterly divided against neighbor. Things got so heated that an elderly handyman for the convent collecting signatures on a Youth Campus petition was beaten by a gang of teenagers from the neighborhood. Fear had turned law-abiding Portola Heights intemperate in no more time than it took to ask, "Why us?"

There was only a month to go before that finite limit that so excited Ray Sloan. He and Dan had been hoping for an issue with emotional impact in the Portola. Ray saw that the Youth Campus was an issue they could exploit, that the opposition was in need of a leader. And Dan's political instinct was that it cut right to the heart of his reason for running, that it was urgently important to give the homeowners, those gut lower-middle-class people, a reason to believe that government could work for them. These were people, he told Ray, who were victimized by criminals, who were too poor to take advantage of tax loopholes, too well-off and self-respecting to avail themselves of welfare programs, forgotten people, his people. Dan's zeal was fired up. Opposition was more natural to him than creative solutions were.

With Mary Ann and Ray in tow, Dan went to visit the sisters. Sister Columba thought that Mary Ann was a lovely girl, and her husband seemed a nice young man, and very persuasive too. Dan told Sister Columba that when he was elected he would help make the convent a home for senior citizens while some other, more suitable place could be found for the juveniles. He seemed very sure of himself. Sister Columba got the impression that the young man figured he could just sweep the poor little nuns under the rug. He talked for a long time and seemed to think that what he was saying was so logical and correct on its face that the sisters would simply change their minds.

When he was finished, she said, "Well, I'm just dismayed that you don't understand that these children are our vocation. Somebody has to look after the children."

Dan was unnerved, Sister Columba could see. After that he turned quite nasty. At one community meeting he told the Mother Superior, "You're lying." And when another nun tried to respond, Dan interrupted her.

"How long have *you* been in our neighborhood?"

"Three years."

"That's not long enough," Dan growled. "Sit down."

The sisters had support from the Archdiocese and, of course, from the mental health establishment, for which Dan had nothing but contempt: overeducated, mumbojumbo-talking pinheads. Dan had no use for shrinks, not then he didn't.

Father Rasmussen of St. Elizabeth's, where Dan had been educated, also sided with the sisters. He explained to Dan and Ray that he was caught between the Archdiocese and his own conscience on one side, and his frightened, angry congregation on the other; therefore, he would do his best to stay neutral even though his sympathy was with the nuns. It was very nice, he told Dan, to get a chance to talk with him, it had been so long since they talked and longer still since he had attended Dan's father at his death. Your father, he said, was a strong, dignified man. Dan was slavishly respectful toward Father Rasmussen, though Ray Sloan didn't understand why.

The man was lying to them, Ray knew. He was out there in the community questioning whether the opponents of the Campus were acting in a moral fashion. Oh yeah, Ray wanted to say, what about your goddamn bazaars? Ray had seen with his own two eyes this Rasmussen giving children dimes so they could bet on the roulette wheel. Ray may only have been a Baptist but this faker encouraged little kids to gamble and then preached to *him* about morality.

The morality question cut much deeper with Dan, who was not from Walnut Creek and wasn't a Baptist. To be opposing the church was an act of apostasy against his own past and his own faith. But his self-righteous zeal to *win* shouted down his own doubts. Time and again he explained that he wasn't against the sisters, nor against the church, nor the children. He was fighting the people on that board from telling his kind of people what their moral obligations were.

The focus of the deep, sore resentment toward these rich outsiders was the Campus Board president, Mrs. Joseph V. Costello. She came to community meetings in clothes that the housewives of the Portola whispered to each other cost more than they could save from their husbands' paychecks in a year. Her speech was gilded with an accent never heard on Leland Avenue, everything about her spoke of a refinement that was forever beyond the reach of their children. They understood perfectly well that Mrs. Costello and her ilk looked down on them as a pack of reactionary know-nothings. They thought: here we struggle all our lives to buy a home, to make a decent, safe neighborhood for ourselves and our kids, and *she* wants to tell us what our duty is.

To save them from Mrs. Costello, behind whose tailored skirts they thought they saw murderers and arsonists lurking, they looked to Dan White, who spoke their language. When the votes were counted on November 8, Dan had 969 from the Portola, and that was 142 more than his nearest opponent. Hardball, Dan against the nuns.

As the campaign headed into the homestretch the pressure was torquing down tighter every day. At one candidate's night Dan was being heckled, and pointing a stern finger down from the stage he said, cold as ice: "I know who my enemies are and I'm not going to forget."

That last weekend Ray was organizing the district-wide doorhanging he had prepared for election day. It was a good little piece, he thought. VOTE TODAY, it said above a picture of Dan and Mary Ann in front of their new home. That covered a lot of bases: civic-minded, married, a homeowner. Beneath the picture, in big block Kelly green letters that covered still another base, it said DAN WHITE. Just three more lines: Democratic Candidate/For Supervisor/Unite and Fight. Ray had hardly been able to believe it that Dan's original piece hadn't mentioned he was a Democrat. Registration in the district was eighty percent Democratic. (Of course Dan had been an Independent when he had declared his intention to run. Mary Ann had been a Republican, but Goldie Judge had straightened them both out about that.)

Ray thought things were looking good. On October 21 the *Chronicle* had run an article, one of a series, describing the district and the campaign there. The thumbnail sketch of Dan had been the first in the story. That put the word out to people who knew how to read between the lines, and in the last week of the campaign the sources and amounts of contributions had begun to change. Southern Pacific, smelling a winner, gave the legal limit of $500, and so did Bank of America. United Airlines and Standard Oil also came across. Ray forsook his salary and loaned the campaign $1,000. Dan increased his own loan by $2,000, to a total of $5,000.

The election-night party was going to be in a storefront just across the street from campaign headquarters, and Kevin O'Malley showed up at 10 P.M. just as Dan and Ray Sloan were coming across the Road. O'Malley was like a lot of the men who had never taken an interest in politics but who volunteered for Dan's campaign. An airport cop, he had known Dan since childhood, they were Vis Valley boys, and even though they had never been the closest of pals it was, to O'Malley, as if his brother were running for supervisor.

Dan had a bottle of beer in his hand. "Kevin," he shouted, "Kevin, didja hear? I'm ahead, I'm *way* ahead. Isn't it great?"

Oh Christ yes, it was great. O'Malley thrust a fist in the air and slammed Dan in the shoulder. Dan banged him back. O'Malley dove into the jam-packed party where everybody was laughing and drinking and dancing and watching the television. Wall-to-wall bodies, all the old crowd, guys he hadn't seen since junior high school.

Dan and Ray lingered for a moment in the dark street outside the party. Dan had more votes than Heinz and Fama combined, he had won in every neighborhood. The two men, whose ambitions had become inextricable when they shook hands in Grison's, stood there together, the noise of the party a muffled din punctuated by sudden war whoops. Ray's crooked, axe-handle face underneath the mica glints of stubble was pale and lined from weariness and lit up with a grin of triumph. Beside him stood his candidate, handsome, cleft-jawed. They were a team, a winning goddamn team. Mary Ann had faded into the background; Dan didn't ask for her help in negotiating the morally ambiguous waters of politics.

Softly, contemplatively, Dan said to Ray: "It's funny, I mean, a lot of people, my whole life there are people who said I was dishonorable. They said it in the campaign, didn't they? And now, they'll all have to call me 'the Honorable.' "

He stuck out his hand and he and Ray shook on it. "You did this," Dan said.

The way Ray felt was almost indescribable. For all his slyness, his cockiness, his hardass exterior, he was easily hurt. In his cups he would write free verse. He hardly ever showed it to anyone, it was for himself. In one he had written, "Nobody has more cosmic debris than me."

They dropped each other's hand and headed into the party. But doubt was already poisoning Ray's moment of triumph. Hadn't that been the moment for Dan to offer him a job as his aide at City Hall? How could he be so selfish?

Two mornings later, on Thursday, Dan and Ray had breakfast together in a coffee shop, to begin talking about what came next. Already the supervisors-elect were exchanging phone calls, getting acquainted. Ray said he would set up some meetings for Dan. Harvey Milk had won in District 5 and his picture, arriving at City Hall on the back of a motorcycle driven by a big lesbian, had appeared on the front page of the newspaper. It seemed a good idea to clear the air of all the bad publicity from Dan's statement about "social deviates," the statement from which Goldie had blue-penciled "cesspool of perversion."

They talked for a while longer and when Dan didn't mention the aide's job Ray told him he wanted it.

"That's fine," Dan said, as if it were no big deal. Then, with a shy, proud grin, he said, "Mary Ann's pregnant. We're going to have a baby."

"You got to be nuts," Ray exclaimed. "How the hell you going to make it on ninety-six hundred a year?" Being a supervisor was supposed to be part-time work, and many of the incumbents had other occupations.

"Don't worry about us," Dan said, adopting his team captain tone. It was a role he had been practicing so long, his whole life really, or at least since Charlie had died, that it was as real as any attitude can be. "We'll be okay, we've still got some savings left."

"You gotta be nuts. That's nuts."

"Hey, I told you, Ray, don't worry. As long as I've got a sleeping bag, a light bulb and my books I'll be all right."

Ray didn't push it. He didn't say what he thought, which was: "Yeah, but what about your wife and the kid?" Instead he decided that as soon as he could he'd better broker Dan some sort of second income.

Dan was on top of the world, there would never be a better time in his entire life; how could there be? He was thirty-one years old and he had fulfilled his destiny, he had made his mark. If he had a son he would name him Charlie and see to it that little Charlie would never want. He had come so far so fast that he was breathless.

He had won without being bought. Of course, he had had to do some buying of his own; his promise of jobs to Glen Porter and the Sons would never be honored. He had won by standing up for what he believed, and if that meant rolling over some nuns and the priest who had administered the last rites to his father, then so be it. What counted was that he had won. He was suffused with an excessive pride, with vanity. He was number one. Perhaps—only he will ever know—his soul was in need of some remedial attention, but winners aren't usually prone to soul searching. That's part of what makes them winners.

Again and again Dan was warned of the financial consequences of winning, but he had been heedless. The victory had cost him most of his savings, and Mary Ann's. There were mortgage payments to be made on the new house and in a few months his wife would have to stop teaching. Being a supervisor paid $9,600, but none of the supervisors looked like they were starving. Besides, he was still a fireman, even though people had warned him he couldn't hold down two civil jobs. But he was somebody now, so he talked it over with the fire chief, who told Dan it was true, he probably couldn't keep his firefighter's job, which paid about $18,000. To be sure, Chief Andy Casper asked the city attorney, and on December 2 received a formal opinion: " . . . the positions of supervisor and firefighter are incompatible."

Dan had had his first brush with the legal rigmarole of public life, the constraints of rules and regulations, and it had taken some of the shine off the crown he had captured. It didn't seem fair to him. Joining the Fire Department had been a homecoming—a fireman had always been somebody special in Dan's hometown, with its history of devastation and its vulnerable wood frame homes now as in 1906 bunched shoulder to shoulder along steep and snakey hills—but now he was being forced out.

With television cameras recording the moment, Dan resigned from the Fire Department directly to Chief Casper, who seldom missed a chance to get his face on the evening news.

"It saddens me to turn my badge over to you," Dan said. He spoke stiffly; being in the electronic eye was new.

Casper smiled into the camera, handed over Dan's last paycheck, and shook hands with him. "Don't forget," he appealed to the Honorable Daniel James White, who a month before had been an ordinary swab, "Our budget's coming up."

7

Number One Queen

District elections had provided Harvey Milk with a bailiwick every bit as much made for him as District 8 was for Dan. He had run for office and lost twice since that first campaign in 1973, but each time he had drawn an increasing number of votes. Operating out of his camera store, the business of which was left mostly to Scott Smith, Harvey had been a peripatetic advocate and ombudsman, a minister without portfolio from the growing number of homosexuals who had waited for so long in the political shadows.

Four neighborhoods were folded together to form District 5: Haight Ashbury, the Duboce triangle, Noe Valley and the Castro. By no means were all, or even nearly all, the forty-seven thousand registered voters of District 5 gay. But if you had to profile that myth, the typical voter, he would be a single man in his twenties or thirties with some college education, a manager or a professional paid $15,000 a year, somebody who had lived in San Francisco for ten years or less and who rented an apartment or a flat. Typically, he voted and his choices were liberal. There was no way Harvey was going to lose in District 5, he vowed, no way at all.

Seventeen candidates were off and running but it seemed that Harvey, or Rick Stokes, who was the choice of the gay establishment and of Mayor Moscone, would become the first openly homosexual city official elected in the United States. Stokes had a campaign kitty more than twice as large as Harvey's, much of it from real estate interests whom Harvey referred to, with his usual tact, as "bloodsuckers."

Harvey ran. He ran and ran and ran, from bus stops to coffee klatches, from Castro Camera to candidate's nights, from labor halls where he won a number of important endorsements to gay bars, where that summer there were signs in the windows that said: "We Serve California Orange Juice Only. NO Florida OJ."

Anita Bryant was Public Enemy Number One in the Castro in the summer of 1977. She had led the campaign that wiped out Dade County, Florida's gay rights law in the first week of June. In the Castro, on the night of the Florida election, a restless, frightened, angry crowd quickly gathered—some three thousand people, ready for action. The police were astounded by the size of the crowd and concerned about its militancy, and because nobody else had any chance at all to control and channel the anger away from dangerous and destructive outlets, they asked Harvey for his help. Harvey led the protestors around the neighborhood and then out through the city, all the way to the tourist regions of Nob Hill and Union Square. He kept them moving, moving too fast and purposefully to do anything they would regret, moving until their anger was as exhausted as their feet. And every chance he got, every time a reporter or somebody in the crowd talked with him, Harvey asked after the whereabouts of his principal gay opponent, Rick Stokes, who was nowhere to be seen. Why wasn't Stokes out there with him? In one brilliant stroke Harvey had shown that he was the best representative of both moderate good sense and gay anger. He was the outsider's insider, always picking fights, unfailingly abrasive, the lightning rod for all the fright and anger inside and outside the homosexual minority. If you were gay, and felt abused, Harvey was your leader. If you were heterosexual and felt threatened or offended, Harvey Milk was a name you knew and hated.

Everything was breaking right; even the *Chronicle* endorsed Harvey. And like Dan, Harvey had his moment of personal bravery. Hearing the shrill call of a police whistle, the sort carried by many gays to attract help if they were attacked on the street, Harvey and a friend dashed to the scene. The friend tended to the man who had been beaten while Harvey chased the assailant, finally bringing him down with a flying tackle that brought back memories of his days as a linebacker on his high school football team.

It had been thirty years since then, when Harvey's high school crowd called him "Glimpy" and didn't know his secret. The shamefulness of the secret, how it ate into his pride and his self-respect, how coming to terms with it had made him courageous, accounted for the speech which he gave again and again during that campaign, the thematic centerpiece of his reason for running.

> The first gay people we elect must be strong. They must not be content to sit in the back of the bus. They must not be content to accept pablum. They must be above wheeling and dealing. They must be—for the good of all of us—independent, unbought. The anger and the frustrations that some of us feel is because we are misunderstood, and friends can't feel that anger and frustration. . . . Because a friend has never gone through what is known as coming out. I will never forget what it was like coming out and having nobody to look up toward.

> And the young gay people in the Altoona, Pennsylvanias and the Richmond, Minnesotas who are coming out hear Anita Bryant on television. . . . The only thing they have to look forward to is hope. And you have to give them hope. . . . Hope that all will be all right. Without hope, not only gays, but the black, the seniors, the handicapped, the us's, the us's will give up. . . .

Harvey's offering himself as the messenger of hope evidently appealed to the Reverend Jim Jones of People's Temple, who volunteered his parishioners to distribute Harvey's literature, especially in Haight Ashbury where half the population was black. Harvey gratefully accepted.

When, apparently in response to an anti-Anita Bryant display which Harvey and Scott Smith had arranged in the window of their camera store, somebody taped M-80 firecrackers to the windows—loud, powerful, almost little bombs—and blew the glass to smithereens, Harvey seized the chance to get his name and his denunciation of violence and hatred on the front page of the next morning's newspaper.

Anita Bryant, the fundamentalist thrust, was to Harvey's drama what the Visigoths were to the Romans; the threat she posed never let him rest for a moment. Back at the beginning of the summer, the night of the Dade County defeat, the angry parade with Harvey at its head came to a halt in front of Most Holy Redeemer Church in the Castro to chant: "Two, four, six, eight/ Separate church and state." The Church and its teachings were resented for good reason: thousands of years of Church-taught morality had been passed down to the Irish and Italian working people of San Francisco who fiercely, stubbornly, tried to shove homosexuals back into that closet without hope.

And Harvey Milk, by God, was not going to let them.

In the end, though, when he won as smashingly as Dan White had, Harvey found himself more troubled than elated. The election had made him the "number one queen," as he would soon tell Mayor Moscone, and the powers-that-be had either to reckon with him or face the political consequences. But in the days after the election, Harvey was drained and full of foreboding. Unquestionably, he felt, his victory had made him a target. He decided to make a will, a political will. Sitting alone and speaking contemplatively into a tape recorder, he named some of the people he would like to see take his place if he should be assassinated, and some of the people—like Stokes—whom he wouldn't. Harvey recorded his statement three different times, each copy to be left with a different friend. Only on one copy did he say, "If a bullet should enter my brain, let that bullet destroy every closet door."

With his arm around the shoulders of his lover, Jack Lira, Harvey led an Inauguration Day parade from the Castro to City Hall, waving and laughing. The parade was a culmination and a spectacle the like of which neither San Francisco nor any other city had ever seen. For every celebrant of this triumph of tolerance, this affirmation that a new era of public mores had arrived, there was a bystander who looked the other way out of embarrassment, or confusion, or distaste. Coming out of the closet was one thing, but a man embracing his boyfriend as he led a parade of homosexuals on his way to be sworn in as a city father, that was something else again. On schoolhouse walls in his own district the graffiti said: "Death to Faggots."

Harvey, who had given up marijuana and his ponytail and gay bathhouses to make himself acceptable, normally eschewed displays of affection in public; he knew what dark passions they stirred. But he had decided that at long last here was a moment for savoring and trumpeting.

He joined an informal rump ceremony that was taking place on the Polk street steps of City Hall. In a light drizzle he and two of the other new supervisors were going to take their oaths of office outdoors, a symbol of these insurgents' closeness to their neighborhood followers, hundreds of whom had come to cheer.

Supervisor Gordon Lau, whom the liberals wanted as board president, was there. So, too, was Carol Ruth Silver, a feminist attorney who had been elected from District 6, just south of the Castro. The district was part brown rice-and-bean-sprouts belt, and part composed of the Mexicans and Central Americans who lived in the area known as the

Mission (after the Mission Dolores, the original church of the Franciscan fathers). Silver lived just a few blocks from the whitewashed adobe church where every day busloads of Japanese and German tourists came with their cameras.

"We're here," she said, in a brief speech, "in an effort to turn things around. We're here to give San Francisco to the kind of people who have come out in the rain." Her listeners, many of whom were gay, applauded her and themselves.

George Moscone was out on the steps too, with an aide holding an umbrella over his head. He was looking very sleek and Italianate, and he was in radiant good spirits. Since taking office, George had reshuffled the composition of city commissions and boards where seats had traditionally been awarded to big contributors and entrenched interest groups. But George had put environmentalists on the planning commission, community advocates on the police commission, a white liberal minister named Jim Jones with a black congregation on the Housing Authority. He had changed the coloration, political orientation and answerability of the people running the city government. Now he was aligning himself with these liberal newcomers, whom he hoped would finally give him a working six-vote majority of the Board. Together they would really wail. The frustrations of his first two years in office, he trusted, were at an end.

More than to any of the others, though, the day belonged to Harvey. Never at a loss for words, he looked up into the gently falling rain, and waving a long finger, told the delighted crowd: "Anita Bryant said gay people brought the drought to California. Looks to me like it's finally started to rain."

8
City Fathers

Quentin Kopp saw the roses in the slim vases on the desk of every supervisor and laughed a mirthless laugh. "That's funny," he said. He didn't mean it. "What's he think this is?" Supervisor Kopp asked nobody in particular. "The high school prom?"

The first Board of Supervisors in the twentieth century to be elected from individual districts was about to take the oath of office in the grand, carved-oak chamber with the richly curtained cathedral windows on the second floor of City Hall. It was a very fine workplace indeed for people being paid $9,600 a year. Five incumbent supervisors and six men and women new to governing the city were there to be formally installed. The lineup of newcomers represented a triumph for the partisans of district elections and a classic array of label politics. There was a black woman, Ella Hill Hutch; a single mother, Carol Ruth Silver; a Chinese-American, Gordon Lau; and a homosexual. There were also two new supervisors who were the latest in a long line of Irishmen to get shiny pants-warming seats at City Hall, Dan and Lee Dolson.

It was Dan and Mary Ann who brought the red roses, thus raising the eyebrows of Quentin Kopp. Actually, Kopp's eyebrows, which are black and bushy with wisps shooting off every which way, are lifted into an arc of permanent incredulity, as befits a man who has been witness to as many shenanigans as he has over the years. It was Kopp's self-assigned role not to suffer fools, loudly.

What kind of a mind was it, Supervisor Kopp wondered, that

would do such a thing? Roses for his colleagues and candy for the secretaries. The kid seemed to be currying favor in some kind of innocent way. "It's funny," he thought again, suspiciously.

Dan was something of an enigma to his new colleagues. They knew that he was a fireman who had come out of nowhere and won big; most of them knew of his remark about "social deviates." And that was about all they knew. Trying to categorize him after his victory, a reporter had written: "If White were a breakfast cereal he could only be Wheaties. Color him All-American." The same article had quoted Dan as saying: "Basically, I'm still a believer in the American dream that a person can do anything he wants when he sets his mind to it. I believe in the old values, especially the value of work. The election, for example. I was determined from the beginning to prove people can raise themselves up by determination and hard work." Such ingenuous sentiments baffled the city's more experienced politicians, accustomed as they were to disguising their provincialism.

Quentin Kopp had already met Dan White. In December Dan had dropped by to see Kopp, who was at home recuperating from a routine but rather painful operation. Kopp was feeling like one very sick boy when Dan came calling, radiating blarney. The two men had sat talking in Kopp's bedroom, Kopp in slippers and pajamas and Dan in suit and tie. Dan did more of the talking. He had been coached in what to say by Ray Sloan, who was trying to broker Dan some power in what looked like a very fluid situation.

Dan expressed concern that Kopp might be left out in the cold when the choice committee assignments were handed round by whichever supervisor was chosen as board president. As everybody knew, Kopp's archenemy was Supervisor Dianne Feinstein. She also wished to be board president. Dan told Kopp that it appeared she had the six votes all lined up, and Quentin would be well advised to accept that graciously. That way, Dan explained, Kopp would be assured of the chairmanship of the powerful Finance Committee, where his snaptrap decimal-point mind would be put to the best use.

Kopp thanked Dan for being kind enough to offer his advice. What he really thought but didn't say was that it was preposterous the way this kid was trying to act like he thought a politician was supposed to. "Don't worry," Kopp said from his sickbed, "things'll work out okay." Kopp was amused by this little charade because he knew something that Dan and Ray, who thought they were being very cunning, did not: Kopp had already promised Dianne Feinstein his vote.

The promise had been made several weeks earlier during lunch at Jack's restaurant, an old and decorous steaks-and-chops place in the financial district. Jack's was *très* San Francisco, one of a handful of restaurants in town which required gentlemen to wear ties. Several of the city's senior conservatives had met there to chew over their chief nemesis, George Moscone. Two of the people around the table, Feinstein and John Barbegelata, had been beaten by George in the mayoral campaign of 1975. Outgoing Supervisor Terry Francois, who had once been closely aligned with George, had moved to the right and parted ways; it was he who was doing the brokering at this luncheon. Francois and Barbegelata were out of office but not out of politics, and they wanted an agreement from the people at the table to all pull together behind just one of their number at the next mayoral election in 1979. The idea was to gang up on George, whom they all opposed and some of them loathed, for turning their city over to new and suspect elements.

Dianne Feinstein was asked by Francois whether she intended to run again for mayor and the lady, as several of the participants remembered it, said she did not; twice was enough.

Would she, then, Francois asked, consider supporting Quentin?

Feinstein's recollection was that she had allowed how she might do that, but others who were there remembered her answer to be less equivocal than that.

In return for her support in 1979, Kopp said, he would help Dianne become president of the board.

They spent a few minutes assessing votes and found they had five, one less than a majority. Dianne said not to worry, that Dan White's vote was securely hers.

So when Dan stopped by Kopp's house to do a little vote brokering, Kopp was naturally trying to puzzle out just what kind of game Dianne was playing with this kid, who seemed so innocent, to put a charitable face on it. Obviously she hadn't told him about the deal at Jack's.

On inauguration day Kopp looked at the roses and figuratively scratched his head. The kid had no idea, no idea at all. They would cut him to pieces.

At eleven o'clock the rump group, including Harvey, trooped upstairs to the chambers for the formal installation. After the speech-making the supervisors chose Dianne Feinstein as their president. The vote was 6–5; all the votes that had been counted up at Jack's had come across. In gesture of reconciliation, Gordon Lau, the defeated liberal, moved to make Feinstein's selection unanimous. Harvey, however, refused to change his vote. And Feinstein didn't let the snub pass unnoticed. In his remarks Harvey had repeated a theme from his campaign: "A true function of politics is . . . to give hope."

In her earnest-college-senior rhetorical style, Feinstein pointed out that, "Hope is fine but the name of the game is six votes."

In just one day at City Hall, Harvey had managed to make quite a splash. A photograph of him with his arm around Jack Lira appeared on the front page of the afternoon newspaper, and it had taken him no time at all to make an adversary out of the president of the board. He was one proud maverick.

Quentin Kopp, meanwhile, went on pondering the red roses, trying to decide whether Dan White was a more treacherous dissembler than anybody understood, or a true innocent. Maybe, Kopp thought, the flowers were his wife's idea, in which case it was certainly innocence, God help him.

Dan knew nothing of Kopp's private musings. He had fetched his grandmothers from the nursing home for the day to come and witness his moment in the spotlight. For Dan it was simply a glorious day, a red roses day. The future looked to him like nothing other than an ever-improving present. The flowers had been his idea.

One morning, not long after the inauguration, Gale Kaufman saw that the door to Dan's office was open just a crack. The young aide to Supervisor Kopp (whom she called "QK"; pretty soon Ray would begin calling Dan "DW") had become friendly with Dan. She knocked and pushed the door open.

Seeing that somebody was coming in, Dan opened a desk drawer as fast as he could and tried to shove the book he had been reading out of sight. He wasn't quite fast enough and there was a stilted moment.

"Oh," Dan said, blushing. "It's you."

Gale said "Hi." She stared at the drawer.

With an abashed laugh, like an altar boy caught tippling the sacramental wine, Dan took out the book. Shyly he showed Gale that it was a vocabulary improvement guide. Gale could see that he was proud of this effort to improve himself.

Effort. Dan was discovering just how much effort it would require to become a capable supervisor. He had never anticipated the pushing and pulling for his attention, the ceaseless clamor of the job. Nothing in his life had prepared him for the polyglot demands of governing a city of 750,000 souls.

The campaign hadn't been so different from baseball or boxing, a contest in which you gave your all and either won or lost. He had supposed he would go down to City Hall and be part of a team, all with the same desire to do what was best for the city. His ideas about government were artless, no more mature than what he had learned in high school civics classes, in which he had done poorly. He was not prepared for the bitter divisions of interests that had to be resolved for the city government to function. Nor was he ready for the cunning and ferocity that the supervisors and a zillion other interested parties employed to gain an advantage. In past situations where he might have sacrificed some part of what he wanted, he had worked himself up into a self-righteous frenzy and quit. Compromise to Dan was a sign of weakness. He had arrived at City Hall quite sure he could persuade the other members of his new team that he was honest and sincere and therefore right. His first few weeks on the job he spent a lot of time in his office doing nothing, waiting for something to which he could react.

Dianne Feinstein, that most schoolmarmish of the supervisors, gave him a first lesson in realpolitik civics. Feinstein had been raised in a family of comfortable means, educated at the best private schools, and was at this time married to her second husband, a prominent neurosurgeon. At quite a tender age she had been drawn into a life in what she called the "public sector," and while at first blush her attitude seemed to be noblesse oblige, beneath the white gloves and the silk blouses with bows at the neck, which were her trademark, she was nobody's fool. Her violet eyes were striking because they were so resolute. She had a lot of what the political technicians called name recognition; in San Francisco if you said "Dianne" there was no mistaking whom you meant.

Dianne had begun to woo Dan just as soon as he was elected. The City Hall types chuckled to watch her draw the young ex-cop into her orbit, just as she had done four years earlier with Police Chief Al Nelder when he was elected to the Board. One of her campaign managers said that the only job Dianne really wanted was Chief of Police. "The trouble is," he explained, "they don't make the uniform in ultrasuede."

Before Dan was even sworn in, Dianne, who at first had been a supporter of the Youth Campus, had switched sides and cast the deciding vote during a preliminary rollcall on the issue that meant so much to Dan. Her change of mind explained why she had been able to assure the luncheon group at Jack's that Dan would support her for board president.

As president she got to assign the supervisors to committees. Not surprisingly, Harvey got no plums and all pits. Dan didn't think that was fair. The way he saw it, each supervisor should be given assignments to coincide with his interests, for the good of the city. Dan knew that Harvey wanted to be chairman of the committee overseeing public transportation. So he took it upon himself to call on Dianne at her home in Pacific Heights and appeal on Harvey's behalf.

The Feinstein domicile was high on a hill overlooking the Golden Gate and Alcatraz. The home itself, the servant, and Pacific Heights, were as much an opium dream for a Vis Valley guy like Dan as Xanadu had been for Coleridge.

Dianne was cordial to his entreaties. As she listened, her shoulders were squared and her posture painfully good. She was tall and slender with long fingers and painted nails. When she smiled you could glimpse teeth that were slightly buck, which might be why her smile was tight-lipped. She was quite handsomely striking in a Kabuki-mask sort of way: there were no lines in her pale, carefully prepared face, and her dark hair was lacquered. There were many sides to this complex and powerful woman. Her only daughter described her as a typical Jewish mother. At dinner parties in her home she would sometimes read Poe's "The Raven" out loud. It was well known that after her home had been bombed by a terrorist group she had begun to carry a small-calibre handgun in her pocketbook. It was a secret, however, that the lady also possessed a .357 Magnum.

Earnestly, Dan explained his mission on Harvey's behalf. And finally, reluctantly, Dianne agreed to make Harvey the chairman of the Streets and Transportation Committee. "One," she told Dan, "you've got a lot to learn. But two, I'm going to give you what you want for Harvey so you'll learn who your friends are."

Dan was so pleased at his success that he went right over to Harvey's camera store and told him the good news. "Harvey," Dan said, "you've got a lot to learn. In politics you have to know who your friends are."

Harvey was amused by the gratuitous advice. He thanked Dan for what he had done. But he also asked him please not to get in the habit of speaking for him.

Harvey was quick enough to see that his authority came from being an underdog and Dianne's vindictiveness suited his purposes. He delighted in slaying the dragonlady and never let up on her. During one early board meeting she objected to granting a zoning renewal for a drug rehabilitation center on the basis that there weren't enough bathrooms for all the residents. Harvey took umbrage.

"Not everyone can afford to live in a mansion with *foah* bathrooms," he lectured her with populist ire. The moment Harvey opened his mouth it was a dead giveaway he was a Jew from New York.

Their attitudes toward Dianne were the least of the differences dividing Harvey and Dan, whose family names were so similar even though White was pure and opaque and Milk kind of puddly. The middle-aged Castro district gadfly had little enough in common with the man who had been a paratrooper in Vietnam while Harvey was burning his BankAmericard to protest Nixon's invasion of Cambodia. Harvey's liberalism and Dan's conservatism may have been responses to some of the same trends—the Manhattanization of the skyline, the breakdown of community spirit, the deterioration of neighborhoods, the neglect of poor and working people—but their analyses of the causes and solutions were opposed.

If they had any sensibility in common it was that they both thought of themselves as scrappers who had come up against all the odds to champion causes. They were curious about each other, Dan more so, and despite Dan's "social deviates" remark Harvey had told his aides to give Dan a chance to live up to their worst expectations. Who knew? Maybe he was educable.

Circumstance brought them together quite often in those early days on the Board. They were the only supervisors to arrive at their City Hall offices—which were really nothing more than cubicles separated by partitions—before nine most mornings. Dan came early because he was shiny bright. Harvey made a point of stopping by the City Hall pressroom in time for afternoon reporters looking for a follow-up story to get a quote from him; he kept count and knew that his name had been in the newspapers more than any other freshman's. Often in those first few months Dan and Harvey would talk when no other supervisors were around. Each of them considered himself an idealist, but there was little about which they agreed. Their chats were never wholly relaxed but Dan's way of handling his bemusement was to make a show of courtliness. Red roses and doors held open for ladies.

Harvey's quick wit and irreverence kept Dan continually off balance. One time, speaking of homosexuality, Harvey smirked at Dan, "Don't knock it unless you've tried it." Dan responded with a tight grin. The nimbleness with which Harvey poked at sore points made Dan feel awkward and slow-witted.

Of course, Harvey knew that, but he was irrepressible and his humor turned on a barbed defensiveness; it was the humor of oppression and assimilation. In their own ways they were both trying to get along, but their mistrust colored their efforts. Harvey was the more mature and experienced man; he had dealt with a lot more people who were uptight about homosexuality than Dan had with homosexuals. For Harvey their relationship was no big deal. For Dan the effort was worth making. He voted along with Harvey, for instance, on a resolution honoring two lesbian lovers, both members of city commissions, on the occasion of their twenty-fifth anniversary. Ah-ha, thought Quentin Kopp, who never missed a trick. The poor dummy must be going along with Harvey because he wants something in return.

Kopp was right. What Dan wanted was Harvey's vote against the Youth Campus. Dan had no other legislative program to speak of. He did think it would be terrific if every neighborhood got up a softball team to play in a citywide tournament to help different kinds of people get to know each other better. But in his first two months on the Board the only legislation he proposed was routine requests for stop signs and the like. From the moment he got to City Hall the single thing he most wanted to accomplish was to stop the Youth Campus.

George Moscone also cared about the Youth Campus. His years in Sacramento had taught him what a bedlam Napa State Hospital was, and it was there, far from their families and friends, that troubled San Francisco children were sent. George thought that his city should do something more to take care of its own screwed-up kids.

When the outgoing board had turned down the proposal in December, George had vetoed their action. He figured the new board might be more sympathetic. To announce his veto he had held a press conference at the convent and spoke with passion. "These children are our own and we must take care of them," he had said. After the reporters had departed George toured the place with Sister Columba, who was a foot shorter than he was. Leaning down to confide in her, George said: "Sister, I'll make a bargain with you. I'll help you get what you want out here but I need your prayers for my daughter. She hasn't been well."

Sister Columba was moved. She pressed an icon into the mayor's hand as a way of sealing their deal.

Maisie Bright met George when he came to a community meeting in a school cafeteria in the Hayes Valley ghetto. One of the reasons George had come was to take personal credit for the awarding of a grant to a community program that Maisie had organized. The grant had been arranged by the fellow Maisie was running around with, a man named Joe who was one of the black administrators George had brought into city government.

The whole thing was pretty heady stuff, as far as Maisie was concerned. It had been only two years since she had hitchhiked from Newark to San Francisco. She was pregnant, on her own, and with nothing to fall back on except her wits and her moxie. She planned to go to law school, but she needed a way to earn a living. She got the idea for the program and found the right man to help her get it funded.

When George announced the grant, he had Joe and Maisie stand up. Then he threw open the meeting to anybody who wanted to say something to the mayor. He was there to listen, he said. Right away there was a whole rash of complaints about trash in the streets. George nodded understandingly.

"I'm going to promise you here and now that something is going to be done about that," he said. "If there isn't a trash bin on every corner in this neighborhood by Monday morning I want you all to call me at City Hall. I mean that, you have my word on it."

"Boool*shieet,*" cried a man in a loud voice. "Where you comin' from with that bullshit, man? Like, what you know about it, man? You gawn back to yo' big house, man, gawn back with the dagos. But us people, we stayin' right here, man. We ain't gawn nowhere. You dig? You dig what I'm tellin' you, dago?"

"Now let me tell you something," George said. "I got four kids, all dagos. And I feed those little dagos. I started on the street, a dago with nothing. And I'm here to tell you that working together we can turn things around. That's what this dago mayor says."

Listening, Maisie thought that was pretty damn slick. Here was this white dude with his jacket off and his sleeves rolled up, like he was just plain folks, and he had all these black folks eating out of his hand. They were ready to lynch the brother who had trashed him.

When the meeting broke up Joe hung around answering questions and sticking close to the mayor, trying to show people how tight they were. Maisie saw right through that, she had Joe sized up. He wore the right clothes and had the right rhetoric but he hadn't tumbled to the essence of the style, the kind of style Moscone had shown.

"Went pretty good, huh?" George said to Joe.

"Hey, it went great, George. These people love you."

Maisie looked the mayor right in the eye. "Yeah, it's really good to know you're available to all of us anytime we just sort of drop around City Hall."

George guffawed. "Hey, as long as I've got nothing else to do. No other fish to fry." He and Maisie laughed together. Joe laughed too, a second after they did.

"Hey, where'd you dig this kid up?" George said. "She's cute."

"Yeah, she's a cute kid," Joe said. The two men laughed. Joe took Maisie's arm. "Well," he said, "we'll catch you later."

"Hey, wait a minute, man. Where you guys headed?"

"Takin' the young mother home," Joe told George.

"You positive you're taking her home? She's too cute to be going home. Why don't *I* take her home?"

Both men were yukking it up like it was all a big joke.

"Hey, that's okay, I'll get her home safe."

"I tell you what, we should all go get a drink." To Maisie, George added: "Does the young mother get a chance to go out drinking?"

"A young mother can go have a drink," she said.

Joe was trying to mask how little the idea pleased him but George and Maisie had taken the play right away from him.

"C'mon," George said. The limo was waiting outside but George told his driver/bodyguard, Gary Wommack, he could take off for a few hours. "Maybe you can meet me later at Africa's," he said.

"Good thing," the bodyguard replied. "This neighborhood was giving me the creeps."

Joe said, "I know what you mean."

"You guys afraid of my neighborhood?" Maisie asked.

"The kid wants to know if we're afraid of her neighborhood," George said.

"Hey, I told you she was cute," Joe said. They all piled into Joe's car. Maisie sat in the middle.

"How's about Henry Africa's?" George suggested.

"What's that?" Maisie asked. "It sound very colonialist."

"Where'd you find her, Joe? She must be a communist, huh?"

"That's what Quentin Kopp called me," Maisie said. "When we were presenting it to the Board of Supervisors." She imitated Kopp's sour tone: "You gotta be kidding. This is a commie program."

George cracked up. "What an asshole," he laughed. "You know

he sued his law partner for alienation of affection? He ran off with Quentin's wife."

It was cause for more hilarity. "Boy, I'm glad to be outta there," Joe said. "You see those dudes down by the mom-and-pop?"

"Hey, that's nothing," George boasted. "This was a tough town when I was growing up."

"I never knew anybody actually grew up here," Maisie said. "I thought, like, everybody just came, you know?"

"Let me tell you what kind of town this used to be," George said. He reminisced for a while. Maisie didn't pay much attention to the details; she picked up, though, on his great nostalgic fondness.

Henry Africa's turned out to be done up with ferns and tinted glass and old war mementos. Chic neocolonialist; Maisie had been right. Willie Brown's law office was several doors away. The minute they got there George was surrounded by people. Just sitting there and listening to him and his cronies was an education. He was very funny. The tears nearly streamed out of Maisie's eyes, listening to him on the subject of Dianne Feinstein. Joe wanted to get her out of there, and as they were getting up to leave after a few drinks, George gave her a look that was as appealing as it was artless.

"Don't forget, this dago's door is always open to a cute kid. Where'd you get her, anyway?" he asked Joe.

Maisie was very pleased with herself. If she ever did need help from the mayor's office she knew she'd be able to get it. And she knew why, too. All that "kid" stuff was only half a joke. He liked her because he wasn't challenged by her. It was easy for him to let his hair down in front of her because she presented no threat whatsoever. It didn't hurt to be pretty either. And the way she was pretty made it even easier for him; she was reedy, boyish, with a sensual, mischievous face.

Dan was a tiger, rounding up every vote he could against the Youth Campus. He appealed to Harvey. Dan was so gung-ho, this obviously meant so much to him, that Harvey didn't want to disappoint him. He said, "Gee, I haven't looked into it, I'll think about it."

Dan persisted. He wanted a commitment.

Harvey bent a little more. "I can certainly see your point of view. I'm inclined to vote with you." It was a hedge.

Dan heard what he wanted to hear, that Harvey would vote with him. Harvey's would be the sixth vote. But Dan's count was just wishful thinking. Even Quentin Kopp was wavering.

Harvey told his aides, Dick Pabich and Anne Kronenberg, that he might do Dan a favor and vote against the Campus. Pabich was aghast. "Look, Harvey," he said. "It's obvious that good liberal people are on one side of this and Dan White and his reactionary constituents are against it."

Dan, meanwhile, was making his first news splash. Some young thugs had gone on a mugging and robbery spree in the Portola and Dan held a press conference to suggest that people in the neighborhood form self-protection groups. "Concerned citizens . . . in my neighborhood are going to see to it that crime goes down." The suggestion of vigilante action got good coverage, and Dan followed it up by attending a meeting at Vis Valley SAFE a few days later. He found a lot of noses out of joint.

Gary Yoes, the chief organizer for SAFE, felt he should have been consulted. It was his turf and crime was his issue. It recalled for him a haunting feeling from the Sunday before the election in November. Gary had reluctantly endorsed White and had been invited to ride on a motorized cable car in a Dan White cavalcade. It was a bright, sunny day and a loudspeaker had been blaring the theme from *Rocky*. As he rode along, Yoes had suddenly felt deeply, deeply regretful; a floodtide of sadness had come over him. For just an instant time had stopped and he could see himself, see all of them, as if they were in a photograph, immutable. In the photograph Dan was smiling and waving. In the photograph, too, were all the little Catholic girls dressed up in their Sunday finery in the sunshine.

At the SAFE meeting Dan found himself having to defend his statements, which made him ill at ease and left him irritable. Afterward, Rudy Kessenheimer, Dan's old scoutmaster, came up to say hello. A long time ago Danny White had been his favorite scout. Rudy was wearing a brown fedora that was too small for his head. This was the first time he had seen Danny since during the campaign, when White had promised him a job.

"Danny," Rudy said, in his slow, guttural way. The only thing Rudy did fast was wolf down his fried eggs at Andy's Cafe on Leland, where he was a fixture. "You still want me for your complaint getter?"

Dan scowled, he was still smarting. "No," he told Rudy. "You stay at SAFE. If you do good work there I'll decide if you're eligible."

It wounded Rudy, the nasty way Danny said this, like he was a louse. He looked appealingly into Danny's eyes but they were dark and impenetrable. He couldn't see any sympathy there.

"Okay, Danny," was all Rudy said.

It was Supervisor Lee Dolson who pointed out to Dan that Harvey wore a navy diver's belt buckle. Dolson was a retired naval officer who taught at a community college. A bluff, confident, freckled Irishman, his belly was so big that his tie didn't reach his pants. If Dan gravitated toward Dianne for her political acumen and her motherliness, he was drawn to Dolson out of respect for the older man's conservative Catholic intellect and his no-bullshit approach. Slick lawyers and single mothers and Robert's Rules of Order—the world of which he was now a part—confused Dan and left him with the vague, troubling suspicion that everybody else understood things that were hidden from him.

Dolson saw Dan floundering. Dan didn't understand that God hadn't made a perfect world, Dolson observed; He had put people in it. Dan obviously held himself to standards of honesty that were too stern for his own good. Dolson suspected that like most fundamentalists, Dan's beliefs were motivated by some hidden desperation. Something in his makeup spurred him to believe what he must, and to confuse what he believed with the way things really were. His vision was afflicted with the myopia of the devout.

Dolson liked Dan and used to invite him along to go swimming at the pool on the Treasure Island Navy Base. On one of those outings Dolson told Dan about Harvey's belt buckle. He had sounded Harvey out about it and come away with the impression that Harvey had been proud of his service on a submarine rescue team in the 1950s. (Harvey also gave out that he had been dishonorably discharged for being found out as a homosexual, a story not borne out by his Navy records but one which enhanced his standing as an underdog.) Dan was suitably impressed to find that Harvey took pride in some of the same kinds of things he did. It made for a kinship.

It was the swimming races on Treasure Island that gave Lee Dolson his biggest insight into Dan's impossible standards. Dan was in near-perfect physical shape; not only that, but he had been swimming his entire life, ever since Charlie White used to take his kids to the pool across from the house on Hahn Street. Dolson, on the other hand, was twenty years older than Dan and thirty pounds overweight. But he was also a competitive swimmer. And he didn't just like to win, he liked to conquer. The older man would loaf along for the first few laps, letting Dan open up a lead until finally he began to cut through the water, fat as a walrus and swift as a shark, and pass Dan by in the homestretch. It happened once, twice, three times. After that, Dan refused to swim with Lee Dolson anymore.

Unlike Dan, Harvey wasn't confounded by his new job. He was bursting with radical ideas, such as eliminating bus fares, or imposing a prohibitive tax on real estate speculation. "The whole real estate market is a market of greed," Harvey explained, waving his hands. He announced he was against condominium conversions by saying, "The city has enough complexes as it is." He had instructed his aides to find solutions to constituents' problems themselves, not shunt them off on unresponsive city bureaucracies.

The onetime hippie activist was discovering what a kick it was to have and use power. The very people who would once have told him to get lost now kowtowed before him. Take the night when a friend called Harvey at home to complain that the Department of Public Works was refusing to do anything about a clogged sewer line that was backing up into his sink and flooding.

"Let me see what I can do," Harvey told him. He called DPW. "This is Supervisor Milk," he said. It wasn't necessary to mention that his committee oversaw DPW.

"Yes, sir," said the bureaucrat on the other end. "What can we do for you?"

Harvey explained the problem and a short time later DPW called back to say it was being cleared up. Now that was hot stuff. Laughing and excited, Harvey kept telling and retelling the story. They had *jumped.* Harvey told Scott Smith that once you were there yourself it wasn't hard to understand why so many selfish, greedy bastards spent huge sums of money to win a job that paid ninety-six hundred a year. He could change the way things were done in San Francisco.

Of all Harvey's many concerns none mattered more to him than ensuring homosexuals protection from discrimination by landlords, employers or the city itself; he had proposed a gay civil rights ordinance as his first order of business after being sworn in. Harvey had always assumed that there would be a problem with Dan on gay rights, so he assigned his aide Dick Pabich to cultivate and educate Dan. Pabich was every bit as clean-cut as Dan himself, a transplanted Midwesterner in buttondown shirts and pressed khaki slacks. His slimness and his aquiline good looks could be misleading. Pabich had a mental toughness that came from not letting his emotions get in the way of what needed to be done. He was as thoroughly professional as Dan was not, and that made it easier for Dan to deal with Pabich than with the unpredictable, mercurial Harvey.

"Do you want everybody to be the same as you are?" Dan asked during one of his talks with Pabich.

"We just want acceptance, the same as everybody else," Pabich answered simply.

"Well, take my advice, then, don't be so far out of the closet," Dan said. "That only antagonizes people. A lot of the other supervisors feel the same way I do about it, they just don't have the guts to say it to you. You know that as well as I do."

Pabich would never have said, "You're suggesting Harvey sell himself out to keep bigots like you happy," but he thought it. Pabich came away from those discussions thinking that for all that Dan wished things would return to the way they once had been, he was probably going to vote for gay rights after all. Every chance he got, Pabich, acting for Harvey, praised Dan. "A really neat thing is how supportive some people around here have been, Dan White in particular," Pabich wrote in a gay newspaper. "He's supported us on every position and he goes out of his way to find out what gay people think about things."

Harvey had given him a commitment, or so Dan thought, and that was on his mind when, early in March, he gaveled to order a hearing before his committee on the gay rights ordinance. The small room was filled with gay men and lesbians who had come to talk and cheer. Sitting at the dais facing the audience—men with earrings; men holding hands, kissing hello; women with their arms around each other—Dan was incredulous that each and every one of these people was a San Franciscan who worked and loved and voted in his city, and moreover that he was about to play a role in seeing to it that their grievances were remedied and their legal rights safeguarded. Of course, he wasn't doing it for them, he wished they'd all go back to wherever they came from. He was doing it for Harvey.

He wanted to get the whole unsavory experience over with as quickly as possible. Dan opened the hearing by suggesting that since his committee was unanimously in favor of the gay rights ordinance there really wasn't any need to take testimony. He couldn't really take these people quite seriously.

"When I was growing up," Dan said, his high, boyish voice amplified, "I had very little exposure to gay people. When I was in the service . . . I learned many lessons. One of them was that when the chips are down and people's lives are at stake all the cards are on the table— you may not be there in the next five minutes or five hours." Without realizing it, he was condescending, more interested in his own attitudes than the aspirations of the people he was talking to.

"I found that a lot of the things I had read about that had been attributed to certain people—blacks, Chinese, gays, whites—just didn't hold up under fire. Literally under fire." He seemed to expect that his audience would find that as impressive as he did. "I saw men I was in combat with perform as admirably as anyone else would perform and I learned right there that people have many problems, we all have our problems, and the sooner we leave discrimination in any form behind the better off we'll be. It doesn't matter what a person is, what his preferences are. As long as they respect other people and they abide by courtesies and values, I think we can all get along."

The moment Dan finished Harvey took the floor and insisted that it was impossible to cut short the hearing, that many people had taken the time to come to City Hall because there were things they wanted to say on the public record. There was cheering in the room. In fact, Harvey said, since there weren't enough seats in the committee room, what they should do is move to the supervisors' chambers. Dan had no choice but to agree.

Several hours later, Dan's committee voted 3–0 to recommend that San Francisco enact the nation's first gay rights legislation. Dan had given Harvey everything he wanted.

That was on a Thursday, and Friday afternoon Pabich and Harvey came by Dan's office and talked for a while with Dan and Ray Sloan. Pabich had persuaded Harvey that he couldn't vote against the Youth Campus after all, and the idea was to let Dan know. Instead, Harvey pandered to Dan's vanity.

"The way you've worked on this," he said, "you've earned your ninety-six hundred on the Youth Campus alone. You've done a just incredible job. Hasn't he, Dick?"

"Uh-huh," Pabich said.

Harvey hoped that Dan would read between the lines and understand that he was clearly not saying he would vote the way Dan wanted him to, but Dan took the opposite message. Sloan listened more carefully, and almost blurted out a direct question, but the atmosphere of the brief meeting was so falsely hearty, and the underlying tension so nervous-making, that he bit his tongue.

The following Monday the chamber was packed with Dan's followers from the Portola; he had invited them to come down to City Hall to witness his great triumph in their behalf, assuring them that he had six votes lined up, that thanks to Dan White their faith would be renewed that city government could work for them. This was the moment that would justify and exalt all his ideals. He was feeling very full of himself.

The debate began and at first was predictable. Dianne Feinstein chastised the mental health bureaucracy. "I don't think the way to handle this is to thrust it," she said. Her remarks were met with rumbles of approval from the hardworking family people of the Portola.

As the palaver continued supervisors left their high-back leather swivel chairs and roamed the chambers, leaning over to whisper to their colleagues, exchanging jokes and asides. The debate was familiar; the clash between compassion and fear lacked the immediacy for them that it held for the homeowners of the Portola or for Sister Columba and her nuns, who were also there. It was all predictable—Dan's angry accusations that city mental health officials had been deceptive in their representations; the appeals on behalf of the children; the fearful warnings of rapists and muggers set loose in the neighborhood; the dry, statistical statements of the bureaucrats—all predictable until Harvey tapped his microphone with a finger to make sure it was working.

Harvey would have preferred for the Youth Campus to be foisted on Dianne and Pacific Heights, but unfortunately that wasn't the issue. "There's no place in this city where people would want a Mafia headquarters next door," he said flippantly. Finally he came to the point: "We have to put aside our own fears," he said, "and accept responsibility for the disturbed children." He was voting for the Youth Campus.

Dan was stunned by the betrayal. Caught unawares, humiliated and beaten in front of the people whose champion he was, Dan swiveled in his chair and glared at the cocky man who, despite all his misgivings, he had tried to understand and support. This was the thanks he got.

"I see a leopard never changes his spots," he whispered fiercely to Quentin Kopp.

"What'd I tell you?" Kopp said. When the votes were tallied Kopp was the first supervisor to rush over and congratulate Sister Columba, even though he had voted against her.

Sister Columba peered up at him over her glasses. "After you voted against us, Mr. Kopp, I'm surprised the good Lord didn't send you to Hell," she said.

Momentarily Kopp was at a loss for words. The pint-sized nun had told him to go to Hell. He laughed dryly. "That's funny," he said.

Dan, meanwhile, stalked out of the chamber in a dudgeon. Sister Columba felt badly for him; she had come to think of him as a spoiled child with very bad manners. After the Board had initially voted against the Youth Campus, back in December, he had led a victory caravan which circled the convent grounds, gloating over a bullhorn. Throughout the wrangling she had often prayed for Dan, knowing that his acts of pettish temper lacked maturity and dignity. If there had been a Youth Campus when he was growing up, she thought, maybe he would have had some help with *his* problems.

Ray Sloan had never before seen Dan so volcanically enraged. For a few days Dan didn't show his face at City Hall. When he did return, it was to teach Harvey he couldn't jerk Dan White around and get away with it. The following Monday the gay rights ordinance was up before the full board. Dan alone stood against it.

His constituents, he explained, had been calling all week to object to the position he had taken in committee. "Gays throughout the state represent a very small minority," Dan said. His anger and his hurt made his words sound even more intemperate than they were. "You have to educate people who disagree with you. A vast majority of people, I'll use Catholics as an example, have very strong beliefs." Homosexuality was an offense to those beliefs.

For a politician to attack gays in San Francisco made as much sense as going to Salt Lake City to attack the Mormon church. Nobody else dared do it, but Dan was forcing Harvey and his kind to listen to just what a lot of people *really* felt. He had the power to make them listen to the truth.

Afterward, Dan was still sulking, feeling self-righteous and misunderstood. He wasn't a bigot, he told Ray. When he had been in Vietnam he had been the point man on a patrol that was ambushed and pinned down by enemy fire. As Dan talked, Ray thought: typical Dan White, he always had to be a hero. Dan continued with his story. The other members of the patrol had all scattered and he had been sure he wasn't going to make it out alive. But one soldier was brave enough to remain behind and provide covering fire for Dan's escape. The man had saved his life, Dan said, near tears. And *he* was gay. How could they accuse Dan White of being a bigot?

Harvey, meanwhile, was in his glory and had no idea of Dan's feelings. He had lost so many political skirmishes himself without ever losing his determination to fight again another day. He asked Dick Pabich to talk with Dan one more time before the gay rights ordinance came up for final passage; a unanimous vote would look good. Pabich found Dan to be absolutely rigid, and as Sister Columba had remarked, "Such rigidity has to break."

When Pabich stopped by, Dan was steely but frank. What he had said in his floor speech, Dan told Pabich, wasn't his truest feeling although it was true enough. What he really felt was that he had bent over backwards to help Harvey—with his committee assignment, with the lesbian resolution, in committee on gay rights—and Harvey had repaid him by lying to him and stabbing him in the back. Never again, Dan told Pabich, would he feel any obligation to Harvey or anything he wanted. He had learned who his friends were. From here on in, he said, it was personal, personal between him and Harvey, tit for tat.

Pabich saw the logic in Dan's feelings, even though its basis was total self-absorption as far as he was concerned. When Pabich reported back to Harvey, Harvey shrugged it off. There were a million things to accomplish and no time to waste worrying about Dan White's bruised feelings.

9
Dry Hustle

Earl Sanders never intended to become a cop.

His brother-in-law was studying for the police exam and he asked Earl to help him out. For months Sanders quizzed him until his brother-in-law said, "Earl, you know this stuff as well as I do. Why don't you take the test too?" Sanders had no other plans and no reason not to. When they posted the results his brother-in-law had flunked and Sanders was second on the list. By 1973, Sanders was a homicide inspector. By then his brother-in-law had made his first million in real estate.

Sanders' partner was Rotea Guilford, whose chance encounter with George Moscone in the New Yorker Hotel had ripened into a friendship. Despite their personal achievements, the lot of black cops hadn't improved. There were no blacks above the rank of inspector and only a token number of sargeants and assistant inspectors. Few blacks were hired, and those who were were isolated and subjected to subtle ridicule in the guise of locker room humor and even more vicious prejudice. Once another cop showed Sanders a handful of dumdum bullets. "Know what these are?" he smirked. "Nigger-stoppers." With a handful of other black officers Sanders and Guilford formed their own labor organization, Officers for Justice. The police chief threatened to fire them. They ignored him.

Sanders was a down-to-earth sort of man who was very good at his job. He was barrelchested and bullnecked. They way he combed his hair emphasized the hand-grenade shape of his head. The smoothness of his light skin was interrupted only by a neat moustache and by a tiny scar at the corner of his right eye. Behind his glasses his eyes were limpid. He looked to be, and indeed was, a proud man in control of himself, with something relentless always held in reserve for when it was needed.

One day in 1973 Sanders, Guilford and a few of the other Officers for Justice were in Guilford's kitchen playing dominoes and grousing about how the lilywhite Police Officers Association was running them around the mulberry bush with the old democracy game. There were about a hundred black and fifteen hundred white officers in the POA, and every time the black cops asked for some injustice to be corrected, the leadership gave them choirboy grins and said, "Sure, it's a democracy, let's put it to a vote." The results were always the same.

Guilford was impatient with the bellyaching. He looked up from the dominoes and said, "Let's sue the bastards."

Sanders took a sip of his beer. It was as if somebody had declared, "We shall fight them on the beaches." Guilford turned over another domino and said it again. "Well, why shouldn't we? Let's sue the bastards."

And so they had. In 1977 the federal government had joined the suit and Judge Robert Peckham had consolidated the two actions. The OFJ part of the suit asked for $43 million in back pay and damages, for a minority hiring quota, and for guarantees of fair treatment. To win they would have to prove that the discrimination against them had been intentional, which was not easy. The federal government's case was stronger, since it challenged only the exam procedures for hiring and promotion and could be proved statistically.

So long as the suit was pending Judge Peckham had enjoined the city from hiring any cops, and the ranks were dwindling. The police department, meanwhile, was loath to make any promotions from existing lists, knowing that they would be challenged. The upshot was that hundreds of white cops who had passed promotion exams were having their higher ranks, and the larger salaries that went with them, withheld. And this at the same time that Chief Charles Gain was declaring that he wanted more women, blacks and homosexuals in the department.

There was a lot of hard feeling and tension, and no real desire for a trial, which would take a long time and exacerbate resentments. The handwriting was on the wall anyway: chances were the feds would win and the OFJ wouldn't. The basis for a compromise existed. Although he had no formal standing, encouraged by the composition of the new board which would have to ratify any consent decree, Mayor Moscone began to hold private negotiating sessions. All the involved parties except for the POA were represented at the parleys in George's office. The POA had been excluded for being obstructionist; they wanted to fight to the finish. Hour after hour George sat at his desk, chainsmoking, rolling pencils in his big basketball player's hands, playing the neutral good guy, even though everybody present knew where his sympathies lay. The compromise which began to shape up galled the POA. It called for setting aside the existing promotion lists, and starting from scratch with minority quotas for hiring and promotion. To the old-boy Irish network that ran the department despite Chief Gain it seemed that George Moscone's idea of compromise was to take away what was rightfully theirs and hand it over to people who hadn't earned it. The crime fighters believed they knew a robbery when they saw one. It was just what they would have expected from George Moscone.

On two separate occasions, in 1975, before the OFJ suit and before Moscone was finally elected mayor, he had met privately in the Hall of Justice with the "downtown force" in the Police Department, the brass and the plainclothes units. The police were a power in the city's politics, even though two out of every three cops lived outside the city. And what they knew about George Moscone they did not like. In part their dislike derived from personal disapproval: his near-arrest in the Fillmore was only one of several such scrapes known to the police; the most recent involved a collision in a Sacramento parking lot—George supposedly had liquor on his breath and definitely had a comely black woman in the car with him; her suitcase was in the trunk. And partly their dislike was political: he had sponsored legislation that all but decriminalized marijuana, he had espoused positions and surrounded himself with people who were soft on law and order. The mood, when George came in to face the upper-echelon cops, ranged from dubious to hostile.

Homicide Inspector Frank Falzon was dubious. But as he listened to George Moscone he softened. George talked sincerely, Falzon thought; he had a smile on his lips and a joke in his heart, a manner that made you want to believe him. By the time George got around to their greatest concern—who he would appoint as their chief—he had the cops laughing along with him at his jokes. In both his pitches to these cops George promised, without equivocation, that he would select a chief from within the ranks; in other words, somebody sitting in that room listening to him would be the chief, the status quo would not be disturbed. By the second time he talked privately with the downtown force the resistance to him, and some of the support for Barbegelata, was no longer in evidence.

And then, after he was elected, George appointed Charles R. Gain as chief. Gain had not been in the room, wasn't even a San Franciscan. A career policeman with a national reputation as a reformer and a history of conflict with the men under his command in every city where he had ever worked, Gain had a defensive arrogance, an "I know better" attitude. He was commanding but aloof, or perhaps shy. He wore an orange toupee on top of a long, narrow head which he held very straight on a high, thin neck. His suits always looked to be a size too large for his wiry frame. There were muscles bunched at his sharp jaw, dramatic planes in his face, and no humor whatsoever in his agate-blue eyes. He was an outsider's outsider, a man whose appointment represented more than a broken promise by George Moscone: it was an outright betrayal. Chief Gain never had a chance.

Why exactly George chose Charles Gain, who was a walking provocation to the men in blue, was never entirely clear. There was, at the time, a U.S. task force investigating the San Francisco police department, and the feds impressed upon the mayor the necessity for bringing in somebody to clean up the department; they insisted that all the old-timers were either corrupt or acquiescent. There were other people who believed that George felt the system of political juice under which the department operated was not consistent either with the times or his own program, that the old ways simply had to be completely reformed, that in order to open up the department to the minorities who in sum constituted a new majority, he would have to bring in a chief who insisted on a strict merit system, a by-the-book man like Charles Gain. The most cynical view involved a rumor that when Gain had been in the Oakland Police Department he had had a hand in suppressing another of George's peccadillos; the argument ran that since George knew his private life made him particularly vulnerable to police pressure, he had to have a chief like Gain or Guilford who had shown a willingness to protect him. Even Gain himself could not believe George wanted him. When George offered him the job, Gain told him: "I'll do it and I'll stick with you but you're crazy. I don't know if you can survive it."

No matter what George's precise reasons were, with the way the city was going it had only been a matter of time before the constabulary came under the thumb of the liberal bureaucracy. Virtually the first official act of the new chief was to eliminate the position of director, a high-ranking post with few responsibilities, a sinecure much coveted by senior officers. Gain spent the better part of his first month on the job familiarizing himself not with his men but with black, Chicano and Chinese community leaders who complained that the department was ingrown, insensitive and self-serving. His department, Gain decided, didn't give a damn about the people they were supposed to police, and he made no secret of what he believed.

He began to reorganize the department, talking to reporters about an "Irish mafia" that had run separate fiefdoms and would no longer; their day had come to an end. And he ordered transfers that showed he meant business. He went public, too, with charges that three hundred active and retired policemen had alcohol abuse problems, and ordered a complete halt to drinking on duty, a tradition as cherished by the cops as the cable cars were by the Chamber of Commerce. He had the American flag removed from his private office. He declared that black-and-white prowl cars would all be repainted a less antagonistic baby blue. In and of themselves these changes, most of them minor and several much needed, might have incurred little resistance had he cultivated his captains and lieutenants, enlisted their help. But that was not Charles Gain's style.

"Nothing comes in my way of achieving goals," Gain said. "It doesn't matter how much shattering of patterns is involved. I just do it. If things get dull I get bored."

Captain Ray Canepeh, who commanded a station house, didn't much cotton to Gain personally; he noticed that his chief didn't meet his eye when they talked. He was nevertheless willing to give the man a chance. But things happened that turned him against Gain, too. One time he called the chief personally to tell him that things at the Sunnydale projects looked bad; he thought they might blow.

"Sunnydale?" the chief said. "Where's that?"

Gain didn't get out and learn the city he was responsible for keeping safe, and he virtually never consulted with his station house captains, who might have been his eyes and ears out in the neighborhoods. In the view of his men Gain had held them up to public ridicule, had debunked patriotism, and had neglected the things that were really crucial to running a department, internal communication and morale. Now he went even further: he invited the fairies into the locker rooms.

When George had hired Charles Gain he had talked over with him the question of hiring gay police officers. "We want gay police officers," George had said. "But let me suggest to you, Charlie, that when you're asked about it you make a general statement along the lines of, you know, 'We do not discriminate against anyone.' "

In line with his community outreach program, Gain met with the editors and reporters of several gay newspapers and told them, "I will absolutely initiate an active recruitment program. Here in San Francisco, of all places, we should have gays on the police force, both men and women." When his remarks were published all hell broke loose. His men were prepared for a lot, but hardly for that. They muttered about him in the station houses he never visited and in the saloons he had placed off limits to them. They hated their chief, and hating him, blamed George Moscone for betraying them.

The hatred was based on symbolic, or personal, or ideological, or moral differences. What happened next—the crackdown on the nude encounter parlors and the incident at the Hookers' Ball—were also symbolic and moral conflicts. But a lot of money was involved too.

As tourism became the city's most important industry and source of income in the 1960s and early 1970s, the coffeehouses, nightclubs and restaurants along the main drags of North Beach became the center of the city's nightlife. Tourists flocked there and flocks are made to be fleeced. Topless strip joints began to sprout like night-blooming mushrooms. Across the intersection of Broadway and Columbus, Carol Doda's red neon nipples winked suggestively at Lawrence Ferlinghetti's City Lights Bookstore. By 1974 nude encounter parlors like the House of Ecstasy and the Sugar Shack were adding a new flagrancy to the fleecing.

A dry hustle is as old as Salome's Dance of the Seven Veils, and a dry hustle is what the parlors were purveying. Johns were led to expect that by paying a little more, and then a little more, and a little more, they would eventually be allowed not only to look but to touch and so on from there. The traveling businessman was encouraged step by step to think he would receive satisfaction in exchange for his money, but he never did. To protect the women from the wrath of frustrated johns they were separated by a plastic barrier with a door painted on it; in the minds of the johns the door was always about to be opened, but that was a patently false promise. In the door, however, was a real slot through which the johns kept sliding their money. A frustrated john might drop a lot of money—hundreds of dollars was not uncommon—and if the john was drunk enough he might be rolled as well. No matter what happened, though, most johns could do no more than holler; they didn't want their wives or their corporate employers to know that they had been inside the parlors. In some places, if a john hollered too loud the consequences were immediate. A tourist from Los Angeles, for instance, was dragged outside where his head was beaten on the sidewalk. Although a suspect was taken into custody—he was a bouncer for one of the parlors—by the time the john came to his senses in the hospital, he decided to go back to Los Angeles without pressing any charges.

Hundreds of complaints, many of them anonymous, were being lodged with the Police Department. Chief Gain declared that North Beach had to be cleaned up. He made it sound like no more than a streetsweep was involved—just mop up some garbage and be done with it. In fact, though, what was really at stake was money, a great deal of money, most of it collected in cash. Successful encounter parlor operators admitted to taking in twelve thousand dollars a week; what they really took in was anybody's guess, but it was certainly more than they were going to report to the IRS. Their money bought them Cadillacs and pinky rings but it also bought them protection; after all, if they ran afoul of the law they would lose their licenses, and there was enough going on so that really diligent police work *would* have put all of them out of business.

At the same time that Chief Gain moved on North Beach, the district attorney, Joe Freitas, was overseeing an investigation of his own. The thing was getting out of hand; somebody would have to take a fall. Among all the people operating the topless joints and the parlors, the D.A.'s office concentrated on two, Sam Conti and Ron London. London, who owned four parlors, had a brutal reputation. The assistant D.A. running the investigation, Candy Heisler, zeroed in on London because his women had been so badly abused that they were willing to talk. "He treated them like whores," said Heisler. "He manhandled them, he forced himself on them, he beat them." He was once observed leading one of his bouncers down Broadway on a leash, whipping him. London ran a coffeehouse where a lot of North Beach patrolmen hung out, and even Chief Gain had heard that cops accepted sexual favors from women London employed.

The other main target of the D.A.'s investigation was Sam Conti, a six-foot-three, two-hundred-fifty-pound operator of three parlors and a topless joint who was driven about in a midnight-blue Cadillac limo. Conti was no worse than most of the other operators. However, his lawyer was Assemblyman Willie Brown, and Willie Brown and George Moscone went together like pepper and salt. Both Conti and London had contributed money to George's mayoral campaign. If *somebody* had to take a fall, why not somebody whose arrest would, however indirectly, involve Willie Brown and George Moscone? Perhaps this was something that the cops and District Attorney Freitas, who was talking about running for mayor, could agree on.

The district attorney's office had gathered quite a bit of information on Conti and on his relationship with Willie Brown, and in April 1977 a good deal of what they had learned showed up on the front page of the *Chronicle.* The paper revealed that Conti had presented Brown with a twenty-five-hundred-dollar Advent Videobeam TV with a six-foot screen. The newspaper attributed the story to documents which had come into their possession, source unspecified.

Another sequence of leaks tended to put both Chief Gain and Assemblyman Brown in a rather glaring light. Conti had applied for a liquor license for one of his establishments and the officer in charge of the vice squad had objected. Soon after, a new captain of vice had been appointed by Chief Gain. The new man, Captain Paul Lawler, had received a telephone call from Willie Brown appealing against his predecessor's recommendation, and Lawler had asked Gain what to do. Gain reviewed the case and withdrew the police department objection.

Whether or not North Beach was being cleaned up was problematical, but it was a sure thing that Willie Brown, Chief Gain and, by implication, George Moscone were being pictured in the shadows of the seaminess and corruption. George, in fact, complained to Supervisor Terry Francois about what was going on.

"I'm having problems with Willie," George said. "Hell, he's making all kinds of money in legal fees and using his relationship with me. I don't get any part of the money but people think I do. It looks bad."

Willie Brown claimed that there was nothing askance with his accepting a TV set in lieu of a fee from a client, and eventually he was exonerated of any wrongdoing. Chief Gain, meanwhile, explained that the transfers in the vice squad had nothing to do with Assemblyman Brown. "Some officers have been in vice for years and years," he said privately. "And some are availing themselves of opportunities to start dealing with drugs, taking payoffs. An officer in vice can get a distorted view of the world; the unusual hours, the narcotics, you get to identify with these people and also to hate them, to want to eradicate them. I think the thing to do is broaden their experience, to set up rotation policies."

However, many cops didn't believe that explanation. They pointed out that one beat cop in North Beach had been zealous in trying to get Ron London for some of his wrongdoing. London began to boast on the street that the cop couldn't touch him. He was immune, London told everybody who would listen, and the immunity was provided by George Moscone. London claimed he was providing the mayor with fourteen-year-old girls, and that George was, among other things, beating them up. There was never any proof of these accusations—indeed there is no reason to think they were anything but lies—but when the cop London boasted couldn't touch him was in fact transferred out of North Beach, perhaps as part of Chief Gain's rotation policies, it didn't look good at all.

District Attorney Freitas, meanwhile, was not taking Chief Gain into his confidence. His principal investigator was instructed to keep his files under lock and key and to open them to nobody. Still another unit in the D.A.'s office began to keep a separate file on Mayor Moscone, filled mainly with rumors.

Conti kept his mouth shut in public and hired himself a well-connected lawyer; eventually his case was dealt out. He gave up his parlor licenses and no criminal charges were pressed against him. Ron London, who didn't shut up and whose lawyer wasn't Willie Brown, wasn't so lucky. He served two years and eight months in state prison. Then he returned to San Francisco to operate a coffeehouse in the Tenderloin which quickly became a favorite hangout for cops.

The other incident that contributed to Gain's unpopularity concerned the Hookers' Ball. The first hookers' masquerade ball had been held during the Gold Rush. The camp followers who had formed liaisons with the forty-niners were not the sort of women a man married; the prospectors, the merchants, the miners began to send back home for wives, and before long San Francisco began to get civilized. In other words, the camp followers and their male friends could go on meeting in the saloons and bawdyhouses of the Barbary Coast, but no longer in public. Out of that cruel separation arose the idea of a masked ball: with everybody's identity hidden, people who could not socialize under normal circumstances were able to spend a night of delicious intrigue in public.

In 1974 Margo St. James revived the tradition of the masquerade ball. When Joe Ryan and the vice squad busted Margo way back in 1959 she had been innocent of the accusations against her; she really had been giving it away for free, a farmer's daughter from Washington who took a shine to George Moscone and the native sons in the cafes of North Beach. By 1974, however, a lot of apples had fallen from that particular tree and Margo became perhaps the best known retired prostitute in American, the founder of COYOTE (Call Off Your Old Tired Ethics) and an advocate of the right of working girls to be free of police harassment. The first Hookers' Ball was a great success: it evoked an old Barbary Coast tradition, it parodied the Policeman's Ball, which had folded its tent when the cops had been overzealous about selling Ball tickets to motorists they stopped for traffic violations, and it raised money for Margo and COYOTE. It had been so successful, in fact, that it began a new tradition.

The relationship between cops and whores was as old as the city itself. San Francisco is a convention town, and in convention towns prostitution is especially lucrative. The police kept an eye on it not only through the vice squad and beat cops but also through the cops who moonlighted as security guards at the big downtown hotels. One way or another it was nearly impossible for a prostitute to operate in downtown San Francisco, where the real money was, without, at a minimum, police knowledge and tacit approval. If a woman or her pimp gave what was asked, many cops would look the other way. Chief Gain did not, in the view of his men, look the other way: he looked the wrong way. The Chief appointed a woman's advisory task force and Margo St. James, with the Chief's full backing, was allowed to ride around in prowl cars, baby-blue prowl cars, observing and reporting on the street scene. In fact, Margo and the task force compiled a list of cops who were especially loathed by hookers and many of them, too, were subject to Chief Gain's rotation policies. The insult to the average cop who learned that prostitutes were calling the shots was grave enough; for some cops, though, it was as if their chief were reaching his hand right into their blue serge pockets.

When Margo asked Chief Gain to attend the 1977 Hookers' Ball he thought it would be fun. Mrs. Gain, however, took extreme exception and refused to go, so the chief left his wife at home. Of course he didn't wear a costume; coming as the police chief was quite enough. The ball was a bacchanal. It was a bazaar of drugs, drink, rock 'n' roll, feathers and finery, and naked bodies; it was separated from everything else by a kind of ravine which the normal moral climate could not cross.

It was a moment in time, just as it had been back in Gold Rush days, where for a single night all taboos, all social restraints were superseded by the libido given license.

By 10 P.M. the 1977 Hookers' Ball was getting a bit out of hand. It wasn't the elephant crowned with a spray of peacock feathers, or the flashers or the fornicators, and certainly not the lady who wore a large plastic penis on her nose, but rather the street toughs who were scaling fire escapes, breaking in windows and doing what they could to gain free admission. Margo grabbed Charlie Gain's arm and started walking him upstairs to a payphone so he could call for reinforcements. On the second level they passed two men who were fighting. One of the men pulled a knife. Chief Gain walked right on by. Such are the privileges of rank.

When the Chief completed his call to headquarters he stepped out of the phone booth, and picking up their cue from that, some revelers began to call him "Superman." Before you knew it a bottle of champagne was being passed around. Spirits were bubbly. Just as luck would have it a newspaper photographer happened by.

"Take a picture," shouted Margo, throwing her arm around the shoulders of the shy, usually reserved Chief who at the moment wore an uncharacteristically gleeful grin. "He's our prince," Margo waxed, "Our savior."

When the picture ran in the next day's paper—in it Gain had one arm around Margo and the other around a drag queen known as Wonder Whore, yet managed to keep his toupee perfectly straight—there were quite a few policemen who thought that Margo was precisely right, their Chief was the whore's savior. To the corrupt cop it looked as if Margo's hand had joined Chief Gain's in their pockets, but to the honest, hardworking son of St. Mary's or St. Brigid's—that is, to the majority of the force, the public display of their Chief in such a compromised pose was tantamount to treason; it mocked their whole lives. And every one of San Francisco's policemen knew who had betrayed them and foisted Charles Gain on their department. George Moscone had.

The notorious picture of Chief Gain and his friends was posted on locker room bulletin boards in the city's station houses, where he seldom ventured himself but where he insisted homosexuals had a perfect right to be. On some of the bulletin boards, right beside the photograph, appeared a copy of a piece of homemade artwork, just a simple drawing of Chief Gain. Superimposed on his likeness were the crosshairs of a rifle sight.

George was in his office when there was a call on his private line. He swiveled around in his chair and answered it.

"Yeah?"

Maisie said, "Is this the mayor?" Shy but bold.

"Of course it's the mayor. It's my phone, isn't it? Who's this?"

"This is Maisie." Putting it right out there.

"The kid! Well, what do you want now?"

"I want something."

"I know, I know you want something. What is it?"

"I really want to talk to you." There was another grant Maisie was after.

"Are you finally going to sleep with me?"

Maisie was flustered, embarrassed. This was the mayor. She was only twenty-three. "Wait a minute, uh, Mayor . . ."

"George," he said. "George, George, George, George."

Maisie didn't say anything, so George said, "Why don't you come over, we can have a drink and you can tell me you'll sleep with me."

Maisie thought, *the mayor.* His wife'll kill me. She wasn't even sure she wanted to. "Well, uh, okay, I'll come over there."

When she arrived George was slipping his suit jacket off the coat rack. Maisie was wearing high heels, which emphasized the slim, almost boyish lines of her body. She was quite sure that George was accustomed to women with more of the usual feminine allure, that part of her appeal to him was her lack of guile. He thought it was cute when she wobbled on her high heels. They were standing alone in the big ceremonial office on a deep, rich carpet. Oil paintings of mayors long gone lined the paneled walls.

"C'mon," he said. "You can tell me what you want and I'm gonna buy you a drink. Where do you want to drink?"

"I don't know," she said. "I don't want to go to another one of those phony fern bars."

That cracked George up.

They walked across the Plaza, beyond the wide expanse of Market Street and its surface car tracks, to a businessmen's bar. Maisie was chattering about the grant she wanted but she could see he wasn't really listening. That was okay too, she knew he wouldn't say no to her. When she was finished George changed the subject.

He began to talk about some of the problems he was having with the Board. Most of them he blamed on its president. "The stiff bitch," he said. "Her problem is she needs a good fuck."

"Is that what you really think?" Maisie asked. "Or is it, uh, you know, just political?" Here she was, talking with the Mayor about Dianne Feinstein.

"Well," George said, "it's that her sense of what's right and wrong doesn't jibe with mine. But she's got a lot of power and I have to reckon with that, so I reckon with it. She knows her place, though," he laughed. "Just barely."

When their drinks were brought to the table George began to tell Maisie about having been a lawyer in Mississippi, helping to register black voters. In Jefferson County, George told her, smiling at the recollection, a white registrar had asked a black applicant if he could read. "Yes, sir." The registrar showed him a page of writting in Chinese. "What does that say, boy?" George paused before the punchline: "Says you don't want no niggers voting in Mississippi."

Maisie understood that George was trying to show her he was comfortable around black people, but it wasn't necessary. She could see that he wasn't uncomfortable or patronizing. As he continued talking George conveyed to her that he had had many relationships with black people, colorful people. Maisie understood that he was talking about women.

"I have a soft spot for pretty black girls. And you're young to boot. Boy oh boy." It was charming the way he said it and looked at her, so undisguised. It embarrassed her anew.

"I know," George said. "You think that there's nothing in it for me to be here talking to you, but that's not really true. The people I usually talk to intimately, on this level, they're stiff like I am, they've got money, they're my age, they've gotten somewhere. The reason I like talking to you is all that doesn't matter to you."

Every time Maisie felt embarrassed she made a fist and whacked him on the shoulder, and each time she did that George laughed. This time he said, "If you hit me one more time, I'm gonna get you for assaulting a public official." They both laughed. Everything was funny, the way it sometimes is.

As they walked back toward City Hall George told her about this lawsuit, this discrimination suit he was trying to settle. "All they're asking for is a fair shake," he said. "Politically it makes sense. A lot of the assholes don't understand that. White doesn't understand that."

"Dan White?" Maisie said. "The supervisor?"

"The asshole," George said, without malice. More like he was annoyed. "I know, you probably think cops are cops, right? You probably don't care. But people believe in me, they believe I'm in their court. I pay attention to these things, I worked hard to get that support, the support of those people."

Maisie told him, "I'm surprised, really, that someone like you, you know, your age and class and a lawyer and everything, that those things matter to you."

"It's not because I'm a fuckin' militant or anything," George said. "It just makes sense. To get anywhere you've got to do things that make sense to people. And sometimes the things that make sense to you, they don't make sense to punks like Dan White. But it makes sense to me, from my gut, and that's how I got here, doing things that make sense from my gut. You see?"

Maisie saw.

"When I'm with you," George said, "I feel kind of like a kid."

10
Upside Down

The new supervisors had drawn lots to determine where they would sit and Harvey had the worst seat, the one nearest to the public gallery on the east side of the chamber. The closer you sat to the citizenry the less prestige you had. To Harvey's left sat Carol Ruth Silver and to her left was Dan's place.

Carol Ruth's face was youthful but its set was no-nonsense. It was a stubborn, intelligent, determined face. She had a sharp chin, thick dark eyebrows, and wore rectangular black-frame eyeglasses. Her dark hair was cut in a longish pageboy. One would expect her to carry a briefcase and drive a foreign-made sedan.

On the board Carol Ruth saw herself as somebody who could maintain a friendly dialogue with everybody and make compromises. Her almost flirtatious kibbitzing baffled Dan and tied him in knots. He appreciated the attention and made a point of holding doors open for Carol Ruth, but he thought it the purest hypocrisy that she could be so cordial and yet oppose him at every political turn.

Carol Ruth sensed in Dan a coiled, repressed sexuality and an intolerance that she was not surprised went along with it. She was careful not to be rude or raunchy around him and during the meetings was always conscious of his disciplined pose there beside her. It looked to her that Dan was trying to hide the fact that he had balls. Reticent macho. It really was a giggle.

The Monday board meetings often seemed interminable. To break the tedium of hopelessly boring debates, Carol Ruth and Harvey would pass the time by whispering and smirking. Smart, tart, glib and certain of what he wanted to accomplish, Harvey could never resist irreverence. He still wasn't comfortable with his new power, and rather than using it with a judiciousness bred of security in his position, he got things done by being an irritant and a baiter.

Harvey would cast a sidelong glance past Carol Ruth, toward where Dan sat concentrating in his soldierly good posture. "He's *got* to be in the closet," Harvey would whisper. "Lookit what a macho hunk he is. You'd have to use salad oil to get into the tight parts."

Dan stared straight ahead, seemingly oblivious.

"What does Mary Ann see in him?" Carol Ruth whispered back. Mary Ann impressed her as a pleasant, solid lady.

"Turn him upside down," Harvey whispered, "And you'll find out."

Carol Ruth cackled.

Dan wasn't oblivious. He talked with Father Tom Lacey about the way things were at City Hall. "They treat me like a junior-grade moron," he steamed.

"Dan," Father Lacey answered in that voice that was so much bigger than his body, "I think that's where it's at."

It hadn't taken Ray Sloan very long to find a setup that would make Dan some additional income. A telephone call had come from Warren Simmons. Simmons was the founder of the Tia Maria chain of fast-food restaurants which he had recently unloaded for $4.5 million. Now he was developing a new tourist arcade along the northern waterfront. Environmentalists had stymied waterfront development since the Cannery had opened nine years before. But Simmons, who had once tried to corner the market on Philippine monkeys imported for Salk vaccine, was one of the city's heaviest political contributors. Five members of the Board and Mayor Moscone had all benefited from Simmons's largesse. Dianne Feinstein listed $2,800 in contributions from Simmons and his employees in her 1977 campaign. In a town as small as San Francisco $2,800 was a lot of money. Not that it turned her head; regardless, she surely would have been behind Pier 39, as Simmons called his new tourist arcade, and her promise to show up in a bikini on the day the ribbon was cut was entirely in character for the lady whom political cartoonists always drew wearing white gloves.

During their telephone conversation, Simmons mentioned to Sloan that he had run into Dianne and Fire Chief Casper at a party and they had let him know about Dan's financial situation. The reason he was calling, Simmons said, was to invite Dan down to his trailer to have a drink and look around at what they were putting together at Pier 39.

The possibilities made Ray's big entrepreneurial nose twitch in anticipation. *Being the arrogant young star I am,* he said to himself, *I had better go along.* Ray was sure that DW would see this for the opportunity it was.

At the trailer Simmons had an elaborate scale model of the arcade and boat landing that was scheduled to open in October 1978. All that was actually up so far, though, was a skeletal shell of two-by-fours. What got Ray's motor racing weren't the piles of sand and sawdust but how well Simmons and Dan were hitting it off. It was as though they recognized each other as being among the world's go-getters. Simmons was a fanatical tennis player, and of course Dan was always more at his ease with physical men. Simmons glowed with vigor, and when he mentioned in passing how he was at his desk at 5:30 every morning, Ray made a mental note to give him a ring at six o'clock sometime soon. You take a guy like Simmons, you call him one morning when the rest of the world is still asleep, he remembers, he knows you mean business.

At the end of the walking tour Simmons didn't beat around the bush. "How would you like something on the Pier?" he asked Dan.

Dan only said he would think about it, which Ray thought was a pretty shrewd response. But he also saw that Dan was thinking it wasn't right for a supervisor to invest in a project that still needed more city permits of one kind and another. Meanwhile Ray's cash-register mind was ringing up yes, yes, yes. When they were driving back to City Hall, sure enough Dan said to Ray that it looked like a good deal but the ethical considerations weighed against it.

Look, Ray answered, Dianne has her husband's money to live on and Quentin and Carol Ruth and the rest of them practice law and whatnot. They all looked after themselves, and they were the ones who made the rules. The way they had it set up a working stiff like a fireman couldn't keep his job. It wasn't fair.

Dan nodded in agreement.

"Simmons already has the lease," Ray persisted. "Sure there's some loose ends with permits but he's already building the thing. It's a settled matter, there's no conflict. You've got to look after yourself."

"Well," Dan said, "let me talk it over with Mary Ann."

It took Dan only a few days to come around to Ray's point of view after all. The next time they talked about it Dan pointed out to Ray that the ethics of it were okay; Simmons already had the lease, right? Besides, if he didn't look after himself, who would?

Simmons treated Dan as if he had rocked him in the cradle. Dan and Mary Ann spent a weekend at Simmons's country club spread in the wine country. Simmons steered Dan toward taking a lease for a potato stand on the Pier. The location was just inside the front door where there would be heavy pedestrian traffic; and being a fast-food millionaire himself, Simmons knew how much money there was to be made. You could take his projection and halve it and still come out with an awful lot of money.

Dan was negotiating a lease when the city Art Commission demanded that Simmons submit his final architectural plans to them as the law required, and issued a stop-work order until he complied. Dan decided to write to the art commissioners, urging them to reconsider. "Innovative and imaginative projects such as Warren Simmons's . . . enhance the mystique of our city and contribute to the welfare of all San Franciscans," he said in his letter. That caused titters around the Board of Supervisors where it began to be said that the boy populist hadn't taken very long to sell out. It gave Dan some pause, but since he believed his motives were honest he couldn't really understand why everybody else didn't see it his way. Under heavy political pressure the Art Commission capitulated and withdrew its objections. Work on Pier 39 went ahead.

The first week in April, Dan, Ray and Dan's brother Tommy signed a lease with Simmons to operate the Hot Potato. It was a good week for Dan, all in all. He went to the Giants home opener at Candlestick Park; the baseball club gave complimentary season passes to all the supervisors. George Moscone was there to throw out the first ball of the season, and when his name was announced over the public address system there were more boos than cheers. Now *that* gave Dan something to think about; people were already asking him when he planned to run for mayor. Sitting in some of the best box seats in the ballpark while his kind of people booed George Moscone, and with a lease signed for what looked like a lucrative business, Dan was able to forget for a while about all the crap he had to wade through down at City Hall and dream the dreams that had always sustained him.

Two weeks later he and Mary Ann took a second mortgage on their house, withdrew the last of their savings, arranged for a loan and thus came up with their twenty-thousand-dollar share of the initial payment for the Hot Potato.

They were in debt for the first time, deeply in debt, but so long as he was a supervisor he figured he'd be okay.

On the first Tuesday in June Californians made big news all across the country by passing Proposition 13, which limited property taxes while fixing the value of real property. It meant that there would be much less money for local government to spend, and it came just when George thought he was finally going to be able to increase his leverage on public policy in San Francisco. The better part of his first year and a half in office had been spent learning the ropes, coping with the municipal workers' strike and then fighting off the Barbegelata recall. Now, just when his time to make his move had come, Proposition 13 straitened his maneuvering room.

Not that his administration was caught by surprise. A proclamation of emergency, removing restraints on the mayor's powers and rolling back or eliminating scheduled budgetary increases, was already prepared. But because San Francisco had voted against 13, George thought there was a mandate to maintain basic services without cutbacks. To offset the huge loss in property tax revenues under Proposition 13, he was asking for new taxes that would take their biggest bite out of businesses and business transactions, out of "downtown." These higher taxes had to pass the Board before July 1, after which Proposition 13 banned any new local taxes.

George and his staff got right to work trying to line up the six votes they would need.

Quentin Kopp's phone rang early, while the supervisor was still at home. It was a modest home out near the ocean. The call was from one of the mayor's aides, inviting Kopp to a press conference George was going to be holding in a few hours. Kopp thought it took a lot of nerve to have a flunky call him.

"Have George call me," he said, and hung up.

George called a few minutes later. He told Quentin how the press conference was supposed to be a show of unity, to demonstrate that they were all pulling together to help the city weather the crisis, that sort of thing.

"What do you want *me* there for?" Kopp barked.

"Well, I want to be able to say I talked to every supervisor."

When it came to George's shenanigans, QK's vision was twenty-twenty. "Well, you don't need me," Kopp said. He never stops trying, Kopp thought. He must think I was born yesterday to get roped into endorsing his program.

Later that afternoon Kopp bumped into Dan White down at City Hall. Dan had attended the press conference and was pleased at the way most everybody seemed to be pulling together. In fact, he and Dianne had met privately with George to say they would go along on his tax package so long as he agreed not to cut the police or fire department budgets.

"Jeez," Dan said to Kopp, "You didn't come to the press conference."

"Why would I want to listen to that shit?" Kopp said.

Dan explained how George had laid out all the figures to show how much trouble the city was in, how unless they did something even the police and fire departments might have to be cut back.

"They always threaten that to bring us in line. It's premature, precipitous and unnecessary."

"I'm not sure you're right, Quentin. Jeez, George's got a lot of information." Dan didn't say something else which he also thought: that George had the best interests of the city at heart, whereas Quentin wanted more than anything else to beat George in 1979 and become mayor himself. He thought that Quentin was grandstanding, and that was one reason why he was already deciding to back George rather than the more conservative Kopp in 1979.

On June 12 the mayor's proclamation of emergency—though not his tax package—was passed by the Board. Dan, however, didn't vote because he was unable to attend the meeting. Mary Ann had gone into labor that same morning and been admitted to Children's Hospital.

The doctor had decided that it didn't hurt to be cautious and keep a close eye on a thirty-six-year-old woman giving birth to her first child. It was a long day, too, for her husband. He would never have said so but the event wasn't an unmitigated joy. As he waited hour after hour he worried, naturally, but he didn't let that show. He took charge of seeing to it that everybody in the family was in good spirits even though there was a dark, downward pressure which he kept shrugging off, not unlike what he had gone through on his honeymoon. He was high, the kind of high you get when you're bouncing away from the threat of a real low low.

A few minutes after 9 P.M. they got the news, a healthy son had been born. After Dan had said goodnight to Mary Ann he went right out to the old age home where both his grandmothers resided to tell them the joyous news about their great-grandson: Charles Edward White, little Charlie.

Dan wasn't about to stint. He not only handed around cigars and candy but gave every one of his colleagues on the Board a bottle of the best, Chivas Regal. Harvey didn't drink hard liquor so he gave it to Dick Pabich and Pabich put it on a shelf in the closet and there it sat. But Harvey did go to the christening and housewarming party.

It was hard to find because you had to go around the big MUNI barn to get there, and Shawnee Avenue was nearly a cul-de-sac. You had to look sharp to notice the narrow street that came to a deadend at an overpass. The house was just about what he expected: a tidy bungalow with a nice fresh coat of lime paint. Suffocationsville. There were lots and lots of people, for the most part the kind of people Harvey didn't spend too much time around. He found himself with a glass of white wine in one hand, a piece of cake in the other, standing in a living room that looked like a picture in a Sears Roebuck catalogue, talking with Joe Ryan, the retired vice cop. Harvey was yammering away about how dope was the source of a lot of crime and Ryan was nodding with this tight, bitter grin. It was only too clear to Harvey what Ryan really thought. In fact, Ryan often enough pointed out, "Ya see a Dianne Feinstein talk to 'em, ya know she goes home and pukes after. Or a Quentin Kopp, he's a family man, ya know he doesn't believe in that stuff. It's all bullshit, everybody's talkin' outta the side of their mouths." And here he was talking to Harvey Milk out of the side of his. How do ya like them apples, his grin said.

Dan was on top of the world, playing the host, showing off his new downtown friends, the star among his family and old friends. It was one of the few occasions where he drank maybe a bit more than he could control; he was ebullient. When he saw Harvey he pumped his hand. Harvey was grinning, nodding, trying to soak up all the details so he could remember them later. They would make great stories to tell to Scott and his friends. All of a sudden Dan reached out and collared an old guy with a big red bald spot and white tufts over both his ears that made him look kind of jolly.

"Tom," Dan said, "Tom, I want you to meet one of the greatest guys I know. Tom, this is Supervisor Harvey Milk."

Dan's uncle Tom didn't know what to make of it. One of the greatest guys he knew?

Ray Sloan liked nothing better than free booze except maybe being the man behind DW, so the christening was really a gas for him. Of course being around Mary Ann was kind of a drag. Nothing that had happened since that first meeting in Grison's Steak House had changed his view of her. A pretty smile and a steadfast wife. Period. And now that they were working together to set up the Hot Potato he had found out she was a tightwad too. Ray was leaving City Hall to work full time on their new business, and he wasn't exactly delighted at the prospect of spending every day in Mary Ann's company. But what the hell, this was no time for dwelling on his instinct that she turned up her pug nose when he was around.

As usual his black eyes were skittering around, trying to notice everything while avoiding notice themselves. He could see how totally committed Mary Ann was to Dan, and how Dan was absolutely crazy about his baby son. Dan loved his wife, too, but Ray saw something else, some flaw in the marriage. Dan wasn't really ready for it, he had a tough time with his sexuality.

When he watched Dan and Harvey together he saw something else again. Dan really—it was a funny word to use but it was what came to Ray's mind—Dan really *loved* Harvey. He also had this grudge against him, he hadn't forgotten the Youth Campus. Dan had tried to approach Harvey man to man and Harvey had burned him. Today the champagne and his joy and pride in his son were making it easy for Dan to paper over his feelings with geniality, but Ray saw beneath that. There were strong, strong feelings that Dan had for Harvey, this wish to be his friend, his special friend, and this bad grudge.

Ray thought there was a lot going on there that wouldn't ever be expressed.

Over the years San Francisco may have grown from a big town into a small city but it still loved a good parade. Chinese New Year, Columbus Day and the Japanese Cherry Blossom Festival were all promoted by the Convention and Visitors Bureau as part of San Francisco's felicity. You would have had to be there, though, to appreciate the grandest and most colorful parade of them all, on Gay Freedom Day. The weather for the fourth annual parade was all that Harvey could have wished for. It was a beautiful, sunny summer day, warm and cloudless. White sails splashed along the azure bay, and Golden Gate Park was jammed with strolling families, bicyclists, roller skaters and busloads of Japanese tourists. Downtown Harvey was riding in the middle of the parade that took more than an hour to pass any one point, waving and blowing kisses from the back of an open convertible and holding aloft a sign that said, I'M FROM WOODMERE, NEW YORK.

Dan came to see the parade for himself, standing off to the side among the dense crowds of spectators who lined Market Street. Only he among the supervisors had voted against the police request to close the route to traffic. "This is our only opportunity to approve or disapprove of what goes on in our streets," he had said. "What we have here is not simply a parade. In the past there have been obscene floats and behavior we wouldn't approve of if it were heterosexual. The vast majority of people in this city don't want public displays of sexuality." He had come to watch the 300,000 and perhaps more people who marched, danced, ran, rode, twisted, twirled and paraded up Market Street to the plaza in front of City Hall where Harvey would speak.

Dan watched men who were barechested except for crossed bandoliers and others in brightly colored silk tanktops; the politicians, like Willie Brown; the tap dancers in spangled shoes; the Dykes on Bikes—all Kawasakis, Hondas, and Yamahas but no Harleys; the lesbian mothers. The deaf and dumb and gay passed him in silence, followed by the National Organization of Women chanting, "Women united will never be defeated." The gang from Maud's Saloon stepped on by and behind them the little boy with the banner that read, I LOVE MY GAY DAD. The lesbian schoolteachers were accompanied by a drum corps and the placards of the Jewish contingent explained that THE LOST TRIBE IS GAY. Somebody carried a sign that claimed, EVEN FEINSTEIN MASTURBATES, and the regular crowd from a bar called the Stud worked up a little rhyme that went, "Black and Blue/Is the Last Taboo." There were too many marching bands, choruses, majorettes and balloons to enumerate, and the baton twirlers had to be especially careful of the streetcar lines strung overhead. The staff and volunteers from the San Francisco Venereal Disease Clinic, which had warned the public of a VD epidemic, held aloft a banner which said they were PROUD OF THE GAY COMMUNITY. The Tooth Fairy marched with the Doctors and Dentists for Human Rights in the health services sector of the parade, where they were joined by the mental health workers whose specialty was ambivalence: "Two, Four, Six, Eight/Are You Sure Your Wife is Straight?" The health workers swept on toward the Civic Center and their place was taken by the San Francisco Blue Boys, who liked to dress up like cops. The first openly gay adoptive parents rode in a Chevy convertible and among the tens of thousands who simply strolled along on their own were a man in cowboy duds and a fellow who looked like a gypsy in a rainbow cloak that appeared to be on loan from Joseph, and which parted like the Red Sea when the cowboy slipped his hand through it. It was that kind of thing which had led Dan to object to the parade; it was disgusting to think of his little sisters seeing something like that. The parade represented everything that had gone sour in his city, the city where he had grown up and which he loved.

At the end of the parade route several hundred thousand people filled the Civic Center plaza, far and away the biggest political gathering ever in the city. To address so many people was a politician's delight and on this occasion Harvey wanted to be more than a politician, he wanted to be an inspiration, to pose challenges, albeit different ones, to gay and straight alike. As he climbed to the reviewing stand in front of City Hall he was aware that as huge as the audience before him may have been, twenty times as many people would see him on the national news that evening. Knowing as he did how this massive outpouring of homosexuals would stun its national audience, Harvey had prepared a speech that threw patriotic pieties back in the bigots' faces.

"My name is Harvey Milk," he began, "and I want to recruit you. I want to recruit you for the fight to preserve democracy from the John Briggses and Anita Bryants who are trying to constitutionalize bigotry.

"We are not going to allow that to happen. . . . I ask my gay sisters and brothers to make the commitment to fight. For themselves, for their freedom, for their country. . . . Gay people, we will not win our rights by staying quietly in our closets. . . . We are coming out.

"Let me remind you what America is." Harvey's amplified voice rang and echoed off the stately buildings which lined the plaza. "Listen carefully. On the Statue of Liberty it says, 'Give me your tired, your poor, your huddled masses yearning to be free.' In the Declaration of Independence it is written: 'All men are created equal and they are endowed with certain inalienable rights.' And in our national anthem it says: 'Oh say, does that star spangled banner yet wave o'er the land of the free.'

"For all the bigots out there: that's what America is. No matter how hard you try, you cannot erase those words from the Declaration of Independence. No matter how you try, you cannot chip those words off the base of the Statue of Liberty . . . you cannot sing the Star Spangled Banner without those words. That's what America is.

"Love it or leave it."

Harvey's glee in the enormity of his audience had not been muted by the postcard on which somebody had typed: "You get the first bullet the minute you stand at the microphone." He was fatalistic; for most of his adult life he had been telling friends that he expected to be killed. His theatricality made his premonitions easy for other people to dismiss.

"Don't be silly," people would say when Harvey told them of how he envisioned his end.

The three partners had agreed that Ray should devote full time to the Hot Potato, so Dan was in need of a new aide. He had met Robin Wonder, the twenty-two-year-old daughter of a judge at a party, and decided that she would do.

Naturally, she was thrilled to get the call. Robin had walked her first precinct when she was twelve and had been around politics all her life. She needed a job and besides that, she had really been smitten by Dan White, so smitten that it had disappointed her to learn that he was married. With as much self-deprecation as she could muster, so it wouldn't sound like boasting, she decided that he must have been impressed at their casual meeting because she was young, upstanding and enthusiastic. She took the bus all the way from Davis to San Francisco to keep an appointment with Dan, but as it turned out he couldn't be there himself so she talked instead with Denise Apcar, Dan's other aide.

Denise seemed to Robin to be a bright lady—pretty, hardworking and absolutely devoted to Dan. Robin knew she had to learn the ropes as fast as possible so she studied Denise—the way she dressed, for instance, in conservative skirts and blazers, and adopted that as her own style.

Dan turned out to be an easy boss. He'd come into the office most mornings and hand out a lot of blarney—"You ladies look just lovely today," that sort of thing. He never asked her to do any personal business for him, the way other supervisors had their aides running to the bank or picking up their wives to take them shopping. Sometimes she or Denise picked him up at home and gave him a lift to work. Robin kind of adored Dan. It chagrined her when her friends said how much he resembled her father, the judge, with whom she was especially close.

A lot of the business that came through Dan's office had to do with the police and fire departments. He was chairman of that committee and she could see he was also a hero to a lot of the uniformed city employees. Cops who were his buddies hung around the office, sometimes even when Dan wasn't there himself. Paul Chignell and the other bigshots from the Police Officers Association were by all the time; it was sort of the unofficial place for policemen to gather in City Hall. The Officers for Justice settlement was a hot topic of conversation; none of them liked it.

By her second month on the job Robin began to notice that Dan wasn't coming in every day the way he had been. Instead he would just call to ask what was going on. He was also neglecting his constituents, and although Robin was only twenty-two she had ten years more political experience than her boss had and she knew what a big mistake *that* was. Dan even began to send her or Denise to community meetings in the district rather than go himself. He wasn't keeping up with the people who had elected him. Already there had been an attempt in the district to recall him, and charges were brought before the district attorney's office that Dan had hidden some illegal campaign contributions. Dan was really bitter about the agitation against him: the recall attempt and the charges of wrongdoing had made headlines, but when the recall failed, or when the D.A. cleared him, you would have needed a microscope to find the items in the newspaper. He took these political maneuvers as attacks on his honor. Dan's attitude was that the people who were out to get him were his enemies, and that they had no scruples. "They're snakes, they're all snakes," said San Francisco's own St. Patrick every time the subject came up.

Pretty soon he seemed to have decided that anybody who wasn't a cop, a fireman, or a friend of at least fifteen years' standing was a snake. It all seemed a little paranoid to Robin. One other thing struck her as being curious: there was no picture of Mary Ann or little Charlie on his desk, no personal mementos of any kind. The bookshelves and desks of the other supervisors were strewn with reports and studies and ordinances and books and letters, but not his. His desktop and office were nearly empty. About the only personal touch was the wall mural. It was the kind you hung in strips, like wallpaper. He and Mary Ann had pasted it up together one weekend, a forest scene, fresh and green and bucolic.

But except for the mural, looking at his office you wouldn't know anything about Dan, or even that he was conducting any business there. One day when he wasn't there Robin went into the drawers of his desk looking for a file, and found that other than a few pencils and some paper clips, the desk had nothing in it.

On June 19 the mayor's package of emergency taxes was up for preliminary consideration, as was the city budget. What George was asking for was based on a political premise, namely that corporations and other businesses should pay their fair share of what it cost to run the city. Dan was ready to go along with him because George had sold him on the idea that the city itself needed his help.

The meeting was convened in mid-afternoon and several hours were consumed by routine business. Then George spoke, calling on the supervisors not to close their hearts. By the time he was finished it was nearly dinnertime, and anticipating a long night, the board took a two-and-one-half-hour break.

When they resumed, shortly after eight o'clock, the chandeliers had been turned on, bathing their arena in bright light. The heavy drapes had been pulled. Outside it was deep dusk, the dome and the steeple were lit, as were the neoclassical facades of the art museum and the opera house. The plaza was deserted except for the seagulls, the pigeons, the winos and the bag ladies. There was something foreboding about the wide, dark public plaza with its scavenger birds and dark lumps curled up on benches.

Had the drapes not been pulled, the supervisors would have seen the top of the communication tower on Twin Peaks obscured by fog, and the red warning lights blinking along its spindly grillwork legs. The tower, that symbol of transformation, made the people who lived near it sick. When the wind rose and played the harp of the guy wires the sound penetrated the closed windows and locked doors of the homes on Twin Peaks, causing headaches and nausea, and creating, so the people who lived there said, a strange melancholy. The city had sent sound wave technicians out to investigate, but their machines could register no sound from the tower that violated the noise abatement ordinance. Nothing could be done.

George's proposed increase in the payroll tax was taken up and passed 6–5, as was the gross receipts tax, with Dan and Dianne holding firm to their promise. The next matter of business was an ordinance to exempt charitable events from a tax on tickets sold at Candlestick Park and other municipal stadiums. It was at that point in the meeting, when the hour was late and tempers strained, that Supervisor John Molinari decided to throw his weight around. For the first time in years the Giants baseball club was in first place, and an attendance record was in the offing. A certain amount of civic pride had been stirred by the Giants' success; Dan was sneaking away from his other responsibilities to see a ballgame whenever he could. But Supervisor Molinari wasn't satisfied with the location of the free seats the ballclub had given him. Molinari was about to teach them who they were messing with: he proposed that the Giants give back to the city part of their share of the ballpark admission tax.

Dan was outraged. Here they were in the midst of a city crisis, with just about everybody trying to cooperate, and Molinari was conducting a personal vendetta. It was soiled politics, contemptible behavior. Dan glowered but didn't say anything. Molinari was voted down, but not before another hour was consumed. The meeting dragged on and on. It was past two in the morning when Dan finally got home and fell exhausted into bed. Mary Ann was already asleep; she had to wake up very early to go down to Pier 39 and open up the Hot Potato. Dan got only three hours' sleep before little Charlie woke him by crying for his early morning bottle.

Dan hauled himself out of bed, prepared the formula, and then sat down in the gray predawn light to cradle and feed his baby. Nothing that had worked before was of any use to him at City Hall. To be handsome, gung-ho, gracious, courteous and even righteous won him nothing more than the lukewarm friendship of some of his new colleagues, an emotion as sincere and abiding as Harvey Milk's word or Molinari's sense of civic duty. To be inspirational, as he had been on so many playing fields, simply had no place in the chambers where the supervisors wandered to and fro, whispering and laughing, so that from time to time Quentin Kopp had to wheel his microphone around and ask in his grating, disdainful tone: "Where are we now. I'm sorry, I was otherwise engaged in colloquy. I'm sorry, where are we now?" Dan couldn't rally this team to the cause because one supervisor's win was another's loss. He couldn't be bullying because every supervisor had one vote, even Carol Ruth Silver who let her single-mothered son play on the chamber floor, irritating Dan so badly that he had frightened the eight-year-old boy by insisting he leave. For the first time in his life, Dan's physical strength was of no use to him: this was no baseball diamond, no battlefield, no burning building, no tavern full of hoodlums. For the first time he faced a situation which did not allow for the bravery with which he had always made his mark. Among the soft-bodied supervisors *he* was a wimp.

11
Summer Fun

Thirty million dollars. That was the price tag that Bill Dauer, the president of the Chamber of Commerce, put on George Moscone's business tax package; that was what he estimated it would cost his people. Every time Dauer thought about what Moscone was trying to do to the business community the disapproval lines so prominent in his face were etched a little deeper and his small mouth puckered as if he had just sucked on a lemon. Thirty million bucks. Surely, there was a more *responsible* way for the city to react to Proposition 13?

One of the figures Warren Simmons, the Pier 39 impresario, was juggling in those first days of July had many fewer zeros attached to it. A mere $8,500, small change, the amount of Dan White's continuing campaign deficit. Virtually all of that amount was owed to Dan himself and to Ray Sloan for loans they had made to the Committee to Elect Dan White. It was in the best interest of the city, of its people, that a fine young supervisor like Dan not be burdened with a debt that could be so easily wiped out. Simmons was sure that the right sort of people, the truly civic-minded, would agree that Dan should not be distracted from the performance of his duties by such a trivial deficit. That way he could keep his mind on business.

Simmons and Ray Sloan got their heads together and decided to throw a fund-raising party at which the people who really counted could meet the young supervisor who was the voice of the working class. Naturally one of the first people they approached was Bill Dauer, at the Chamber, who thought that their idea had a certain arithmetical beauty. Six votes for the business taxes minus $8,500 usually added up to five votes in his experience, and five votes was one less than a majority for Moscone's $30 million tax fiasco. Good government, that was the bottom line.

A new committee was formed, a date and a location were selected. "The Friends of Dan White" settled on July 20. The place would be the restored three-masted, square-rigged sailing vessel *Balcuthe* that once upon a time had braved its way around Cape Horn hauling the forty niners to the gold fields of California.

Simmons arranged for Dan and Ray to break bread with Bill Dauer and some of his people from the Chamber. It was at that lunch that Ray Sloan realized something he had never fully appreciated before, namely that Dan was the smartest inexperienced man he had ever met. The get-together was cordial enough until the subject of Dan's campaign deficit came up, when Dan suddenly unloaded on Bill Dauer.

"I want you to know that you weren't there when we needed you," Dan told the president of the Chamber. The Chamber, Dan reminded him, had contributed to one of his opponents, a real also-ran as it turned out. Their mistaken judgment, their underestimation of Dan White, had played a part in his being saddled eight months after the election with a heavy debt.

Dauer replied that he had no idea Dan was still angry about that, but he offered both an explanation and a way he could make it up. The lack of a contribution, he said, had really just been a misunderstanding, the Chamber had not understood that Dan was going to win. But now that he *had* won the situation was, of course, different, and he personally would consider it an honor to serve as a principal fund-raiser for the Friends of Dan White. Graciously, Dan accepted Dauer's offer. Ray thought that was really slick.

Never before had Dan rubbed elbows with so many men who had achieved his lifelong ambition to become rich; if he were rich he would never have to suffer the hardship his mother and father had known, if he were rich little Charlie would never have to triple up in a bedroom and wear hand-me-downs. The way these guys were courting him made his head swell. They wanted to be his friends, his new friends. It made the old neighborhood seem awfully far away.

One of his new friends was Mo Bernstein, an avuncular millionaire and supplier of funds who was the city's premier power broker. Bernstein was a member of the airport commission, and in the city's new economy, controlling airport expansion was a fulcrum of power and riches.

Commissioner Bernstein was a friend to any politician seeking his friendship, but his closeness with Dianne Feinstein, who had dropped the suggestion to Warren Simmons in the first place that Dan was in need of a way to make money, was something special. It was Commissioner Bernstein's pleasure to convene some meetings of the fund-raiser for the Friends of Dan White at his club, the Concordia, which had been formed in response to the exclusion of Jews from the city's most prestigious private clubs. Usually they met for breakfast at seven.

Once Dan stopped by briefly to be introduced to a few of the businessmen in attendance, and to thank them for the help they were giving him. It was just a week or so before the final vote was due to be taken on the mayor's business tax package, so Simmons, who was not noted for his discretion, asked Dan how he was leaning. "Why don't you just wait and see?" Dan said to Simmons.

After Dan had departed from the breakfast group, Commissioner Bernstein, who had been doing this kind of thing for a long, long time, upbraided Simmons for having been so vulgar. His remark, Bernstein said, had smacked of bribery, whereas the truth was nothing of the sort. Simmons just laughed off the dressing down, but word that Dan was wavering reached the mayor. There was very little that happened in the city that George didn't know about. One source of the power held by men like Mo Bernstein was information, and the experience to understand who would find it most valuable. At any rate George asked Dan to drop by for a chat. They talked for a while, and while Dan didn't say how he would be voting, he didn't renew his commitment, either. George didn't like that one bit, so right after Dan had left he dictated a letter thanking Supervisor White for his staunch commitment, freely given at the press conference in June. The letter would document Dan's turnaround if indeed he did renege. Someday it might be a useful bargaining chip.

On July 10 the final vote was taken, and sure enough Dan and Dianne had switched sides, the business taxes were beaten, and once again George's stewardship of city policy was dealt a blow. Proposition 13 was by then in effect and no new taxes could be considered. The game was over and George had lost, thanks to Dan White. The way Bill Dauer at the Chamber saw it, though, was that Dan had hit a ninth-inning homerun with the game on the line. Taking pen in hand,

Dauer also sent out a letter, on the stationery of the Friends of Dan White.

"This vote," Dauer wrote to the member organizations of the Chamber,

> will save the business community an estimated $30 million annually.
> . . . Supervisor White has proved to be a conscientious and con-
> cerned legislator and was the one who provided us with the neces-
> sary swing vote on this all-important issue. . . . On July 20 the
> Friends of Dan White are organizing a cocktail reception from
> which we hope to raise enough funds to eliminate his lingering
> campaign deficit. Due to the brief time before Dan's event I am
> enclosing two tickets which I hope you or your firm will purchase.

When the checks finally stopped arriving for Ray Sloan to deposit, many a prosperous San Franciscan could say in all honesty that he had already given at the office. Big corporations like Foremost-McKesson, Bechtel, and Standard Oil of California kicked in, as did the utilities and the larger department stores. If you lumped them all together and called them downtown their contribution was $2,000. Hotels, Ghirardelli Square and other elements of the tourist industry ponied up $750 and the Simmons crowd, who would become full-fledged members of the tourist industry when Pier 39 opened in October, came across with another $1,300. Banks and savings and loans associations dipped their hands into the till for $700. But the generosity of the real estate people put them all to shame. Relieved as they were to have seen the property transfer tax killed, they were still apprehensive about two measures pending before the Board, one of which would impose rent controls and the other of which, sponsored by Harvey, called for a prohibitive tax on real estate speculation. They weighed in with $2,425. Even Dan's old commander, Fire Chief Casper, bought two $25 tickets.

Taken all together the list read like a liberal community activist's worst nightmare. These were the people whose investments had changed the skyline of San Francisco, whose preferred policy had made it a white-collar town, a tourist town where the likes of Dan White felt squeezed and beaten and robbed of the city they had once known and would always love. Very few people from District 8 had been asked to buy tickets, but John Marshall had. Marshall was a heating contractor whose plans to expand his business had been rejected by the Planning Commission. Marshall had asked Dan for help, and Dan had sponsored a resolution overruling the Planning Commission. Now Marshall showed his gratitude with a $50 check. Dan was learning how the game was played.

Afterward, Ray Sloan remembered the party only dimly. His lasting impression was that it had been a great drunk. When it was all toted up there was enough for Ray to be paid the $1,000 he had loaned the campaign plus the $1,600 he was owed in unpaid salary, and Dan was reimbursed in full for what he and Mary Ann had taken out of their own pockets to help him get elected. What with the house, the business and little Charlie the money was most welcome. The Police Officers Association got the $300 that the campaign had borrowed from them, and in fact the entire deficit was retired. There was enough money raised to pay both Mary Ann and her father, the retired fire department lieutenant, $700 each for what was described on the statement filed with the Registrar of Voters as office work. Somehow they had kept the three hundred people who crowded aboard the *Balcuthe* well-oiled all night and yet the liquor bill submitted by Commissioner Bernstein's Smarty Party Shop was for only $251.97. Ray supposed it was a special price, for a friend.

Maisie and George were at a public event so they pretended they weren't together. Naturally a lot of people approached him to talk or ask questions, and each time that happened Maisie marveled at how George suddenly became The Mayor. Turning it on and turning it off. She had never seen anybody do it with such fluidity. When he was alone for a moment, smoking and leaning against a wall, she asked him about it.

"They expect to see the mayor," George said, "So I have to be the mayor."

"Yeah," Maisie said, "I know that's what you're doing. I'm not making fun of you or anything, but don't you get sick of having to give your 'mayor' routine?"

"It bugs the fuck out of me," George said.

When they were leaving, George asked Maisie if she didn't want to be rich.

"Well," she said, "There are more important things in life than being rich."

"What's *that*?" George asked, turning the tables, "Your 'community girl' routine?"

Maisie laughed. "Yeah. My 'poverty girl' routine."

"You should be rich. Why not? It's easy to be rich. Think about what you could buy, your kids wouldn't have to worry about anything, you wouldn't have to run around hustling grants. You could go to a regular law school, work in a downtown firm . . ."

"But I wouldn't be happy doing that." Maisie said it kindly because she understood what he was telling her, that she could be as boring as the rest of them but she wasn't. By that time they had reached George's little sports car. The used Alfa-Romeo was his pride and joy. It was still daylight but the sun was moving west, creating that blinding, golden California glow that is such a cliche and yet so overpoweringly real.

"You want to go to the beach?" Maisie asked him. George laughed. "The kid wants to go to the beach." George drove fast, weaving in and out of the afternoon traffic, smoking a cigarette and concentrating on his driving while keeping up the conversation.

"My sister works out of there," Maisie said, pointing to a motel near City Hall. "Her, um, patrons, you know, are like people who work at City Hall, judges, you know, anybody. She's seventeen."

George told her he could empathize with the poor Joes who were doing that kind of thing, cruising around picking up streetwalkers. He said he had done that kind of thing himself, when he was younger.

Maisie had been portraying them as villains but George said, "They're sad, basically, I mean if you really look at them they're just poor shmucks."

When they arrived at Ocean Beach the Pacific was roiling under the setting sun, the whitecaps exhausting themselves against the sandy shoreline as far south as they could see. George parked the car where there was nobody around and got out.

"Hey, wait a minute," Maisie said. "I don't have my gear. I mean, look how I'm dressed. If you think I'm gonna walk around out there dressed like this you're crazy." The wind was picking up, the temperature dropping.

"It's not cold out here," George said, leaning over to stick his head back into the car. He was so handsome he might have been a movie star. "You're crazy, c'mon."

So Maisie got out too and they leaned against the hood and George produced a joint. "Sensimilla," he said, squeezing the word out while he held the smoke down in his lungs and passed the joint to her.

She said, "I don't like this stuff."

George exhaled. "You're just used to that cheap rag. This is the good stuff."

"I don't like it," Maisie said. "It doesn't make me laugh."

"Wouldn't the cops love to catch me, huh?" George said. He was stoned. "You know, my wife doesn't exactly approve of me using this stuff too. And I got to maintain an image with my kids."

The mayor. The husband. The father.

He began to tell her how one time he and his buddies were at his house, passing a joint around, when his oldest son Chris walked into the room just as George was handed the joint. He didn't know what to do but he decided to go ahead and take a drag. A little while later he went and talked with his son about it. The boy was a teenager. George told him he was trusting him with his secret but he didn't want the boy's mother or the other kids to know about it.

"How did he react?" Maisie asked.

"Like, uh, relieved, kind of," George said. "Like, well at least my old man isn't a square." Maisie saw that a sadness had come over him. Maintaining his closeness with his kids wasn't the easiest thing when he was away so much. Now that he was back in town he had time to play basketball with Chris; and his younger son, John, would come by the office after school and flop down on the carpet to do his homework. He always had to remember when he walked in the door of his house that he was daddy and not the mayor. "All this probably seems ridiculous to you," he said, "but I feel all these obligations. You probably think I could just chuck it. But where would I be then, what would I have? A job in a downtown law firm making lotsa money?" The joke cheered him up.

By this time they were walking up the beach. It was windy enough that neither one wanted to stay out for long. Back in the car George produced another surprise, a couple of grams of cocaine.

"Wow, wait, I mean, wait a minute." Maisie cracked up.

"Nobody ever checks my car, right?" George said, starting to cut up the coke with a razor blade. He did it awkwardly, giving Maisie the impression that he knew what he was doing but he hadn't done it often. While they were snorting the cocaine George said that he knew how much the cops would love to bust him, how he wasn't one of them. And how he could imagine, if he had to fear the cops, how powerless ordinary people must feel.

"Well, you can't worry about it too much if you keep it in your fucking car."

"Well, I can't keep it in my fucking house. You'll never guess where I got this from." The way he said it told her it was somebody high up, like himself.

"I don't care," Maisie said. "I don't want to guess."

"That's something I like about you, you're not nosey. You know, if I was younger I would have already made out with you like eighty times." There were a lot of ways to approach a woman and George knew most all of them.

Maisie didn't know about that. She tried to explain to him that she really wasn't interested in him because of that. It was more what she was learning—how people like him with power weren't gods, and how it was helping her learn to deal with things she wanted to be able to deal with.

"That's smart," George said. "That's what you should pick up. Can I kiss you?" His mouth was loose-lipped, and always seemed on the verge of either a smile or a leer.

They kissed, and Maisie had a funny sense. This wasn't the first time she had been with a married man but it was the first time she had such a strong sense of a man's wife while she was kissing him. She enjoyed kissing him but she wasn't exactly encouraging. George looked at her from up very close.

"Hey, I'm used to them falling at my feet."

That cracked them up all over again. It was apparent to Maisie that they were both genuinely enjoying themselves, and that meant more to her than anything else because she didn't want it to be sleazy, she emphatically did not want that. It was not okay with her to be the black girl he fucked.

When George dropped Maisie off at her home—by then it was well after dark—he said, "Well, I know you wouldn't take any money from me even if you needed it."

"You're probably right," Maisie said.

"But," George continued, "I know you wouldn't take two dollars but you'd take a hundred."

"I would," Maisie said, laughing, "I would take a hundred."

"The kid would take a hundred," George said, nodding. "I like that. You're gonna go far."

"The trouble with George is, after he's had two drinks he thinks he's invisible." It was one of those sayings you heard often enough around town. Some people attributed it to Willie Brown, but whoever had said it first really didn't matter, it had a life of its own, the same way calling Dianne "Goodie Two Shoes" did.

Gina Moscone remained very much in the background, having consented to only two interviews in the nearly three years that George had been mayor. When she was interviewed at their new home in St. Francis Wood, an exclusive middle-class enclave where homes began at about $200,000, she was wry about her husband's public life and perhaps a bit forlorn. When supper was ready, she explained, she and the children ate since they never knew if George was coming home. "We don't wait," she said. "The children would starve."

"Saying that everything about him is public is something I can't buy," Gina Moscone said. "Not when the family is involved. People can say what they want about the issues. That's okay. But not the personal attacks. They're unfair and do damage to the family."

She seldom made public appearances on her own. Once, recently, she had agreed to serve as the chairwoman of a fund-raising dinner. Partway through the speechmaking George showed up, apparently unexpected, and he took the microphone away from his wife, saying: "I'm sure the chairwoman won't mind being upstaged." A reporter covering the event, Randy Shilts, found himself squirming sympathetically. Beside her husband, thought Shilts, Mrs. Moscone seemed colorless. But it was more than that. His instinct was that being in public beside George somehow humiliated her.

George thought he was invisible, but of course he wasn't. An investigator for the district attorney's office had been sitting in his car watching when George came out of a North Beach motel with one of his aides and three girls, and another time two newspaper reporters trailed the mayor and a woman to a parked car in front of a venerable church and then stood by observing as the windows fogged up. Then there was the incident in Sacramento when he was stopped for drunken driving with a young black woman beside him, her suitcase in the trunk; that one had even made the papers. The anticorruption unit in the office of District Attorney Joe Freitas, who very much wanted to be mayor himself, kept a file on stories and rumors that reached them about George's peccadillos—one of the rumors had it that George was a kingpin in the local cocaine trade—and one columnist swore that Freitas had bought him lunch in a pricey French restaurant and, over chocolate mousse, informed him that he had "the goods on George—

places, times, names." When the columnist repeated the story, however, Freitas called him a liar.

George knew they were watching and whispering. He would say to his press secretary, Corey Busch, that so long as a man was doing his job whatever else he did had no bearing. But there was something resigned about the way he said it, as if he were also saying, "See, that's what they do to you for trying to open up the city."

Nobody was more bothered by George's illusion of invisibility, however, than some members of the SFPD, the paid enforcers of the moral code. The vice cop Joe Ryan, for instance. "He's so high and mighty," Ryan grumbled, "and he's pulling these capers and getting away with it."

The department was still smarting over George's broken promise to give them a chief from among their own ranks. Charlie Gain had such a stiff neck, every time the POA attacked him, which was every chance they got, his attitude hardened. Up yours, he told them, this is a military operation and I'm in command. The POA brass, guys like Paul Chignell and Jerry Crowley, the same ones who looked to Dan White as their man on the Board, were bound and determined to win the power struggle. Their strategy seemed to be to keep Gain's name in the newspapers embroiled in controversy until George was forced to decide that his chief was too much a political liability to be kept on. Quentin Kopp also saw Gain as George's Achilles heel and unloaded on the Chief. But for George to capitulate to all that pressure was impossible; he had come to think that Gain was, indeed, a liability, somebody who had achieved a purpose by shaking up the old ways in the department and outlived his usefulness, but if he were to fire him now it would look like Kopp and the POA were calling the shots and he couldn't allow that.

George would talk about it with his police chauffeur/bodyguards, Gary Wommack and Jim Molinari and they, in turn, would try to explain to the POA leadership—the "bluecoats," as they were called—that if they would back off for a while and give the mayor some breathing room, Gain would soon be gone. Every time Wommack brought it up, though, he got the same message: no quarter, not an inch. It was a stalemate.

For more than a few cops, what George was doing in private and what he had done in public by making Gain their commanding officer were intertwined. "Look," said an inspector who had worked for many years out of Northern Station and patrolled the Fillmore in the days when it had been George's playground, "we saved his rear end many times and he stuck it up ours, giving us Gain. We saved his ass, we drove him home, we kept it out of the papers. He has 'em right up in his office, the mayor's office. That's what I hear."

If they felt George Moscone was in their corner they might have said the same things, but because he wasn't—the proposed settlement of the Officers for Justice suit being only the most recent and most expensive of a dozen examples any cop could cite like a rosary of grievances—the way most cops talked about George had a cutting, bitter edge to it. When the bluecoats gathered in Dan's office, or at Northern Station when Dan dropped by, the same resentful grumbling went on. At times one cop or another even said they should get George Moscone and Charlie Gain, get them once and for all. The rancor was corrosive but the threat empty: it was just the way cops talked sometimes.

The consent decree on the Officers for Justice suit that had been negotiated in George's office was working its way through the legislative process with intense lobbying on both sides. It called for back pay for officers who had been discriminated against, for setting aside existing promotion lists until women and blacks were hired and trained, and for meeting quotas for minority members in higher ranks. Earl Sanders wanted to talk with Dan White about the consent decree, and even though Rotea Guilford was sure it was a waste of time, he couldn't see how there was anything to be lost, so they set up a meeting at Dan's City Hall office.

Sanders did most of the talking, reminding Dan of the similarity between this situation and what had happened back in the fire department in 1974, arguing that standards had not slipped, that it was best for the police department to reflect the diversity of the city it had to patrol. For the most part Guilford listened and watched. Both of them had known Dan when he was a cop and they shared the opinion that it was a good thing he had left the department; he had been too intense for the streets, not flexible enough. Studying him now, as Sanders was making their case, Guilford could see that nothing had changed. Dan was listening but he wasn't really paying any attention. His jaw was clenched and the veins in his temples were popping with tension from how uncomfortable the conversation was making him feel.

Sanders knew where Dan's head was at; Dan was a creation of the Police Officers Association, they had turned out the troops to help elect him, they had given him money, and he was their supervisor. Sanders supposed that Dan didn't brush his teeth in the morning without calling Paul Chignell first to ask if that was okay.

When Sanders finished saying his piece Dan wouldn't meet his eye. "On this issue," Dan said, "I can't help you. You understand, Earl. I don't have to go into all the reasons with you, you know how it is." But then his tone changed, he sounded apologetic, and he looked at Sanders almost imploringly. "But come see me on other things, there are things we can agree on. I want you to feel free to always come to me."

On the final vote in mid-August, the consent decree that George had worked on so hard for so many months lost 6–5. Dan was the last to vote on the rollcall. It was one of those opportunities Goldie Judge had talked to him about way back when, a chance to broker his vote in order to get something he wanted out of the mayor. Even a reconsideration of the Youth Campus might have been possible, and certainly George would have agreed to endorse him for re-election, which would have neutralized any liberal challenge in the district. But that kind of political cunning, that ability to see where interests coincide, which is the essence of democratic process, was beyond him.

Judge Peckham set a trial date for the first week in November and made it clear there would be no more delays. He was keeping their feet to the fire. It looked like every lousy grievance that split the police department was going to be aired in court, and for no good reason. In the end Judge Peckham would probably impose a settlement much like the one the Board had rejected. All the bitterness and the expense would be an exercise in futility and the divisions would be deeper and sorer than ever.

It was pretty clear to George that he would be losing a lot more 6–5 votes. Dan had double-crossed him on the business taxes and lined up against him on the OFJ settlement and would continue to be a key to his losing on other things he wanted, progressive things, things that were good for the city. George would dearly have loved some leverage, some way he could lean on Dan White to bring him around, but there wasn't one. Sometimes when George had played hardball in order to bring some recalcitrant politician around he used a particular phrase to describe the exercise of power. "I had to rub his dick in the dirt," he would say. Maybe someday there would be a chance to teach young Dan White a lesson or two, teach him how the game was played—if necessary, rub his dick in the dirt.

Meanwhile it was summertime, time for fun. For years the mayor and his staff had played an annual softball game against the Board of

Supervisors and their aides. The idea was to sheath the long knives for a day and pal around in the sunshine.

The game was played at Funston playground in the Marina where George had been playground director long ago, strutting around with Gina Bondanza on his arm. George was scheduled to make a speech somewhere else later that Saturday afternoon so he showed up in a suit and tie, but he took off the jacket and rolled up his sleeves and joined in with everybody else. Even Dianne was playing.

The mayor's team was up first and George led off with a soft line drive that somebody wearing sneakers could have beat out easily, but slipping and sliding in his Italian loafers as he ran up the first baseline, George was making the play close. Quentin Kopp was playing first base for the supes, hollering for the ball, and as George reached the bag he yanked Quentin's mitt. It was a funny thing to do, George made no effort to hide it, and the two political antagonists stood there side by side smiling at the gesture. For the politicians—and everybody there was a political animal—it was a delightful acknowledgment. Everyone knew that they would be going head to head in the 1979 election, but for the moment they were just two guys standing, laughing in the sunshine. It set the tone for the day, it would be clumsy softball, camaraderie would be more important than winning or losing.

Dan played shortstop for the supervisors and batted third. There was no question but that he was the best athlete on the field. His first time up he hit a prodigious homerun, it took off on a line and kept rising until it landed maybe fifty feet over the left-fielder's head. Everybody marveled at how hard the ball had been hit. But Dan had the wrong attitude. He was playing all out, arguing with calls, never cracking a smile. Dan didn't know how to play except all out; when he stepped onto a baseball diamond he didn't know how to give anything less than a total effort. And maybe he had something to prove as well. When they all sat down in City Hall Dan was the guy the rest of them were laughingly carving up and serving for lunch. Now he had these people where he could show them something about what kind of man Dan White was.

One play in particular made the point. Dan lined a vicious single into left field and never slowed down going around first base. The mayor's assistant press secretary, Josh Getlin, was playing second base. When he saw Dan coming toward him at full throttle, his muscular thighs pumping, suddenly launching himself into a hard, mean slide, Getlin, who was thirty pounds lighter than Dan dripping wet, didn't even try to apply a tag, he just got out of the way as fast as he could. It was as if there were two different games going on: the one the rest of them were playing, and Dan's.

There were dark, puffy bags under Harvey's deep-set eyes and the lids drooped even more than usual. It was years since he had taken a vacation and he was pale and tired, very tired and determined. There was no prospect of a respite anytime soon, nor did he really want one. There were problems and pressures in every corner of his crowded life, but Harvey reacted to pressure the way a light bulb does to an electrical current. It was one of those times when each moment takes on a certain urgency, and weariness is a feeling behind the eyes and a dry taste in the mouth.

The new Castro, which he had done more than any man to legitimize, was a boom market. Yet the direction his neighborhood was taking dismayed Harvey. It seemed a day hardly went by when some longtime merchant wasn't replaced by a clothing, antique or gift boutique, a restaurant or a bar in which women were unwelcome. The greengrocery where he and Scott had once shopped for their dinner vegetables was gone, and so was the family pharmacy which had ruined their snapshots and given Harvey the idea of opening a camera store. At its best the camera store had never earned more than enough for the two of them to eke out a living; business was always secondary to politics. The public part of the store was furnished with an old dentist's chair, a legless faded maroon sofa with springs coming through the cushions, and a counter heaped with photographic supplies. It was ratty but at least marginally presentable. The rear of the store was partially hidden by a partition made of cardboard carpeting tubes festooned with a motley assortment of remnant patches. Behind the partition every surface and much of the floor was piled high with stacks of leaflets, flyers, position papers, posters, placards, documents, correspondence and god knows what all else. It was a clutter Harvey knew from the bottom up; he could reach halfway into a foot-high pile of dusty papers and pull out what he was looking for. There was a refrigerator, a multilith, two toilets—one of which actually flushed, a closet-sized office out of which Harvey conducted much of his political business and a coffee maker that was always perking. The store was the best possible portrait of Harvey's life.

In March their landlord had informed Scott and Harvey that the rent was going up from $350 to $1,200 a month. Twice before they had thrown themselves into bringing the business back from the edge of financial collapse, but it no longer seemed worth what it took. Although they rented a tiny storefront about two blocks away on upper Market Street it was clear they would soon close Castro Cameras altogether. Harvey told Scott he would help find him a job at City Hall.

When they had first moved to the Castro, which Harvey continued to call Eureka Valley the way the old-timers did, a kind of urban pioneer feeling had existed. The gay style had been eclectic then, but that, too, had changed. Preppie macho was now in vogue. Pressed jeans and knit shirts with little alligators embroidered over the pectorals showed off sleek or bulging muscles to the best advantage. Flannel shirts, sweaters draped over the shoulders, and construction workers' boots, so long as they were unscuffed, were often to be seen. Neatness seemed to count and hair was worn short. The Ralph Lauren scent called Polo was popular. The sameness led to sneers that the gays were "Castroids" or clones. For their part, the young men of the Castro contemptuously referred to heterosexuals as "breeders." There was a sullen resentment back and forth, and fag bashing was a Saturday night sport for carloads of drunken white or Latino teenagers. Though the city's image-mongers and most of the politicians tried hard to pretend that it wasn't true, there was a simmering sexual integration crisis in the Castro and adjacent neighborhoods.

For all that Harvey had played a critical role in the extraordinary transformation that had taken place, he didn't want to see the Castro turn into a ghetto. When the Board of Education threatened to close the local elementary school because of declining enrollment, Harvey took an active part in the successful community resistance. It was important to him to keep families in the neighborhood.

Most of Harvey's time was devoted to being a supervisor, and he was winning a good deal of respect at City Hall. In six months on the Board, Harvey had proposed a blizzard of substantive legislation. He had asked for a municipally-sponsored network of recycling centers, had demanded that the South African Consulate be closed, and had wanted to enact a ban against discrimination by landlords who refused to rent to families with children. He was the sponsor of a prohibitive tax on quick-turnover real estate speculation. When he stepped into a pile left behind by a dog in order to publicize his call for a scooper ordinance, every television station and newspaper in town was there to record the moment. Harvey had brought along a brown plastic replica and made it seem as if his stepping in the real thing was an accident, but the truth was that like a real trouper he had arrived early and located a choice lump.

Coverage of the supervisor with the smeared wingtip was played above a story that said District Attorney Freitas had a grand jury investigating favors by Warren Simmons to city officials who had helped approve plans for Pier 39. (Something about the juxtaposition, perhaps, interested Dan because he saved the entire front page and kept it with other newspaper clippings on a small desk in his basement den.)

Being a full-time supervisor and leading spokesman for gays everywhere, performing ward heeler's functions in District 5, coping with the eviction and looking for a new apartment would have been quite enough for Harvey to take on, but there was more. His lover, Jack Lira, was drinking heavily and causing scenes. Lira couldn't hold a job and Harvey was trying to support both of them. That, in turn, enraged Scott Smith, who objected to spending the marginal profit from the camera store on Lira's weakness when neither Scott nor Harvey could afford the new clothes they needed. A wardrobe belonging to an elderly man, recently deceased, had been given to Harvey, and the best suits he had were the dead man's. Harvey called them his geezer clothes. Scott and Dick Pabich, among others, wanted Harvey to dump Lira, who at his most domestic moments seemed like a frightened rabbit, hovering and serving tea. Harvey refused. Lira had a powerful sexual hold on the lover who was nearly thirty years his senior.

And then there was State Senator John Briggs. An archreactionary from Fullerton, in Orange County, Briggs had led a petition drive that placed an initiative on the November 1978 ballot that would ban homosexuals from teaching in California schools. From the steps of City Hall Briggs declared that San Francisco was "a moral garbage dump of homosexuality." Harvey responded: "Nobody likes garbage because it smells. Yet eight million tourists visited San Francisco last year. I wonder how many visited Fullerton?" The pointedness of the riposte in no way diminished the threat, however, and it seemed Harvey never slept.

Dan, letting bygones be bygones, stopped by Dick Pabich's office and wrote out a check for one hundred dollars for the anti-Briggs campaign. "Everyone has the right to earn a living," Dan explained.

One Sunday there was a story in the paper about Harvey, Quentin Kopp and a few other notables being made up as clowns at a big downtown hotel for a charity benefit. The writer, Ira Kamin, described the transformation that took place:

> Harvey Milk got into the chair. Ron Severini painted his face white. Milk's green eyes looked ghostly and haunted. "How do you feel?" he was asked.
>
> "I'm getting into sadness."
>
> . . . It was as if, "getting into sadness," he was picking up the horror, the real horror of the world. . . .
>
> "You look older," someone told him.
>
> "Impossible," he said. "When you're old you can't look older."
>
> Boom. Something snapped. What had snapped was the sadness. It snapped into sheer joy. . . . Can you imagine how happy Harvey Milk is to be a supervisor? How hard he tried and for how long?
>
> . . . he ran, not walked, ran with kids' fearless feet into the street and told these tourists on cable cars who wouldn't know a supervisor from a parking meter, "Hey, I'm a supervisor. I pass the laws. I run this city. I'm an elected official."

The story ran on Sunday; on Monday, at the Board meeting, his scooper ordinance was passed. The meeting ended unusually early and it was still light when Harvey began the walk home to the flat he was sharing with Jack Lira, even though he was spending more of his time with another man, a new lover. Inside the front door there was a trail of voter registration forms leading all the way back into the dining room where the way was littered with wadded-up anti-Briggs flyers and empty beer cans. It was quiet in the apartment, deathly quiet. At the very end of the trail, on the enclosed back porch, was a black velvet curtain hanging from a beam. There was a note pinned to the curtain. "You've always loved the circus Harvey," Jack Lira had written. "What do you think of my last act?"

Harvey pulled back the black velvet and saw Jack's dead body hanging from the beam.

A reporter named Phil Tracy, recently arrived, found the state of investigative journalism in San Francisco to be puzzlingly supine. He had been raised in one of the toughest neighborhoods in New York and the lessons he learned there he applied to the practice of political reporting: the idea was to seize the jugular of the bad guys and squeeze.

That way you performed a public service and won yourself a little respect. He had already written and published a scathing attack on George Moscone's performance in office. In the summer of 1978 he had a new target: the white pastor of a predominantly black congregation in the Fillmore district, the Reverend Jim Jones of People's Temple.

Jones's church had received nothing but adulatory press in the several years since it had moved from Mendocino County on the north coast and settled in an abandoned synagogue. Even the muckraking weekly, the *Bay Guardian,* had praised the minister: "Rev. Jones . . . has instilled in his members a willingness to get involved where human life is at stake. . . . It's as if he has found a way of translating and dramatizing the old Christian message that serving one's fellow human beings is an end in itself . . ."

But a different version of what went on behind the guarded doors of People's Temple was reaching Tracy. It began when a reporter for the *Chronicle,* Marshall Kilduff, undertook an investigation. His findings were never published, however, because the city editor at the *Chronicle* killed the story. The editor, as it turned out, was a devotee of Jones and often attended services at the Temple. So Kilduff brought the story to *New West* magazine and he and Tracy teamed up for a further investigation.

Jones, they found out, had been appointed by Mayor Moscone to the City Housing Authority and designated as its chairman. At first it had been George's intention to appoint Jones to the Human Rights Commission, even though Jones hadn't been in town long enough to be eligible for a city position. At the last moment, with the press release written and reporters gathered in an anteroom for the announcement, Jones had refused the Human Rights appointment because he felt the position wasn't important enough. A few months later George gave him the more influential job at the Housing Authority.

Nor was George alone in admiring and rewarding Jim Jones. Virtually every liberal politician in town, from District Attorney Joe Freitas to Assemblyman Willie Brown to Harvey Milk had some association with the pastor. Freitas, for example, had hired an attorney who was the president of the Temple to lead a unit in his office investigating charges of election irregularities. The thing was, the charges were made against People's Temple. Assemblyman Brown was forthright in telling Tracy and Kilduff why Jones had such clout. Jones was able to turn out more election volunteers—disciplined, hardworking, well-dressed volunteers from among his flock—than anybody in town. In a city where candidates ran without party labels and where the party organizations were poor and ill-organized, that really counted for something.

Tracy was finding that there was a reluctance to attack the pastor whose congregation was lauded as the very model of brotherhood, and who had such influence at City Hall. Jones had made his political patrons dependent on him.

Tracy's investigation was no secret. A whale of a man with an adenoidal New York accent, he cut an unforgettable figure and thought it was his job to make waves. Once, he was walking on the street and began to feel paranoid because everyone was staring at him. He stopped and looked in a store window and saw reflected a man with lank gray hair that would not stay in place spilling over his collar, yellow aviator shades over misfocused eyes, a loud plaid sport coat and a clashing fire-engine-red Hawaiian shirt. That made him feel a lot better: he would have stared too.

As he went about his job it became clear to the liberals and Moscone loyalists that it was not his intention to write another puff piece about Jones. Nor was it unknown that Quentin Kopp and John Barbegelata were helping Tracy. The people around George began to feel that the reporter was the instrument of a reactionary cabal. When Tracy went to George's press secretary to request an interview with the mayor he was turned down cold. "There's nothing to talk about," he was told.

The story might have gone into print with no greater revelation in it than the extent of Jones's political influence had not the pastor and his indebted friends gone too far in trying to dissuade *New West* from pursuing the investigation. As many as fifty phone calls and seventy letters a day were flooding the magazine's office, many from members of the congregation and others from prominent people such as Cyril Magnin.

The pressure only increased Tracy's suspicions that something didn't smell right. So he decided to apply a little pressure of his own, and leaked the crusade to kill his story to a friendly columnist. The resulting column, and a story in the afternoon *Examiner* about an apparent break-in at the *New West* office during which the People's Temple file had been tampered with, produced phone calls to Tracy of a different nature.

Former members of the Temple began to call anonymously to say that Jim Jones practiced great cruelty. Tracy and Kilduff told all the callers the same thing: unless they agreed to the use of their names, and to allow their accusations to be tape-recorded, the reporters were not interested. In the end a dozen former members of Jones's flock agreed to their terms.

"Based on what these people told us," Tracy and Kilduff eventually wrote,

> life inside People's Temple was a mixture of Spartan regimentation, fear and self-imposed humiliation. As they told it, the Sunday services to which dignitaries were invited were orchestrated events. Actually, members were expected to attend services two, three, even four nights a week—with some sessions lasting until daybreak . . . members . . . were often compelled to stay up all night and submit regularly to "catharsis"—an encounter process in which friends, even mates, would criticize the person who was "on the floor" . . . these often humiliating sessions had begun to include physical beatings with a large wooden paddle. . . . Church leaders also instructed certain members to write letters incriminating themselves in illegal and immoral acts that never happened. In addition, temple members were encouraged to turn over their money and property to the church . . . those who didn't ran the risk of being chastised severely during the catharsis sessions.

When it appeared certain that the story was going to be published, Jones fled to a twenty-seven-thousand-acre enclave he had purchased in Guyana and made arrangements for about one thousand members of the church to join him there. Soon after Jones left the city, forever as it turned out, there was a dinner at the Press Club which Tracy attended. A large table was set up for the mayor and his party. A little while later, when the lights had been dimmed and speeches were made, George came in and stood quietly at the edge of the room, all by himself. Somehow his isolation seemed poignant. Within a moment or two of his arriving, though, there was a buzz of whispers in the room: "The mayor's here." As soon as the lights were turned on again George was surrounded by people. As he was being led to his table, however, he saw Tracy, and followed by his political strategist, Don Bradley, he headed instead in that direction.

George said hello and sat down. For the next three hours he remained there, swapping stories, getting up once to shoot a few games of pool, and shooing people who tried to take him away. Never once did George allude to the blistering profile that Tracy had published the previous year. Tracy was expecting that George would ask about the

People's Temple story. After all, the chairman of the mayor's Housing Authority had just fled to South America in anticipation of its publication. In fact, Tracy had the galley proofs for the story in his pocket and had George asked he would have shown them to him. But he never did ask.

At first Tracy figured he was being hustled with charm; his estimation of George was not very high. He sized him up as some sort of Tennessee Williams character, at one and the same time bagging black teenage whores (so he had heard) and a hero in the ghetto. Just the right mayor for San Francisco, where the corruption was really raw. After New York everything in San Francisco seemed so melodramatic, so personal, so small-town. Gradually as they drank and talked about nothing in particular, just reminiscing and telling political stories, he began to think that maybe George was no worse than a well-meaning guy whose old man had been a drunk, who had always had to work hard for everything he got, who had gradually been sucked down.

As the second hour passed, and the third, Tracy's suspiciousness relented. It began to dawn on him that the reason George wasn't an effective mayor was that he wasn't very interested in the job, that he would rather sit and drink and shoot the breeze and chase tail than run the city. Maybe that was why things jammed up and nothing ever seemed to get done. In the final analysis, Tracy decided with a sudden, clarifying insight, George was just a small-town guy who really wanted nothing more than to be one of the boys. A San Francisco guy.

12
Call It Quits

San Franciscans who have migrated from back East are always being asked if they don't miss the sharp turnings of the seasons. Everybody knows that it never snows in San Francisco and that a ninety-degree day in summer is a rarity; the city is famous for its God-made air conditioning. New arrivals do at first find the sameness of the seasons monotonous and even melancholy, but when they have stayed on long enough they begin to appreciate the subtle differences between, say, the high summer afternoon fog blown in through the Golden Gate and the low-lying tule fog which carpets the city on winter mornings. They find themselves anticipating balmy weather not in July but in September and October. They see that though the spicy eucalyptus and the Monterey pine are evergreen they can look forward to the sycamore trees in the Civic Center shedding their leaves for winter.

The city gardeners hate the sycamore trees because they are so much work; their broad, heavy leaves plop into the reflecting pool and have to be removed at once or else they clog the drains and make an awful mess. By the end of September the sycamores are usually bare. Every year, beginning after Christmas, they're not merely pruned but polled, cut back to the trunk. When the dense, bushy leaf cover falls away the trunktops of the sycamore are revealed to be grostesque: rounded and bumpy and shiny, like stumps of amputated limbs.

On the other side of Polk Street from the sycamores, within the beaux arts City Hall, the great question of the day in September 1978 was which of two competing voting machines would be employed at polling places. It was a question of absolutely no importance. Both systems—one called Votomatic and the other Datavote—could apparently do the job. But because George favored one system his opponents, most vociferously Quentin Kopp, favored the other; the usual dog and pony show was playing. The Registrar of Voters, caught in the political crossfire, was in imminent jeopardy of losing his job and charges of corruption and payoffs were thick as gnats. As Dan watched this spectacle of San Francisco government it seemed to him every bit as grotesque as the glistening stumps of the naked, polled sycamores.

During the election of 1977, Registrar of Voters Thomas Kearney had ordered a return to the use of the Datavote machines, which had for a time been discarded in favor of the Votomatics. There had been a series of delays and snafus that ostensibly had given rise to the hue and cry to return to using the Votomatics. However, it was soon common knowledge around City Hall that a businessman who had contributed a lot of money to George's campaigns was also the head of the firm that marketed Votomatics. And a second businessman, one of Commissioner Mo Bernstein's friends, manufactured the machines.

The wrangling was taking on epic proportions. But to Ray Sloan the salient fact, the only salient fact, was that the Votomatics had the more influential friends. Ray wanted to establish himself in San Francisco and it seemed quite clear that this was a chance to go along and make some friends. So he asked Dan as a personal favor to vote for the Votomatics. The Board was split as usual 6–5 and if Dan did switch, then Ray could let it be known that he had delivered the winning vote. Ray was dismayed, however, when Dan didn't immediately agree. Instead he crossed his arms over his chest and said, "I'll think about it."

Ray wasn't happy with the response. "What's there to think about?" he asked.

Representatives of both companies had brought around scale-model replicas of the machines for the supervisors and their aides to try out. The replicas were like toys and trying them became a popular game. Harvey's jokes when he pushed the little prong through the perforated holes were the most pointed. It was all a lot of fun for everybody—everybody, that is, except the supervisor from District 8. Stubbornly, and despite laughing entreaties, Dan refused to try out the Votomatic gizmos; refused with a stony expression that brooked no argument. Dan's behavior seemed so pettish that Harvey and Carol Ruth Silver couldn't help imitating it. Harvey arranged that plastic face of his into an expression of mock severity, wrapped his arms around his skinny chest and shook his head back and forth like a silent Indian Chief. Even Robin Wonder, who was so loyal to Dan, had to laugh.

Though it never came up during the debate—none of the supervisors, perhaps, having a fondness for historical parallels—voting machines had been at the bottom of the most notorious scandal in the city's political history. In the first decade of the century Boss Abe Ruef had been instrumental in electing a mayor from the Union Labor Party, but had had no luck getting Union Laborites elected to the Board. Finally Ruef and Mayor Eugene Schmitz had devised an ingenious solution: they introduced voting machines to San Francisco. They had calculated, correctly, that most voters would be so intimidated by the new-fangled machines that they would rather just pull the straight party lever under Schmitz's name than diddle with a whole lot of levers. It worked: a Union labor board was swept into office, and several years and numerous cash-filled envelopes later, Boss Ruef was swept into jail.

Seventy years later the showdown vote between Datavote and Votomatic was set for late September. On that Monday Dan put a long arm around Ray Sloan's shoulders and gave him the bad news.

"I looked at all the information," Dan told him, "and I'd like to do it for you but it isn't right. I mean, the facts and figures don't add up."

Datavote lost 6–5 and another opportunity to go along, to do a favor, to win some friends, had passed by. Ray was no more secure in San Francisco than he had been before because Dan wasn't willing to do him an inconsequential favor. Dan's view was that certain kinds of favors were corrupt; that was what George Moscone was up to with this whole voting machine scam, and Dan was not going to be pulled down into that slime.

The suggestion of corruption was everywhere. A federal grand jury was investigating charges that Howard Hughes, the reclusive billionaire, had been buying favors from California politicians. A political consultant and Hughes operative who was also an old friend of George's had, according to rumors seeping out of the grand jury, siphoned ten thousand dollars to George under the table. George vehemently denied it—he went so far as to telephone the FBI in the presence of two reporters—but the rumors persisted.

The frustrations, demands and infighting that came with being mayor were greater than George had anticipated. He had been a consummate legislative tactician but was a less effective chief executive. As a legislator he had been a master of forming a consensus. In Sacramento the goal had been to pass a bill to solve a problem and then to send the governor both the problem and the possible remedy. As mayor, when a problem arose he had to cajole and bludgeon a solution through the Board, not as a colleague but more like an antagonist. And even when he succeeded, the problem, in the form of an ordinance, came right back to his desk. Because the town was so small the consequences of his actions were on his doorstep within moments of his making the decisions. And George's style, his desire to get everybody who had been excluded from city government involved, combined with his affability, encouraged a deluge of requests and recriminations.

Perhaps worst of all, the leadership of the Board was politically hostile. Dianne was philosophically opposed to George. The intentions of Quentin Kopp were as benign as those of the spider toward the fly.

By the fall of 1978 George was on the defensive, and he was tired. Even the reporters who had sat in his office while he dialed the FBI to ask if he were accused of wrongdoing had commented that he seemed fatigued. And to people who had known him longer and more intimately, some spirit seemed to have gone out of him. The political attacks, the administrative problems, the bare-cupboard state of his personal finances, the unremitting hostile scrutiny of elements within the police department and the district attorney's office, and perhaps the greedy, sybaritic way he lived were catching up with him. He was, after all, a chainsmoking, congenial-drinking, pasta-loving man of nearly fifty.

All requests for street closings to accommodate the popular neighborhood street fairs, as well as for the traditional celebrations such as Columbus Day, had to be okayed by the Police, Fire and Safety Committee, Dan's committee. In general the requests were standard fare, and approval by the police, the fire department, and the supervisors little more than a rubber stamp process. That was not the case, however, with the 1978 Columbus Day parade, which was the *grand* event of the year for San Francisco Italians. A bicycle race through the steep and narrow streets of upper North Beach and Telegraph Hill was being sponsored by a neighborhood merchant's association, and the police and fire departments had their doubts about whether they would be able to respond to an emergency in a timely fashion.

The supervisor from District 3, where the race was going to be held, was John Molinari—"Jack" to his friends. With the possible exception of Carol Ruth Silver, nobody on the Board was less liked by Dan than Molinari, whose public manner was backslapping, congenial, a good-old-boy; behind the scenes Molinari wielded considerable power and influence. Among his colleagues and the cognoscenti Molinari had the reputation of being amenable to the right kind of persuasion from his principal contributors, the prosperous merchants of North Beach, the same *pèzzo gròssos* who were sponsoring the Columbus Day bicycle race. Ever since Molinari had tried to stick it to the Giants baseball team because he was dissatisfied with his free season tickets, Dan had disapproved of him.

As Dan listened to the testimony before his committee about the potential dangers of the bicycle race he was disturbed. Leaning toward Molinari—whose broad, freckled face seemed to convey that life was just a rollicking collection of secrets, jolly secrets best suggested by a knowing grin—Dan whispered, "We need to sit down and remap this thing, this isn't good."

"I don't want to touch it," Dan thought he heard Molinari whisper, grinning. "These people own me."

Dan could hardly believe his ears. He flushed from anger and shame for his colleague. When the street closing came before the full board he adamantly argued against it. Dianne Feinstein was sitting in the president's oxblood swivel chair, behind the raised dais with its handcarved *fleur de lis* scrollwork. She could see how upset Dan was. She had noticed from the time that he had been elected that Dan was "kind of lost in terms of the polarizations." From her long experience she had learned that the supervisors, in her words, "live in a provocative arena, that's part of what we have to handle."

Dianne had gone out of her way to befriend Dan, the Board's policeman-in-residence, and his wife, Mary Ann. There were those, like Quentin Kopp and Lee Dolson, who thought that her solicitousness toward their youngest colleague was manipulative, that she had wrapped Dan and his vote around her elegant pinky. They noticed that his political innocence was so great that his outsize admiration for Dianne didn't even embarrass him. Dianne was accustomed to such smears and innuendos. As far as she was concerned her intention had been to teach Dan how things were done, to help him; that, in her view, was her responsibility as president of the Board. And besides that, she liked the young man, she really was fond of him. She had entertained Dan and Mary Ann at afternoon tea in her sumptuous home, she had even shared confidences with Dan and knew that the financial and political pressures he was experiencing had caused some "marital stress," as she was to put it later.

At any rate, when she saw how disproportionate his reaction was to the possible dangers of the Columbus Day bicycle race, she covered her microphone and gestured to him to come up to the dais.

Dan came, scowling.

"What's wrong?" she asked softly. "Why do you feel this way about this issue?"

"There could be an accident," he said. "The rapidity of those bicycles, and with the streets closed, the people won't be able to get out, emergency equipment won't be able to get in." He did not mention, however, Supervisor Molinari's casual admission.

Dianne was not able to calm him. In the end the route was approved. Dan's reaction had left her wondering, mildly troubled. In the past when he had been so self-righteously hot under the collar—over the Youth Campus or the Gay Freedom Day parade—there had been some sound moral or political reason for his inordinate reactions. But a bicycle race? She did not know, however, what Dan thought he had heard Supervisor Molinari say. And so she did not understand. She had no way of knowing how the world of politics at City Hall looked to him at that point. How, whichever way he turned, he saw the same thing: defeat and corruption.

Nor did she have any way of knowing something about Dan of which people who had been watching him for a longer time were aware. It was something that Frank Falzon had seen, and even Dan's mother had noticed: how her son got interested in something and then put it aside and turned his enthusiasm in a new direction. Dianne had no way of knowing about the incidents in Dan's past when he had been asked to do something he believed was wrong. Or how his idea of what was right and wrong depended entirely on his conviction that he knew the difference rather than on any set of principles. Or how, when those requests to do something he thought was wrong came at a time when he was under pressure, he had each time done the same thing: worked himself up into a frenzy of self-righteousness. And how, each time, as if to say "I'm too good for this," he had quit.

Warren Simmons was one of those self-made men who liked to think of himself as a peasant at heart. "I'm a peasant," was his regal boast, "I put up what pleases peasants and they love it." The opening of Pier 39 on October 4 proved him to be at least half right.

The grand opening ceremonies were part circus and part civic event. The mayor was there to make a short speech about the revitalization of the waterfront, and Dianne, true to her word, and with prodding from Simmons, who had sent her a singing telegram, showed up in a bodystocking under a bathing suit (but not the promised bikini), her hair and her makeup mannequin-perfect as always. There were clowns, balloons, jugglers, strolling bands, and a man who jumped off a high tower into a bucket of water. The new pier resembled a Hollywood sound set; it was a replica of something that had never existed: a long promenade lined with psuedo-turn-of-the-century shops selling everything from giant chocolate chip cookies to expensive jewelry, from "I ♥ SF" tee shirts to fur-trimmed leather jackets. It differed from Ghirardelli Square and the Cannery in that it was not a restoration, an architectural revitalization of the past. To say that Pier 39 lacked taste or grace would be a redundancy. By itself, had it been set down in the boondocks like Marriott's Great America, Pier 39 would have been no worse than any other gaudy eyesore. But its location on one of the most beautiful and valuable stretches of urban waterfront in America was the final, unpardonable offense.

Dan and Mary Ann, however, were far less concerned with the architectural quality of the tourist arcade than they were with the opportunity their new potato stand afforded them to set their financial house in order. Mary Ann was putting in full time at the Hot Potato, as were Ray Sloan and Dan's brother Tommy. Other brothers and sisters were working there as well. Their low labor costs, their location just inside the fast food arcade at the foot of the pier where pedestrian traffic was heaviest, and the exorbitant markup on potatoes all were encouraging. Although they could not expect an instant profit, their prospects looked good. Mary Ann and Dan were each drawing a salary of about $350 every two weeks, and so the moment of its opening provided relief from the crushing burden of trying to make it on Dan's salary as a supervisor. They weren't exactly on easy street, but their income had crept back up toward respectability.

In other ways, though, the pressures on Dan and Mary Ann were only increased by their new business. Dan would rise early most mornings to give little Charlie a bottle; he was deeply devoted to his infant son, and would often be seen wheeling the little boy in his baby stroller. Before 8 A.M. Mary Ann would drop Charlie with the babysitter and start the seven-mile drive in the family station wagon to Pier 39. In the evenings, when she was back at home tending to Charlie, Dan would often be at the pier helping to close down for the night, counting the receipts, sometimes even slicing the potatoes for the next day. One night, quite late, George's old friend Art Bierman was having dinner on the pier. Strolling out past midnight he passed the fast food arcade and saw Dan, bent over a sink of hot suds, scrubbing pans. "Who but an Irishman could think he'd make money selling potatoes?" he asked himself. But almost from the beginning the Hot Potato showed a profit. Simmons had steered Dan into what would prove in a couple of years to be a sound investment.

A sound investment, but hard work, like assigning yourself to permanent KP duty: sweaty, repetitious, dull, demanding, time-consuming, and when the heavy sacks of potatoes had to be carried, back-breaking work. Perhaps the only one of the partners who was finding any enjoyment in operating the Hot Potato was Ray. The pier was his playground. "Thirty bars, for chrissake," he said to his friends, smiling his lopsided smile. Every day he would reach one of those bony hands into the till and take out a couple of bucks and go imbibe his lunch. And each time, he caught a look from Mary Ann, the same look that the former third grade teacher gave a naughty boy. He shrugged it off. They had never liked each other.

Dan, meanwhile, was both frenetic and withdrawn. There were still the board meetings to attend every Monday. More and more Dan hated going to City Hall. He had yet to propose a single piece of substantive legislation, and he was constantly outmaneuvered and beaten by the same people who were laughing at him; as the betrayals and the corruption piled up, he increasingly found City Hall a place to be avoided. He hated it. His lobbying on behalf of Pier 39, combined with his responsiveness to the real estate industry that had given so generously to the Friends of Dan White, and his stubbornness, made him an easy butt for jokes. "The boy populist," as some people had begun to mockingly call him, seemed to have been bought. The City Hall crowd would not have been especially biting about that—after all, Dan wasn't the only one who cast an expedient vote—but his self-righteousness toward the compromises made by other supervisors made his posturing comical. To his own mind he always weighed the facts and did the right thing, but that wasn't how other people saw it. Every time Dan got up on his high horse the snickers began.

Certain responsibilities were unavoidable: with Mary Ann gone all day at the Hot Potato, he had to help look after Charlie; he had to help out at the Hot Potato, he had to be at the Monday meetings and the committee meetings, he had to be available to the Police Officers Association and to his new friends. What suffered, what he chose to neglect, were his constituents. The champion of the neglected San Franciscan, the blue-collar hero, was too busy and too self-pitying to pay attention to the people who had elected him.

But Dan didn't blame himself; he blamed his constituents. At a meeting of the Outer Mission Merchants Association in mid-October Dan pleaded with his audience to help him out. He accused the merchants of not supporting him, not staying in touch with him. Roland Percival, Goldie Judge's good friend, was in the audience and after the meeting he called Goldie. "You had better go see your friend Dan White," Roland told her. "He looks terrible."

Denise Apcar had accompanied Dan to the meeting and thought it had gone very well. The leader of the merchants had been complaining of Dan's neglect, but at the conclusion of Dan's remarks he had joined in the applause. Denise was euphoric about the warm reception Dan got; she had expected far worse. They walked outside of the bowling alley where the meeting had been held and got into her car. Whenever possible, Dan had one of his aides drive him. Being driven around was one of the perks of his office he especially enjoyed.

Dan was played out by the emotional effort the speech had required, and now he was let down. He asked Denise to stop by a doughnut shop on the way home and he wolfed down several doughnuts. Denise was rather shocked; she had never seen Dan eat sweet stuff so ravenously. In fact, she had hardly ever seen Dan eat sweets at all. In his courteous, old-fashioned way Dan avoided junk food around Denise and Robin, both of whom were always trying to lose weight. Their weight problems were a constant source of banter among the three of them—"Y'know, Denise, you're a real fine-lookin' gal. But you've got to lose five pounds," Dan would tease her, echoing her own frequent lament—and it just would not have done for him to ingest Cokes and french fries and chocolate cones, as he had loved to do with Alma, and when he was a cop, in front of them. Around his young female aides he watched his diet, went along with their concerns, talked about the weight he had gained himself. Since 1968, when Dan had joined the police department and tipped the scales at 175, he had, indeed, put on five pounds. Of course he was no longer twenty-two and he no longer had the time to exercise every day. Now that he was thirty-two and inactive, those muscles built up with years of weight work and competitive athletics were turning a bit fatty. He was even getting jowls the way his father had.

The day after his speech to the merchants, Goldie Judge, who had not seen Dan in months, went down to City Hall. First she stopped by to see Denise and Robin. Goldie asked how Dan was doing and both women said he was fine, just fine. Goldie next went to a hearing room where Dan was presiding over a committee meeting.

She was shocked by the way Dan looked and acted. Goldie noticed the jowls, and the way he was pale as a goddamn ghost. His eyes were wandering, it was apparent he was paying no attention to the hearing. She intercepted him on his way out.

"Hello, Dan," she said coyly, in her Brooklyn-Louisiana dialect. He walked right on by, as if he hadn't seen her. Goldie was one of the "snakes," as far as he was concerned.

Goldie reached out and grabbed his arm. "Wait a minute, Dan. How *are* you?" His eyes were red-rimmed, as if he hadn't been getting enough sleep.

"Oh, I'm doing fine," he said. "What are *you* doing down here, checking up on me?" He broke away and walked out.

If he was irritable with Goldie—who had walked out on his campaign—he tried not to be irritable at home, which was the only place he could escape from the pressures and demands on him. The campaign had been a tremendous kick, it had made him the focus of attention and admiration. As was always the case with Dan, however, he had not looked down the road with anything like a realistic appraisal of what his victory would bring him. The man who had wanted to be a writer, to sail around the world, to open a delicatessen, to learn to fly an airplane, to beat the house in Las Vegas, to be a cop, a fireman, a supervisor was not a man who took the long view. And now it was costing him. Being a supervisor was an agony for this uneducated, physical man with his overwrought, even precious code of right and wrong, his deep-seated moralism that had been inculcated in him when he was only a child at St. Elizabeth's studying his catechism; who had tried hard his whole life to be what he thought a man should be. He had been determined to win, and he had won, and now he was paying the price. His vanity was taking a bad licking. When it all became too much he would go home and go off into the bedroom or down to his den and do as little as possible. For several days at a time he wouldn't bother to shave or sometimes even to get dressed. He simply gave up trying. He would watch television or read and play with little Charlie. At times like that he was uncommunicative and easily irritated. Even eating a meal seemed like too much trouble. Potato chips, doughnuts, Cokes and candy bars were all he wanted, just something to fill his stomach and give him a quick hit of blood sugar. His stubborn code, though, and his consideration for the pressures that Mary Ann was also under, stopped him from complaining. How could he burden her with *his* problems? He felt down on himself; it was his duty to provide for his wife and his son and he was doing a lousy job of it. Moping around the house he would sink into a deep, self-accusatory gloom, a kind of adolescent gloom in which the world was phony and devoid of sunlight and he was a wretch in his own eyes. A man's real responsibilities were a dreadful burden. The roamer who had once lived in him, the romantic Jack London figure, had been banished but not disposed of.

To Dan, complaining was weak, and to ask for help was tantamount to complaining. A man, the kind of man his dad had been, the kind of man he wanted to be, just found the strength to keep going. And did it with a smile. That was the face he had always turned to the world; Dan was the one who rallied and inspired other people to greater effort. But under the weight of his heavy responsibilities—as husband, father, homeowner, provider, businessman, supervisor—he was staggering to a halt. And so he detested himself. Even with cancer destroying him his father had never stopped fighting. A man never stopped fighting.

When Dan was deep in his Irish gloom Mary Ann would often take Charlie and get out of the house, get out of her husband's way, go shopping with a friend or just for a drive. Dan was left alone in self-pitying, self-loathing misery. At other times she tried, God knows she tried. This was not the same man she had married, the exuberant, exciting man who had promised her that no matter what, their life would always be an adventure (or was it? There had been the honeymoon, after all). At times they would sit together in their small, tidy kitchen and Mary Ann would tell Dan that something seemed wrong, and ask how she could help.

"Well," Dan said once, "Well, I can't really think of anyone else when I don't even like myself."

Mary Ann would listen to her husband say it wasn't her, it was just him. She had learned over the four years of their marriage that there was truth to that. But it *was* her. She should be able to help, help him through these hard times, and she couldn't. It had reached a point where he seldom slept with her. Turning and tossing, restless and plagued by demons of debt and guilt, he would slip out of bed, take a sleeping bag, and flop down on a couch or the floor. A sleeping bag, a bare light bulb, his books: his carefree days.

Their sex life diminished and dwindled and finally all but evaporated. Mary Ann said to her husband, "Maybe if you went to see a doctor, do you think, maybe he could give you something?" Something to sleep, something to help.

"No," Dan said, "No, I can do it. I can do it by myself."

Harvey was near the end of his campaign against the Briggs amendment, and he had run himself ragged. There had not even been time to grieve for Jack Lira. He refused to turn down a single invitation to speak anywhere in the state, and yet somehow managed to pop into City Hall almost every day. Sick with terror that Briggs might win—the polls showed it to be very close—Harvey had persuaded himself that the worst possible outcome was in the cards, persuaded himself so convincingly that when the early returns on election night showed the initiative going down by about one million votes, and that three out of every four San Franciscans were contributing to that margin, he was still despondent. He had geared himself up for martyrdom and suffering but in a blink of the electronic eye he had to adapt himself instead to triumph.

About 10 P.M. George, who had fought Briggs too and whose chief political strategist, sad-faced Don Bradley, had coordinated the campaign, showed up at the headquarters in the Castro where a giant party was in progress. George spoke and received a thunderous welcome, the kind of reaction that always pumped him up. A few minutes later Harvey arrived. He and George embraced, and then Harvey spoke and the crowd just went wild.

Harvey had won, the bigots had been beaten back, his summer of peril and personal suffering had ended at long last. Politically and personally he was stronger than he ever had been.

Dan's thinking on the morning of November 10, a Friday, ran from guilt-torn visions of little Charlie at a babysitter's house and Mary Ann up to her elbows in spuds and suds, to the way he was neglecting his constituents and the way some of them were snakes out to get him, to the humiliation and corruption of City Hall. He was wearing a groove in his mind, caught inside this prison of his own devising. And then, as if by magic, the guilt subsided to be replaced by resolve. He would walk away from the corruption, somebody else could look after his constituents, he would provide for his wife and child. His duty as a man came first, had to come first. He would walk right out of that door, out of the gloom, and into the sunshine again. He would resign.

He was already moving. He shaved. He put on a good suit and a dark tie and tied a big, loose Windsor knot in it. He wanted to look his best.

Down at the Hot Potato Mary Ann was surprised to look up and see her husband standing there, shiny as a silver dollar. She could see at once that the gloom which had been so palpable was lifted, blown away. "Danny." she said.

"Hi."

Mary Ann dried her large hands on her apron. It was lunchtime. Ray was out, as usual with some money from the till, playing in his playground.

"What are you doing here?" she asked.

"I'm going down to resign."

"Are you sure that's the best thing?"

"Uh-huh. I thought it all over."

She could see how relieved he was. "If you think that's best," his wife said.

They talked some more and then made arrangements to meet at home later. Dan proceeded to City Hall. Up the shallow front steps, around the metal detector the way all the supervisors and high officials went, up the broad marble central staircase and into his office with its nearly empty desk. He sat there alone for a few moments and then he called Denise.

"I'm here," he said when she answered.

Denise came right across. Like Mary Ann she was surprised to see him all dressed up. Recently when he had come to City Hall any day except Monday he wore the kind of clothes he needed at the Hot Potato, khakis and open-neck shirts. She was really pleased to see him and doubly pleased that he was dressed as if he meant business. Denise began to chatter, to tell him about some of the things that were going on. He didn't meet her eye. When she paused for a moment he said, "Denise, I'm going to resign." Quit was not a word he would use, not about himself.

It very nearly knocked the wind out of her. She sat down, at a loss for words. So many thoughts and reactions were jostling each other that she was able to say only one word: "Why?"

Dan answered her but her head was spinning, she was barely able to pay attention to what he was saying. He hadn't consulted anybody, she thought. He didn't even know how to resign, he was asking her how to do it. He hadn't thought this out at all. But she could see in his face that he meant it.

"I'm really sorry," Dan said to her.

"You can cope," she answered. "I know you can."

"No." Dan asked her to type up a letter so he could submit it to the mayor. Denise had to compose herself first; she went off in tears toward the ladies' room, stopping first at her office to grab her pocketbook. A moment later Robin Wonder came into the office she shared with Denise and aides to other supervisors. One of them said to her, "Denise just went off in tears. Something's wrong."

Robin knew instantly what it was, that Dan had decided to leave. Her first feeling was relief, relief for him. She had seen that the job was a thorn in his side. In the next instant she realized that this meant she was out of a job. Just then Denise returned. She had fixed up her face and though she was still awfully upset, she was in control. Denise began to dictate a letter for Robin to type. When Robin finished a draft Denise took it over to show to Dan. He was nervous, anxious to have done with it. They corrected the letter and made some changes and Denise returned to Robin, standing over her shoulder and saying sternly, "Don't make a single mistake." The situation was not conducive to errorless work. Denise was breathing down her neck, barely in control of herself, and Robin was a terrible typist. But somehow she did it.

"Dear Mayor Moscone," the letter began. It continued:

I have been proud to represent the people of San Francisco as their elected Supervisor from District Eight for the past ten months, but due to personal responsibilities which I feel must take precedent over my legislative duties, I am resigning my position effective today.

I am sure that the next representative to the Board of Supervisors will receive as much support from the people of San Francisco as I have.

Sincerely,
DAN WHITE

When it was finished and Dan had signed it, Denise brought the letter over and hand-delivered it. George said he'd like for Dan to come over and talk about it. While he was waiting, George read over the letter. He knew what the kid was talking about, about "personal responsibilities." Kee-rist, a potato stand. He felt sorry for Dan White.

When Dan showed up he was obviously nervous but looking very determined. George asked him how come he was doing this. Dan told him what he had been telling everyone else, that he couldn't support his wife and son and work at the new business and see to his duties as a supervisor. As Dan talked, George thought how young he looked. Perhaps it crossed his mind that he had made the opposite decision, had put his family second to his public life, and maybe he felt some regret.

"Are you sure, absolutely certain, that you've explored every avenue, every financial alternative?" George asked. Warren Simmons would buy him the Taj Mahal, for chrissake.

"This is what I've got to do," Dan said. He didn't mention the stink of corruption but it blazed in his eyes. He had seen a way out and nothing could deter him.

"I admire that," George said, "putting your family first. You do what you have to do." They shook hands and Dan was gone.

George felt truly sorry for him. They had always found it easy to jock around together and George had a soft spot for anybody who was an athlete. He had even enjoyed Dan's spikes-flying competitiveness during the summer softball game. He realized that he'd have to say something to the press. Christ. Another political headache. Somebody would have to be appointed to the vacant seat and he'd have to do the appointing. He barely knew who were the right people to talk to out there. The Outer Mission. The Outer Mission, who the hell was there in the Outer Mission?

Denise had gone to the City Hall press room and told the reporters that Dan would be holding a press conference. That wasn't one of the most exciting things the press room wags had ever heard. One of them said: "What's he gonna do, quit?" It got a chuckle.

Meanwhile, Dan was crossing beneath the great rotunda, back to his little cubicle. The reporters trooped in and Dan went through it all again. "What is happening," he said, "is that neither my family is being taken care of as they should be nor are my constituents. I wanted to be . . . to give it one hundred percent and that meant forty hours a week. I didn't have any time. . . . My wife and I had a very difficult time coming to this decision but now that I've made it I feel it was the right one." Though the reasons he gave might have been a hybrid of truth and public relations, he looked as relieved as a prisoner just released.

Word of what Dan had done was spreading fast. Harvey was in his camera store with Doug Franks, his new lover, when he got a telephone call. When he hung up he jumped with glee. "That's terrific," he yelped. "I can't believe it, it's so terrific. Now I've got the sixth vote."

Dan's high school baseball coach, Jim Witt, heard the news on the radio. "I'll be a son of a gun," Witt thought. It was history repeating itself.

"Now this next boy"—Jim Witt's amplified voice rang throughout the Woodrow Wilson auditorium where the baseball coach was presenting Block *W*s—"this next boy, now if I ever had a son, I'd like him to be like Danny White."

Blushing and scowling, Dan stepped forward to accept his high school letter. It was hard to tell whether he wanted to cry or to slug the coach. Dan wasn't Mr. Popularity but he was known and respected; the white kids, on one side of the auditorium, applauded and whistled. On the other side of the aisle a black boy named Marvin Robinson leaned toward a pal and whispered, "Floodwater." Dan's chinos reached only to his ankles; above his sneakers showed six inches of white sweatsocks. Quintessential honky.

Wilson had opened its doors in mid-1963 and at once became a racial battlezone. The city's other high schools had dumped all their hard cases on the only high school in the southeast part of town. Dan was a member of an all-white club, the Spiders. He was also a hardass, you didn't mess with him unless you were ready to back it up.

The teachers did everything they could to keep the peace but the fights went on every day regardless. One of the worst took place in November when two Vanguards had messed up a white boy really bad in the locker room. That same afternoon the football coach rounded up a bunch of the black and white athletes.

"Let me give you guys an example of what happens when people don't obey the law," he said, "when fighting and violence are the way people try to solve their problems. Somebody just shot President Kennedy in Dallas. The President is dead."

For a few days there was a shared sorrow and then the primacy of the code reasserted itself and the rumbling began anew. Dan's willingness to fight had won him respect and distinction. He was one of the best athletes at Wilson, too, the captain of the football team. His eagerness to fight made trouble for him, too; in fact it was the reason he was at Wilson. When Charlie had died Dan was attending a Catholic school, Riordan. Dan's grades had plummeted and there had been a really nasty fight and the priests had told him to get out. Eileen was very upset. Dan felt guilty about letting his mother down but he had a chip on his shoulder. When Charlie died not only his mother but his younger brothers and sisters had turned toward him instinctively. Dan wanted to measure up, to be worthy. At seventeen it seemed to him that the right thing to do was to act like a man, and being a man meant hanging tough. Showing your feelings was weak and he had to be strong. Charlie had died but he went on living in Dan as a standard of right conduct, an ethic.

Sometimes, though, this crazy angry wildness took hold of him and when it did he had to *do* something. Once he was standing with a buddy right next to a bunch of Egyptians and said in a loud voice: "You know something, man, I really hate these jiveass niggers." The sudden tension, the certainty that any second he would ball his fists and crash them against another boy's skull was a form of relief from the welter of inchoate resentments. He wasn't the sort of boy to assess his sudden devil-may-care rages; it wasn't within his makeup to examine why he felt so furious.

After Charlie's death he threw himself into sports with fervor. At Riordan his grades had fallen so low that when he transferred to Wilson he was at first ineligible for athletics. But Coach Witt sized him up as a stickout kid. Witt could see that Danny White could handle responsibility and he wanted to utilize him some way, so he made him the student manager and third-base coach. Danny was sharp, a holler guy and a natural leader. Witt trusted him to flash signs. Witt would signal a bunt, and standing in the third-base coaching box, clapping his hands and chirping encouragment, Danny would relay it to the batter.

They talked together a lot, the slim, wiry kid with the earnest expression, and his navy-tough coach. Witt had been the executive officer of a destroyer and the navy was in his bearing. The coach was aware that Danny had recently lost his father and although it wasn't something they discussed, it colored the coach's feeling for the boy. He was not one to get personal with his players; he had an officer's reserve with his young men. Yet he let himself get closer to Danny White than to any of his other boys, in or out of the navy. When they talked they never mentioned Danny's family or private things, feelings. Dan would boast about some black tough whose butt he had been forced to kick. Witt admired that. The kind of thugs that had been dumped on Wilson was shocking. Why, he told Danny, some of them—not the black boys on the team but the other kind—had actually used the *F* word to him.

And they talked about Dan's future. He wanted to be a major leaguer, he thought he had the stuff. The 1964 season was Dan's only chance to get himself a contract or an athletic scholarship to college, and there were professional scouts checking out Wilson's games. Wilson was winless going into its game against St. Ignatius. It would have given the Wilson boys special satisfaction to whip SI, the rich kids' school. SI represented something beyond the grasp of these kids, most of whom would spend their lives working with their hands and their backs. In both social privilege and the league standings, SI was top of the heap and Wilson the bottom.

In the next to last inning the score was tied 4–4. Wilson had runners at first and second with nobody out, and a chance to move the winning runs into scoring position with their two best batters due up next. From the third-base coaching box Jim Witt gave Danny the sacrifice sign. Danny was his best bunter and he knew he wouldn't miss the sign. Witt flashed bunt and Dan tipped his cap to acknowledge that he understood.

Danny stepped into the batter's box and toed the ground and waved his bat back and forth. He looked like a hitter. He dug in and the SI pitcher wound up and fired and both Wilson runners took off. But Danny didn't bunt, he took a full cut, just nicking the ball and fouling it back.

Oh jeez, Witt said to himself. He walked down the line and shouted, "Hey, Dan, I gave you the bunt!"

"I know, I know. But I didn't want to."

"Dan! You know there can be only one captain and I'm the captain of this ship."

Dan didn't say a word. He glowered at his coach. And then, right before Witt's amazed eyes, he tore his jersey over his shoulders, wrenched it over his head and slammed it down a few feet up the third-base line. He was red in the face and kicking the dirt and shouting invectives at his coach.

"Who the fuck do you think you are?" Danny screamed and stomped off the field.

Dan never came back. He never again spoke another word to Jim Witt; a couple of times he avoided him in the school hallways. The coach was shocked and angry and hurt. The boy he had trusted above all others had disobeyed his orders and used the *F* word to him. Danny White, who was like a son to him.

On November 10, 1978, Jim Witt heard how Dan had quit and he thought: "He did it again."

That night Dan and Mary Ann found someone to look after Charlie and went out to dinner. Danny was more relaxed than Mary Ann had seen him in months, and in her heart she began to hope that maybe at long last they would have the life together they had planned when they used to sit in her living room on Sanchez Street and look out over the city, over City Hall and the Cathedral glimmering in the night. With all her heart she wanted to believe that. And yet she sensed that he still wasn't satisfied, something was still troubling him.

She thought, "He resigned but he also thinks he quit. And that's just Danny, my Danny, who never quits anything."

13
Seventeen Days

It is customary, as when the soothsayer warns Julius Caesar to beware the Ides of March, for fate to arrive onstage in the person of a minor player. On Sunday, two days after his resignation, Dan and Mary Ann sat laughing and cheering in their complimentary box seats near the fifty-yard line at Candlestick Park watching the Forty-Niners game, happier than they had felt in months and full of hopes and plans. They would not have believed it for a moment, they would have scoffed, if somebody had warned them that whatever turns and twists the next two weeks held in store for them, their destruction had already been sealed on Friday, November 10—by a zealous clerk.

Gilbert H. Boreman had for about three years been the clerk to the Board of Supervisors, responsible for keeping its records. During the board meetings he sat immediately below the president's dais facing the ten other supervisors in the chamber, keeping track of board actions, and, when called upon, providing procedural advice. Boreman was a rather colorless fellow with a long, horsy face and thinning hair that was gray at the temples. Around City Hall he was universally well liked; he saw to it that he did not offend. When word had reached him late on Friday afternoon that Supervisor White had resigned his seat, Boreman walked across City Hall to consult with an assistant city attorney who agreed with him that they'd better have it in writing. Boreman returned to the west side of the second floor of City Hall and obtained a xerox copy of Dan's resignation from Denise Apcar. Immediately, he took the copy to his own office, stamped it with the time and date, and put it in his file for the board meeting the following Monday, November 13. He had no way of knowing, of course, what the ultimate consequences would be of his performing his duty in such an efficacious and timely fashion.

Monday, November 13

The phone in Goldie Judge's kitchen rang just a few minutes before Sunday midnight.

"This is Goldie."

"Goldie!" It was a man's voice.

"Who's this?"

"This? This is the mayor of San Francisco, George R. Moscone."

"Ohhh, my secret lover," Goldie drawled, shaking a cigarette loose of the pack. "I wonder what it'd be like being in bed with you."

"Well, c'mon over right now and you can find out." They both guffawed.

"So tell me, Mr. Mayor, what's on your mind?" As if she didn't know, right?

"You know, I was just wondering what's going on down there in your neighborhood."

"We're all asleep," Goldie said. "Everybody's gotta be to work in the morning."

"Yeah?" George said. "Well, what're we gonna do about Dan White's seat?"

"*We're* not gawna do anything. That's not my problem, paisan, that's yours. What're *you* gawna do?"

"Goldie," George crooned. "How about helping me out on this one?"

Goldie understood what he wanted: a name, a recommendation. "Nope," she said.

"How come?" George asked. "What about Goldie Judge?"

"C'mon, be serious. All right," Goldie said, "I'll ask around."

"Now, that's my sweetheart. I'll be in touch," George said. "Don't forget me."

Monday morning Goldie began to work the phone. Everybody was being coy about their own ambitions, but one theme was universal: embarrassment, even shame, among the politically oriented people of District 8 at how Dan had made them look. They had always approached City Hall with a feeling of being poor relations, and now this; ten months after they had elected him to carry their message, Dan White had just walked out on them, made them laughingstocks. The embarrassment, and the anger, were so universal that Goldie called Gil Boreman and demanded, in the name of the voters of District 8, that Dan's nameplate be removed from his office door at once, if not sooner.

Boreman said he would comply with her request just as soon as the board meeting was adjourned and Dan's resignation had been officially accepted. He was a compliant man but above all, orderly.

Later that Monday morning Harvey's aide Dick Pabich was coming down the Polk Street steps of City Hall and passed Dan, dressed casually, on his way into the building.

"Hi, Dan." Dick stopped.

"Hey, Dick."

"Well . . ." Dick said.

Dan explained, "I'm just heading up to clean some stuff out of my office." He seemed lighthearted.

Pabich couldn't bring himself to say he was sorry. "Well, good luck," he said instead.

"Hey, thanks. Thanks a lot." Dan continued on his way. Pabich turned and almost stepped in a pool of blood on the City Hall steps. Somebody yelled, "Watch out!"

"What *happened*?" Pabich asked.

"Guy had a seizure," said Dick Weinand, the policeman assigned to permanent duty in front of City Hall. "Banged his head pretty bad."

Pabich had more important things to think about. The mayor and Harvey had worked out a deal to get some city and federal money for a gay community center, and the political infighting over control of the purse strings had led to an FBI investigation of whether the federal funds had been deceitfully obtained. The vote on the gay community center was set for Monday, November 27, two weeks hence, and so far Harvey and George had been able to line up only five votes. Harvey had already visited with George since Dan's resignation and extracted a commitment that whoever the mayor appointed to fill the vacancy would vote for the Gay Community Center. That was what Harvey had been thinking of when he had exclaimed, upon learning that Dan had quit, "I've got the sixth vote!"

The Board convened that Monday afternoon at 2 P.M. As soon as it was in session, Gil Boreman read the letter from Dan White to Mayor Moscone and indicated that a motion to accept it would be appropriate.

The motion was made by Quentin Kopp and passed unanimously. When the meeting adjourned Gil Boreman had one of his assistants strip Dan's old office door of his nameplate. Boreman had already pro-rated Dan's salary to November 10 and seen to it that the former supervisor was taken off the city payroll.

Tuesday, November 14

Denise Apcar was still terribly upset by what Dan had done. She and Robin Wonder had decided to continue working until they were terminated by the city. The little things would affect Denise: for instance, should they go on answering the phone with "Dan White's office," or should they say, "District Eight"? The phone rang and rang all day Monday and Tuesday. A lot of the people who wanted to talk to Dan called Denise first to find out what the hell was going on. Some of them were pretty hot under the collar about what Dan had done, like Paul Chignell of the POA. By walking out Dan was leaving the way clear for Moscone to resubmit the Officers for Justice settlement to a board with six friendly votes. Bill Dauer from the Chamber of Commerce wanted to talk with Dan, to convince him that he should not resign; his voice was needed, Dauer said, it was a sensible voice and if Moscone filled his seat with another ultraliberal, the Chamber would be losing a lot of close votes that they had been winning. Ray Brown, the realtors' lobbyist, had the same concern; they had plowed an awful lot of money into Dan White. Commissioner Mo Bernstein rang up too. Denise talked with each of them and all of them said they would call Dan. But from the district itself there was silence.

Denise and Robin had also met with Bernard Teitelbaum, one of George's chief aides, who asked them to recommend a replacement. Denise suggested a federal housing administrator who had also been one of the founders of a District 8 community group, Don Horanzy.

"Horanzy?" Teitelbaum said. "I never heard of him."

Phones were ringing all over the city. Dan's resignation had caused the politicians to begin choosing up sides, like kids in a schoolyard. Denise felt that something *had* to be done. On Sunday night she had seen Ray Sloan at a party and the two of them had agreed to meet on Tuesday for a late breakfast. Relations between Ray and Denise were one-sided, it was Robin Wonder's observation that Denise admired Ray, looked up to him and sought his approval. Ray, on the other hand, treated Denise with a kind of cavalier disregard. When he needed her for something he was ingratiating, but most of the time he acted as if she were part of the furniture. Now Ray needed Denise.

When they sat down together in a coffee shop near City Hall, Ray was intent on persuading Dan to ask for his job back, and he wanted Denise's help. They talked back and forth about how peculiar Dan's abrupt departure had seemed. Ray even said that the guy might need a psychiatrist, but fat chance he would ever tell him to his face. It was the sort of thing Ray felt free to say to Denise but not to Dan. Because of the force of Dan's personality, Ray couldn't help but treat Dan like the All-American hombre. Dan was so much more the regular guy than Ray had ever been; Ray admired "DW" but he never felt they were friends, not personal friends. And besides all that, Ray needed Dan; Walnut Creek seemed closer by the moment.

Together, Ray and Denise determined to talk Dan into changing his mind. They knew about all the others who had done the same thing, and that Dan had turned them all down. Ray understood that the appeals were made to Dan's sense of duty, either angrily or sympathetically. But because he and Dan were so alike—both were scrappers—he understood instinctively that an appeal to duty was only half the trick: you had to give Dan a *challenge*. Ray didn't think that Dan was a quitter, it was just that once he had acquired things he lost interest in them. Give DW a challenge and the old fire might return. They drove out to Shawnee Avenue but nobody was around so they went to talk with Dan's mother for a while.

Mrs. McHugh told them that she, too, had been stunned by what her son had done and couldn't understand it herself. And she encouraged them to try to change his mind. Over the weekend, she said, there had been a lot of discussion among the family about Dan's financial situation, and it seemed that quite a large amount of money in interest-free loans could be put together if that would help. Also, she said, some of her younger children would be glad to work at the Hot Potato for no pay until things righted themselves.

About 3:30 Ray and Denise went back over to Shawnee Avenue and found Dan at home. He let them in and they all sat down at the dining room table. There was a window in the dining room looking out toward a tiny interior vestibule in which stood a statue of a saint. Denise explained to Dan that they had come because they—everybody, really, his mother, his friends—were concerned, upset. She didn't think he had thought through what he had done. She, all of them, wanted him to reconsider.

"My mind's made up," Dan said.

Denise pressed her argument. His financial bind was only temporary, as the business prospered it would ease. His family would lend him money; there were a lot of people who wanted to help out.

"How *could* you just walk out like that?" Denise asked. "After you worked so hard, how could you just walk out on all the people who elected you, who depend on you?"

"I don't owe anybody anything." Dan paced. "I can't let my family down, they've got to come first. I'm not a crybaby but those people down there are basic shits. I just chose not to be part of it."

"Listen," Ray said, his blood boiling, "I did *not* walk and work all those days and nights for you to quit willy nilly. If you don't like the job you can quit in two years, three years, whatever, when the term's up. You've got to ask George to give you your seat back."

Dan was scowling. "You don't understand politics," he said to Ray.

"The hell I don't," Ray said sharply. "Who the hell pulled your goddamn campaign together?" Hadn't Dan said to him the night he was elected, "*You* did this"? "Where the hell do you get off," Ray shouted, "telling *me* I don't understand politics?"

"Look," Dan said, like trying to explain long division to a child, "Moscone won't give me my seat back."

"The hell he won't," Ray answered, sensing the shift in direction of Dan's responses. "You won in a fuckin' landslide. He's got to give you your seat back. He's gonna need District Eight when he runs for re-election."

Dan erupted, it all came spilling out. "I've had it!" he shouted, his voice growing higher. "Had it! I don't want to go back. None of them tells the truth, you know that. They're corrupt as hell, they don't stick by their word. They don't care about the people, they care about their goddamn cocktail parties. You know what the difference is between me and all those goddamn punks down there? Basically, I'm different from them. The goddamn job doesn't mean anything to me. They're so fuckin' concerned with being so socially prominent, and basically that doesn't mean shit to me. Nothing." He was flushed, fired up with righteous indignation.

Ray saw his opening and seized it, threw down the gauntlet. "Fuck *them,* fuck *them* all, you're afraid he won't give you your seat back, is that it?"

"No I'm not," Dan said, but his tone had changed entirely. It had been like this for days now. Chignell had called him a quitter, they had all suggested he was a quitter. *Was* he a quitter? Every one of them had said he owed them, and said, too, it was his duty to put out for them, they had put out for him. His precious liberty, the momentary sense of escape, the freedom to be just himself again, was receding with every second. He would *show* them Dan White was no quitter, and he would show Ray he knew what he was talking about.

"All right," Dan said. "I'll call him."

Denise dialed for him and then handed him the phone. When George came on the line Dan said, "Can I come see you? It's important."

"Not now," George whispered, "I'm in a meeting. What is it?"

"I want my letter back. I've changed my mind."

"Oh," George said. "Why don'tcha come down at six."

Dan hung up. "He'll see me at six," he said. "Denise, be a good girl and iron my good suit, it's kinda wrinkled." He had rounded the corner so fast he hardly seemed to realize that he was on another street.

Denise went happily off to get the suit and set up the ironing board.

"Okay," Dan said to Ray, much subdued. "What do I tell him?"

"Tell him you made a mistake." Ray followed him into the bathroom where Dan was taking a couple of aspirin, something Ray had never seen him do before. "He told you you shouldn't give up the seat, to explore every avenue, right? So tell him he's right, he was right and you should have listened."

"Denise," Dan shouted, "hurry up with my pants."

Not ten minutes ago DW had been sulking and defiantly stubborn and now, right before Ray's eyes, his whole demeanor was changing. He was holding his head higher, his strong jaw was jutting, his eyes, which had been vague and unfocused, were clear again. You could sense his great physical strength in the way he moved. That's what it took, Ray thought, a challenge, some obstacle to surmount. It was like watching a fighter psych himself to get into the ring. The corny phrase you always heard on television popped into Ray's mind: "The thrill of victory, the agony of defeat." That was DW all over.

They were in the bedroom now. Denise carried the suit in and Dan started to get dressed. "A three-piece occasion," he said.

"Look," Ray said, "It's time you started playing the game. If you want this back you've got to play George's game. Tell him you'll support him for mayor, you were gonna do that anyway if Quentin ran. Tell him that."

"You think I should?" Dan asked, looking in the mirror, knotting his tie. "Yeah, that's right. That's the way to do it. I'll tell him he was right and I support him. Okay, that's what I'll do."

It was a damp November night. When they arrived at City Hall and parked the car, the stationary spotlights were trained on the pale green dome and the spire above it. The winter fog was swirling through the plaza, insinuating itself among the bare sycamore trees. Inside the building many of the lights had been turned off for the night and it was dim and eerie. The only light was cast by big bulbs set in globes atop claw-footed fixtures. Side by side they trotted by the broad central steps that led toward the supervisors' chambers. While Ray waited, Dan started the long walk to the east side of the building, where the mayor's office was. Ray stood by the supervisors' chambers and listened to Dan's footsteps fall on the polished marble floor and echo through the rotunda. He could see Dan's shadow wheel across the floor as he passed between the pillars all the way across the building. When Dan had disappeared into the mayor's suite Ray went into Dan's old office—he was shocked to see that the nameplate was no longer on the door—and sat down to wait.

After George had received the call from Dan he had hung up and turned to one of the men who was with him. "Can you believe this?" George said. "Dan White wants his resignation back, he's rescinding it."

"What are you going to do?"

"Hell, give it to him of course. He's just a kid, you know? Everybody has the right to change their mind, we all make mistakes."

George brought the resignation letter out to Cyr Copertini, his confidential secretary, and told her Dan White would be coming by at six, to give him the letter and set up an appointment for tomorrow morning.

In just a few moments Dan rejoined Ray.

"Well, I guess you can call me Supervisor again," he announced. He was grinning from ear to ear. In the excitement of rising to the challenge he had forgotten all his doubts, forgotten how much and why he hated being a supervisor.

"Right on!" Ray exclaimed, jumping up. "Right on!"

"C'mon, Ray, let's go celebrate. Let's go get a drink." They walked up Polk Street toward a bar called the Irish Embassy which was a popular City Hall hangout, its name an unintended mockery of the way things had once been and were no more at City Hall. Denise had gone off to take care of something or other, but Dan called and left a message for her to meet them at the Embassy.

Usually, Ray had noticed, DW was the kind of guy who nursed a single drink for two hours, which was one of the reasons Ray had never wanted to socialize with him. But tonight Dan was matching Ray drink for drink. And the liquor, on top of the exhilaration, loosened Dan up. He was talking with Ray in a way he had never spoken before; his team-captain persona was in the locker and his true feelings about things were coming out.

"This isn't really a money situation," Dan confided. Of course Ray had never believed that; they seemed to have some savings—after the event on the *Balcuthe* they had been paid back what they had loaned the campaign, and when you added up Dan's salary as a supervisor with the wages that he and Mary Ann were both drawing from the Hot Potato, they weren't hurting all *that* bad.

"It's not money," Dan continued, "but I'm going to say to the press it's financial, I'll tell 'em how my family is going to give me a loan. What else am I gonna do? Slam 'em? I mean, say they're fools and idiots like they really are? You know, I can't deal with those goddamn people. You don't know what it's like, Ray. I have to sit and listen to fuckin' Carol Ruth Silver's gibberish and then when she's done, that fuckin' Kopp spouts his lawyer bullshit for forty minutes, about nothing, some minor point. So I'll say it's a financial situation."

It was just about the most sentences Ray had ever heard Dan string together all at one time, and probably the most honest. Just as luck would have it, Denise showed up then. Ray's heart sank. He didn't need her anymore and he wasn't happy to see her. He knew it would change with her there, for the first time DW was opening up to him, for the first time he didn't feel like some goddamn Iago. Denise would spoil that, Ray knew she would.

Sure enough, Denise started right in babbling, as far as Ray was concerned saying the wrong thing at the wrong time, missing the mood. But at least Dan had asked for another round when he ordered a drink for Denise. Ray could see that DW was stewed. Ignoring Denise's chatter, Ray asked Dan the question that had been on his mind for an hour: "Why do you think he did it, gave it back?"

"Oh," Denise answered, "The mayor knows how they *love* you in the district, he knows the people would never stand for anybody else taking your seat, he knows that, he . . ." Denise went right on playing hearts and flowers but Ray was watching Dan's face. The happiness drained out of it as swiftly as if an eraser had been wiped across a blackboard. It was replaced by a look of such intensity as Ray had never seen.

"You know," Dan said, cutting Denise off, "you know, you don't understand me, not really." He was speaking with a feeling so strong Ray would have been tempted to call it desperation. "You don't know what I wake up and feel like in the morning. Nobody knows. Nobody knows what goes on inside me."

Ray, who had often enough felt like a piece of cosmic debris himself, who knew the loneliness that existed on the far side of poignancy, saw then what he had missed before, so strong and smooth had been Dan's shell: he saw that the team captain was hurting, really hurting bad inside, and couldn't fall back on anyone, felt he had to see it through alone.

It didn't surprise Ray when within a few minutes Dan shrugged off the mood and suggested they go on out to give Mary Ann the good news. Feeling so alone, naturally he would want to be with his wife. Then, in the car, Dan's mood changed again. He was happy drunk, loud and expansive, falling in with Denise's chatter. Ray sat quietly considering what he had just understood and pondering, too, the machine-gun rapidity of Dan's transformations. In something like five hours he had watched DW go from stubbornly defiant, to determined to meet a challenge, to doubtful ("What do I tell him?"), to ebullient, to confiding, to desperately lonely and now to raucously celebratory; like a little boy with a good report card, marching into the house, through the vestibule and into the dining room, announcing in a loud voice, "I am the supervisor, *I* am the supervisor."

Mary Ann was at the dining room table with Dan's sister Nancy, the sister to whom Dan was closest, and Ray saw the two women exchange a quick glance. Then Mary Ann met Ray's eyes and gave him a look that said: what have you *done?* The look wasn't incredulous, and it wasn't sad or angry. It was the look of a lost soul, of someone who had been buffeted one time more than she could absorb, the look of a woman who did not know what to do. She didn't say a word.

The way Ray had sized things up was that Mary Ann hadn't ever wanted Dan to be a supervisor, especially. She enjoyed the perks—tea at Dianne Feinstein's mansion, weekends at Warren Simmons's spread at Silverado—enjoyed them more than Dan did. But they really didn't matter. She had just wanted him to do whatever made him happy, whatever satisfied him. She sensed his continual dissatisfaction and it frightened her. She had been thirty-four when she married, now she was thirty-eight and a mother for the first time. What have you *done?* her look said. Ray sat down at the table across from her.

Dan was talking loudly, drunkenly, about what had happened as he went off into the bedroom to change his clothes, oblivious to what Mary Ann was feeling. Ray saw them all of a sudden as two lonely planets in orbit around the *idea* of their marriage, their home, their son.

Quietly, Ray began to explain to Mary Ann and Nancy what had happened. In a minute, Dan returned in chinos and an old shirt and sat on the floor to put one of his Irish records on the stereo. He was pumping a fist in the air in time to the beguiling call of the old country, the land where he had found the people friendly, the countryside green and gentle, the life a true life of contentment. He kept pumping his left arm, the one with the shamrock tattoo.

Quietly, too, Mary Ann said to Ray, "You'd better tell me what to do. Maybe it's time you outlined what you want me to tell him."

Ever since that first moment they had laid eyes on each other in Grison's Steak House—it seemed like a hundred years ago—and had taken an instant dislike to each other, Ray had made up his mind about Mary Ann. She was a disapprover, and she was the power behind the throne. Whenever there was a big decision to be made, especially if it involved money, Dan had always said he had to talk it over first with Mary Ann. All along Ray had assumed that her's was the determining voice in his decisions. Now he realized it hadn't been that way at all, that when Dan "talked it over" with his wife, he told her what he was going to do, or what Ray had said he should do, and Mary Ann had simply endorsed it. If Danny wanted it, that was okay with her.

Ray could see how frightened she was, how torn up. Something was wrong, terribly, terribly wrong with their marriage, with Dan. Still singing along with the Irish Rovers in a loud voice, Dan joined them at the table.

Mary Ann turned and smiled at him.

Wednesday, November 15

The headline in the *Chronicle* said: REP. RYAN ARRIVES IN GUYANA.

In the wake of Phil Tracy's revelations about Reverend Jim Jones, subsequent investigations by newspaper reporters, and the exodus to Guyana of one thousand members of People's Temple—some of whose kin were claiming they had gone to the jungle under duress—Congressman Leo Ryan of San Mateo, just south of the city, was undertaking a fact-finding mission. Both San Francisco dailies had sent reporters along.

At nine that morning George stepped out of the back door to his office and went into the offices of the city attorney. A senior deputy named Jim Lazarus was standing in a corridor. George put his arm around the attorney's shoulders. "I've got to talk to you and Tom in private," George said. "You're not going to believe this." They stepped into the office of Tom Toomey, another deputy.

"Dan White is revoking his letter, he wants his resignation back," the mayor said.

"Well, I've never heard of that before," Lazarus said.

"I suppose he has the right to change his mind," George replied.

"Give him back the letter, it's only a piece of paper," Toomey said. "But it's an awfully interesting legal question, I bet it's never happened before. I don't know if you have the power to, uh, undo it. And there's the question of whether he's entitled to rescind it."

"I did already," George said. "I gave him his letter. I want you people to look into it. I don't want to hear about it until you're through looking into whether I can reappoint him."

"This is too important, uh, we shouldn't do it hastily," Tom Toomey said. "It shouldn't be verbal, it should be a formal opinion."

"How long will that take?" George wanted to know.

"A week, give us a week," Toomey said. "I mean, it's never happened before."

"Okay, a week," George said.

When Dan arrived, he and George talked privately for a few minutes. George was concerned about Dan's situation, about the legal questions, about Dan. Finally George told him that as long as there were no legal impediments—and speaking as a lawyer he didn't see why there should be—he would consider the resignation rescinded. And, he added, in case there was a legal question he would then reappoint him.

"That's great," Dan said.

George got up. They shook hands and George put his arm around Dan's shoulders. "I'm glad it's all worked out for you," he said.

A few minutes later George told the same thing to the reporters who had been alerted. George looked particularly dapper that morning in an Italian-cut dark blue suit with his silver gray hair cut short to look like Cary Grant. He fielded their questions from behind his desk, playing with a pencil. He didn't smoke on camera.

Denise Apcar stood right there among the reporters and listened to George say that he would reappoint Dan if that became necessary, that Dan had been a good supervisor. When everybody except his own people had left, George said, "Can you believe that? I mean, really, can you *really* believe that?"

Meanwhile Dan was holding a press conference of his own, with his letter of resignation safely in his pocket. "People unknown to me plus my family and friends have come to me and stated that they want me to stay in office," Dan said, mentioning the loan, making it sound like a financial question. "The majority of my district doesn't want to have someone appointed that they didn't elect, and I'm going to stay in my seat." Mary Ann stood beside him, her head cocked, looking uncomfortable in the public eye.

Harvey had been standing nearby listening. The moment the press conference broke up he came over to shake Dan's hand. He began to talk quite glibly, waving his arms around and telling Dan there might be legal problems with his getting his seat back, seeming to know a good deal about it. Dan stood listening to Harvey with a tight half-smile, a near-grin that said, I see right through you, pal, and you're full of shit. His expression had in it about equal parts of mockery, anger and hurt. As soon as their little tête-à-tête was over, Harvey went to work.

For the second time since Dan had resigned Harvey paid a call on the mayor. Listen, he told George, you're up for re-election next year and don't think the gay community is going to overlook it if you give that jerk his seat back. That man, Harvey said, is the leading opponent of gay people in this city. We will not forget it if you reappoint him. And furthermore, I have your commitment—a *commitment*—that whoever you appoint to that seat will vote for the gay community center. What are you going to do about this?

George told Harvey to take it easy, not to worry, it would be at least a week until there was a city attorney's opinion and a lot could change in a week.

"It had better," Harvey said, and huffed out.

Dan, meanwhile, thought it might be a good idea to see the city attorneys himself and find out what was happening with the legal questions George had mentioned. His initial experience with city attorneys' opinions was still a bitter memory.

Jim Lazarus was already researching the question when Dan showed up. Dan told Lazarus and Toomey, who was called in, that he had rescinded his resignation. They said they knew, they were looking into it under instructions from the mayor.

"Well, don't worry about it too much," Toomey said. "Uh, we haven't got too far but so far I don't see any, uh, problems."

"Well, my biggest concern is to get it, to have you get out your opinion as fast as you can. Because the people are behind me, they want me to represent them." Toomey gathered that Dan was worried that the situation might change if too much time elapsed, if political forces started gathering.

Lazarus explained to Dan that it looked like the mayor could probably appoint him to the vacant seat. The more serious legal question, what might be the sticking point, was that because the resignation had been voted on and filed by the Board, Dan might not be entitled to rescind it. In other words, it looked like Gil Boreman's quick action had left the question right in George Moscone's lap.

Just then the phone rang. Lazarus answered.

"Yes?" he said. "Uh-huh. Yes, I am. Yes. Well, uh, Supervisor, it may take a week. I understand, I understand your concern, Mr. Milk. I don't know yet. I will, I sure will. Okay."

Lazarus was ill-at-ease. "That was Supervisor Milk," he said.

"Uh-huh," Dan said.

Thursday, November 16

The political pressure on George was building. Again and again people who had supported him in 1975 and were ready to back him again in 1979 were giving him the same message: if you appoint Dan White, you're a one-term mayor. To most of them George was replying, "Look, I'm just giving the kid a chance. He did a stupid thing, if I did a stupid thing I'd want a second chance."

It made quite an impression on George that several supervisors also told him, privately, that they thought he should dump Dan. John

Molinari, for instance, whose political acumen George respected. And of course Harvey, nobody more adamantly, more persistently than Harvey. Harvey had seen a meeting in Dan's office among Dauer, Chignell and some other POA honchos, and the realtors' lobbyist. Those people were his enemies, the enemies of progress. Harvey had even suggested a candidate to replace Dan: Helen Fama, a community activist and women's advocate who had finished third in District 8.

But not all the advice that George was getting was opposed to Dan. Commissioner Mo Bernstein, whose financial backing George was relying on in 1979, had a good word to say about Dan. And there were others; people whose judgments George trusted and whose politics were far to the left of Dan's had responded, as George had, with sympathy. Sympathy and practicality. Look, they said, you barely beat Barbegelata in District 8; Quentin will be even stronger there. If you axe a popular supervisor your name will be mud in the Outer Mission come 1979. George was still planning to honor his promise to Dan, but was keeping his options open.

The scales began to tilt the other way, however, beginning with the rally on Leland Avenue that Goldie Judge organized Thursday afternoon. The rally yanked the rug right out from under the practicality argument.

On Sunday George had asked Goldie to test the waters for him in Visitacion Valley and to help him find a candidate for Dan's seat; that was before Dan had asked for his letter back, of course, but George hadn't called Goldie off, and Goldie had made up her mind to fight Dan to the finish. The rally was being held in an empty lot on Leland Avenue near Andy's Cafe. The people sponsoring it were calling themselves Citizens for Responsible Representation—a coinage that had come to Goldie in the middle of the night—and under its umbrella crowded Gary Yoes from SAFE, many of the more influential merchants and community groups, all of Dan's major opponents in the 1977 election, and even Reverend Mark Coonradt, who had endorsed Dan. They all felt that he had gone downtown and deserted them.

It was a cold and overcast morning and Goldie, who was to speak first, was bundled up in an overcoat and a rainbow beret she had knit herself. Television crews had been invited and were standing by when Goldie began to castigate Dan for having brought disgrace to the neighborhood. Goldie had finished and an elderly gent named John King who had been one hundred percent with Dan in the election was ready to say his piece when suddenly Dan himself stepped forward with Ray and Denise trailing behind.

As Dan came marching toward the little platform that had been set up in the lot, the TV cameras began to roll. Brusquely, Dan stepped past John King and began to speak, jabbing his finger.

"There's not one person or one editorial that's ever been written that is politically against me or politically for me, and that goes all the way to the top as far as Mayor George Moscone." He was squinting, blinking as if his eyes were not focusing. "Every one of them right down the line says I've represented District Eight to the best of my ability and the District Eight people are getting fair representation . . ."

Goldie was still standing on the platform, beside Dan. Deciding she had heard enough she hissed at him, "I resent this, White," and put a shoulder into his chest, shoving him aside. As Dan stumbled his jacket fell away and Goldie saw, strapped to his belt, a revolver. A gun. Her stomach flopped.

Dan regained his footing—the cameras were still rolling, the sequence would be on the evening news—and shoved Goldie back. "She can shoot off her mouth so much . . ." he began to say.

But Goldie was incensed, she was shouting him down, her wet lips moving rapidly. "I'll tell you people something else, when we needed this SOB he was nowhere around. White," she screamed at him, "you go peel potatoes on San Francisco Bay."

Dan shrugged his shoulders—he was glowering, blinking even faster, and pouring sweat despite the cold—and turned to John King. "John," he appealed, "tell them what kind of man I am." King stepped onto the platform.

"I say here today that former Supervisor Dan White has brought disgrace, that Dan White holds us in utter contempt. Who is he accountable to any way—his constituents or the Police Officers Association and real estate interests downtown?" King said.

As King was speaking, Dan abruptly shouted, "Isn't anybody on my side?" Casting around, his eyes fell on Rudy Kessenheimer, his old scoutmaster, who had been so wounded by Dan's refusal to let him be the "complaint-getter" on Leland Avenue. "What about you, Rudy?" Dan asked.

"No," Rudy said, slowly shaking his head.

As the rally was breaking up, Dan was approached by the reporters who had been present. "Don't listen to them, they're just a bunch of snakes," Dan told the press.

"Losers," Ray Sloan added. "This was organized by a bunch of losers who want to jump on Dan."

But the damage, the political damage, had been done. That evening George invited Goldie and the others to meet with him the next afternoon, Friday. If Dan didn't have support in District 8, George was thinking, if there was such resentment against him on his home turf, and not just among his opponents but among people who had been with him in the election, then the practicality argument didn't cut the mustard. If that was the way it was, then it just came down to sentiment, to sympathy with a young man who had made a mistake—and who had a nasty habit of casting the sixth and conclusive vote against George Moscone.

Friday, November 17

Calls went out from Denise and Ray: Dan had to have a rally too, down at City Hall, right under the mayor's nose. Several carloads of real estate agents and their office help showed up, and the top brass of the POA, as well as a few of Dan's sisters and stepsisters. There were perhaps fifty people listening to Dan make a brief speech from the front steps. It was not a showing that would have impressed George. The cops and the realtors had never been in George's corner; he didn't have to listen to them on this one.

Far more significant was the 5 P.M. meeting with Goldie's group at which George heard their unified opposition to Dan. When they had finished, George urged them not to fight among themselves, not to get angry, to stick together. And he gave them a hint about how he was thinking.

"I've got a problem," George said. "Dan White had not been a friendly vote. I don't know what I'm going to do, but I can tell you this, if I reappoint him, and I'm not saying I will, but if I do, well, that would be a political favor. There would be an indebtedness."

Goldie left thinking that her paisano was tired, tired and uncertain.

His hands thrust deep into the pockets of his trenchcoat, Police Inspector Earl Sanders was headed out of City Hall, looking, as always, stolid and self-contained. The Officers for Justice trial was coming to the end of its second week and it wasn't going well. Sanders had been the first witness for the plaintiffs, and on the stand his claims of discriminatory practices by the police department had been undercut by the defendants' lawyers. They had made quite a point of his swift rise to inspector. Even more embarassing to Sanders personally, and damaging to the suit as well, was a little trap set and sprung by the defense team. Sanders had testified that he had had to suffer racial epithets.

"Of course," a defense lawyer had said when crossexamining him, "you would never use racially derogatory terms yourself, would you, Inspector?"

"No," Sanders replied, "I don't."

At which point the defense introduced photographs and a script from an annual dinner roast. In the photos Sanders was dressed like a witch doctor with a bone in his nose. He was on stage with a Japanese officer.

"You Nip!" Sanders shouted in the script.

"Don't mind if I do," the Japanese replied.

"Oompuh, oompuh, chugga chugga lugga," Sanders had responded, producing a flask from beneath his loin cloth.

At the end of Sanders's testimony Judge Peckham had called the plaintiffs' attorneys to the bench and conveyed to them that they had to do better than that.

With the lawsuit going poorly, Dan's resignation had seemed a godsend. "We hear," one of the lawyers told Sanders, "that George is going to resubmit the settlement to the Board once he fills White's seat." That was where things stood as Earl started out of the building on Friday afternoon and came upon George Moscone standing there in conversation.

"Hey, Earl," the mayor called, waving him over.

"How ya doin'?" Earl said.

George wagged a finger at him and winked. "Earl," he said significantly, "this one's gonna be all right."

"Hey, I'm glad to hear that," Sanders said. George's message had been understood; there would be a new supervisor, and he would vote in favor of the settlement of the Officers for Justice suit. That made Sanders feel pretty good, even though he understood that political commitments were ephemeral. Twice George Moscone had promised jobs to Sanders's main man, Rotea Guilford, squeezing his shoulder and assuring him, "You can trust me on this one," first as Police Chief and then as Sheriff. After all, George owed Guilford, if it hadn't been for Guilford his political career would have deadended in that crummy room in the New Yorker Hotel many years ago. And twice George had backed away from what he had promised, circumstances had changed, and all political promises were subject to circumstance. As Guilford himself had said after each of his disappointments, "In politics there is no such thing as a promise."

It was that same afternoon when Ray Sloan put Dan's nameplate back on the door of his old office. After all, they had the mayor's word.

Saturday, November 18

"To date," the mayor's press secretary told a reporter who called on Saturday to ask what was happening with the Dan White situation, "the only person who has come into this office indicating that Dan White should be reappointed is Dan White himself."

While the statement was not literally true it was a good indication of the problem George was facing. The city attorneys had already made it clear to George that the power was his; under the charter Dan could not rescind his resignation. The seat was George's to fill and the meeting with Goldie's people the previous afternoon had made it equally clear that to appoint Dan White would not necessarily be politically popular, not even in his own district. The time had come to play a little hardball. George had Cyr Copertini arrange for Dan to drop by at noon.

The two men met alone in the mayor's ceremonial office. In the eight days since Dan had resigned both men had wavered; Dan had changed his mind once, and now George was ready to give Dan an opportunity, an opportunity to help him so that he wouldn't have to change his mind too. The mayor explained to Dan the problem he had. There was a lot of opposition to Dan regaining his seat, opposition in his own district, and not just from his enemies but from people who had been behind him in the past. In light of that, it might not be prudent to reinstate him.

George explained that his sympathy was still with Dan, he wanted to be able to appoint him, but Dan had to make that possible, he had to come up with concrete evidence of support. To begin with, support from his constituents, letters, petitions, that sort of thing. But there was more involved.

Politics, George explained, made for hard choices. As a supervisor Dan understood that, didn't he? Dan, he pointed out, had opposed him when his vote would have made a crucial difference; Dan's vote, in fact, had impaired his ability to govern effectively. On the business taxes, for instance, Dan had reneged on his commitment to vote with the mayor. Then there was the Officers for Justice consent decree, just to pick an example at random. George would dearly love to resubmit that item to the Board if he could be assured that it had a sixth vote. Those were his problems, George explained, and of course Dan had a problem too, and George wanted to help.

If he appointed Dan—and, he explained, that was still what he hoped to be able to do—then that would be a *political* favor, and such a favor meant that Dan would be incurring a political debt. In order for him to appoint Dan, George continued, Dan must assure him of his support. As mayor, with an election coming up, faced with political pressures of his own, he had to be sure of Dan's support when he needed it. Dan understood that, didn't he?

All along Dan had viewed this as a personal rather than a political situation. His myopia, once he had his letter back and George's word, had prevented him from appreciating the dimensions of the mayor's problem. Now they had reached the critical juncture: how to respond to George's offer. If, for once, he saw beyond his own self-righteousness he might be saved, if he finally came to grips with the political fact that every victory had its price he might get his seat back.

Eagerly, Dan assured George that he would have evidence of Dan's support, the people in District 8 wanted him as their supervisor. The majority were still behind him, the ones the mayor had been hearing from were his enemies, they were snakes. Don't worry, Dan said, there would be proof of support. He'd get right to work on it.

Okay, George said, he'd give Dan as much time as he could, he'd tell the city attorneys to take their time, he wouldn't make a final decision for another week. Meanwhile, George said, keep it quiet what they had talked about. Dan left.

In a way, George thought, he respected the kid. He had given him a message that a seasoned political pro would have read without any problem. But the kid didn't understand politics, George could see that, and that's why he had stopped short of rubbing his dick in the dirt, telling him exactly what the score was. George leaned back in his chair and lit another cigarette. It was becoming pretty clear what he would have to do, and the thought didn't make him particularly happy.

Dan, meanwhile, went straight to Denise Apcar. "The mayor's going to reappoint me," he said. "All I have to do is show support. I just have to get letters from my supporters into his office." Denise went out and bought a thousand envelopes and a thousand stamps. All weekend they would work at sending an appeal to their friends in District 8 to write to the mayor urging Dan's reinstatement.

If Dan had understood what George had been telling him, he couldn't face it, it would mean mortgaging his honor to redeem his position. If he didn't play ball with George he'd be letting down all his friends, his old friends who believed in him and his new friends who said he owed them, who needed him. If he did play ball with George he'd be letting them down even worse. Walking out of the building Dan was so caught up in his own thoughts that he walked right by Bernard Teitelbaum of the mayor's staff without acknowledging him.

"Hey," Teitelbaum said, "Dan." The two men had always got on well.

Dan looked up slowly. "Oh, hi Bernie."

"How'd it go?" Teitelbaum jerked his head toward the mayor's office.

"Go?" Dan said. "Oh. Fine. It went fine."

Sunday, November 19

REP. RYAN SHOT

In bold black letters the Sunday paper gave the news. Members of the People's Temple had attacked and killed not only Congressman Leo Ryan but four other members of his party on an airstrip in Guyana as they were prepared to depart.

All day Sunday radio and television were carrying further fragmentary bulletins. A massacre or mass suicide was taking place in Guyana, and the people who were dying were for the most San Franciscans. Jim Jones had gone over the edge, slipped into madness, and taken his congregation, that disciplined congregation so valuable at precinct work, with him. Jim Jones, who had been Mayor Moscone's housing commissioner; Jim Jones, whose people had turned out for every liberal politician in town; Jim Jones, who the mayor, the district attorney, and Assemblyman Willie Brown had defended against Phil Tracy's accusations, was a mass murderer. Corpses were piling up in the heat of the jungle. Nobody knew how many. Hour by hour the body count increased.

Sunday evening Dan met Ray at the Hot Potato and together with

Denise and some other people they went back to the apartment Ray had rented within walking distance of Pier 39 to continue stuffing, sealing and stamping letters urging his supporters to let the mayor knew how they felt. As they worked they kept the television on for news from Jonestown. When it was announced that a large number of people were dead from having drunk cyanide-laced Kool-Aid, Dan made one of those remarks which sounds much worse when repeated than it really is, one of those flippant remarks it is so easy to make when faced with a horror of such a magnitude.

"You see that?" Dan said. "One day I'm on the front page and the next day I'm swept right off."

In just eight days Dan would be back on the front page, in type every bit as large as that which the *Chronicle* used to report on Monday that 400 STOOD IN LINE TO DIE.

Monday, November 20

Ray Sloan thought Dan should pin the mayor down behind his commitment, so Dan wrote George a brief letter in which he said: "Your stated willingness to reappoint me to my own position if it becomes legally necessary is much appreciated."

Since that was not what George had tried to tell Dan during their meeting on Saturday, and since Dan's letter would probably be released to the press, George thought it advisable to draft a reply.

"Dear Dan," the mayor wrote,

> The last thing I want to do is deprive the citizens of District Eight of their necessary representation. . . . As I told you this past Saturday in my office, however, I have received a great many communications from the residents of District Eight—some from your public opponents, others from your past supporters—which have urged me not to reappoint you. . . .

> As I informed you this past Saturday, I am going to take an additional week in which to review this situation, and to receive further communications . . . some of which may conceivably benefit you. But I must reiterate that I have not made a commitment of any kind to appoint you . . . to the position. . . .

> *Further communications . . . some of which may conceivably benefit*

you. It was like a message in code, the private meaning within a public letter. When George released the letter he told the City Hall press corps that Dan had taken the uncertainty "like a man."

The reporters immediately trooped over to Denise and asked for a reaction from Dan. She promised to get one for them. When they had departed, she called Dan at home, fuming at what she construed as George's betrayal. She read him the text of the mayor's letter; in no uncertain terms she expressed her contempt for George Moscone. She was surprised when Dan didn't seem as angry as she was, didn't seem angry at all. But then there were things Dan understood that Denise didn't know anything about.

"Jeez," Dan said. "George told me to keep it quiet, and there he goes writing a letter."

Tuesday, November 21

Regardless of what Dan was unwilling to acknowledge to Denise he understood the import of George's letter. However many letters from the district were sent to the mayor, however many signatures gathered on petitions, it didn't really matter. Support of a different kind was what mattered, political support for George. Just thinking about what it would mean to have to vote for something like the consent decree in the Officers for Justice suit made him sick, listless and devoid of the will to carry on the fight to regain his seat. The challenge which Ray Sloan had so cleverly calculated to light a fire under Dan had burned itself out in one week. Once again Dan had taken up a challenge only to come up against the need to accommodate, against the hard choices, and once again he quit. Dan took to his bed. He climbed into bed and stayed there, wishing the world would go away and leave him alone. His emotional life had become a roller coaster, the ups and the downs coming faster than ever, but always round and round on the same track. He could not withdraw his candidacy now, it was too late for that, but neither could he fight on. As far as he was concerned, it was all over.

George had more or less reached the same conclusion. On Tuesday he met with Don Horanzy, the federal housing official whose name had been suggested by Denise Apcar and who had, in addition, the backing of several influential politicians. Horanzy impressed George sufficiently for his name to move to the top of the list of candidates to replace Dan White.

Meanwhile Dan's letters of support were beginning to arrive at the mayor's office. On Monday Dan had been using a City Hall Xerox machine and his handiwork had fallen into the hands of the mayor's staff and become the subject of amusement. Dan's letters were all identical, another sign of rank amateurism. Somebody in the mayor's office leaked Dan's appeal for support to a gossip columnist for the *Chronicle* who printed a little item which ended: "The Mayor's office is braced for a deluge of 'unsolicited' letters proclaiming that White is Beautiful." Dan read and clipped the item. It seemed unfair for George to encourage him to solicit letters of support and yet to encourage the press to make fun of him for doing it. The whole way George played the game seemed to Dan to be raw, dishonorable.

On Tuesday afternoon, also, the city attorneys' office finally released its opinion which concluded that Dan's resignation had been effective as soon as Gil Boreman brought it before the Board and it had been filed; that the return of Dan's letter of resignation had no legal effect; that the seat was vacant, and that George could appoint anybody he wanted to fill it, including Dan. The opinion came as no suprise, nor was it encouraging to Dan who knew that he could not comply with what George had set as his private terms. Dan continued to mope around the house, filled with self-pity and self-loathing.

Not knowing either the true cause of Dan's loss of heart, or the real depths of his distress, Ray, Denise and Dan's other allies determined that the time had come to launch a legal fight. They had been consulting all along with a lawyer and now the idea arose to seek a temporary restraining order to prevent the mayor from appointing anybody else to the vacant seat. It was the last in a weeklong series of tactical errors; you could not be asking the mayor to do you a favor on the one hand and be fighting him in court on the other. Pugnacity was out of place, but pugnacity was the only way that Dan and Ray knew how to go after something they wanted.

Wednesday, November 22

If there had still remained even a shred of hope, the flimsiest of possibilities that George's sympathy for Dan's financial and family plight would win out over the practical political considerations, the threat of a lawsuit was the final tear.

The lawyer with whom Denise and Ray had been consulting read the city attorneys' opinion and saw a flaw in its legal reasoning. He talked with Denise about it and Denise carried his message to Dan, but Dan balked at the idea of suing. It seemed pointless to him. By this time, though, Dan had lost control of the efforts undertaken on his behalf. Acting on instructions from Denise, Dan's lawyer drafted a response that zeroed in on the zealousness of the clerk, Gil Boreman. The city attorneys, in finding that Dan's resignation was valid and could not be rescinded, had stated that "although Supervisor White addressed his letter of resignation to the Mayor, *he did cause* the letter to be delivered" to the Board.

In his response Dan's lawyer, Peter Bagatelos, argued that his client did *not* cause the resignation to go before the Board; that had been Gil Boreman's doing. On Wednesday afternoon Bagatelos met with Toomey and Lazarus and told the city attorneys that he would be going into court on Friday to seek a temporary restraining order until this legal question was resolved.

That same day, Wednesday, Congressman Leo Ryan was to be buried, his body having been flown home. The body count in Guyana had topped five hundred. More immediately frightening were the rumors in the city that Jim Jones had programmed several of his adherents in the United States to begin a series of assassinations. The police gave a certain credence to these rumors of People's Temple hit squads which were supposed to be operating under the code name of "White Knight." Security measures were implemented, among them instructions to City Hall employees to enter and leave the building only through the front and back doors where metal detectors were set up. The metal detectors weren't foolproof, but they were some help in trying to prevent a would-be assassin from carrying a gun into City Hall.

George attended Leo Ryan's funeral and something happened. As George was entering the church in a long line of public officials and dignitaries, a woman dashed out of the crowd of onlookers—like Sara Jane Moore, like Squeaky Fromme—and headed right for him. He shrank back in fright but all the woman did was grab hold of his arm and say that she wanted to attend the funeral service with him. The cops took her away but George's fright didn't subside.

When he returned to City Hall late Wednesday afternoon, Toomey and Lazarus came by to tell him that Dan White would be going to court on Friday to seek a restraining order. For a while George discussed the legal merits with them, assuring himself that they were prepared to argue the city's case, his case.

"Tomorrow's Thanksgiving," he finally said. "Why don't you do what I'm gonna do and enjoy it and forget about this until Friday." They left.

George prided himself on being a good lawyer even though it had been a long time since he had practiced. If Dan White wanted to take him to court, that was jim dandy with George. The mayor had a legalist's turn of mind and it seemed obvious to him that Dan had backed himself into a corner: how could he argue in court that he was still the supervisor from District 8 and at the same time be pushing politically to be appointed to the vacant seat? He couldn't have it both ways, but since he had chosen to try, he wouldn't have it either way. Dan had made this an adversary situation and George was feeling powerfully contumacious. He had given the kid a chance, and the kid had blown it.

Meanwhile, it was Thanksgiving eve. It was George's habit at the end of every workday to retire to the sitting room behind his formal office with a few friends, or with some members of his staff, to have a day-end drink and shoot the breeze. That little sitting room was where he unwound; it was his favorite part of his office, where he took people with whom he wanted to feel intimate. When he stepped out of the ceremonial office where he worked and into the sitting room, he also stepped out of being mayor, with all the constraints that implied, and into being Georgie Moscone. A day-end ritual had come into being. George would point at somebody—his bodyguard, Gary Wommack, or his secretary, Cyr, for instance—and say, "Pick a number." They'd guess and George would say, "Jesus, you missed again." And whoever missed would have to pour drinks. Every few times, though, George would say, "Sonofabitch, you guessed it," and pour the drinks himself.

On this Wednesday before Thanksgiving, with the state legislature in recess, Assemblyman Willie Brown was in town, and when Willie was around he usually dropped by for the day-end drink and story swap. Willie had, in fact, been stopping by every day that week; he and George had a lot to talk about—the political fallout from the People's

Temple massacre, for instance. The two men had known each other ever since they were dead-broke law students, their political fortunes had risen along parallel lines, they valued each other's advice and company. At times, in private, each would suggest to other people that he was the senior partner, but when they were together there was an equality and an intimacy born of fifteen years' mutually advantageous political maneuverings and personal understandings. Willie had never stopped practicing law, and he was by far the richer of the two men. In comparison George was a pauper who could hardly pay his bills. But Willie appreciated George's attitude; Willie was a Porsche man himself, but George got as much pleasure out of his used Alfa. George had that rarest of human capacities: he was able to enjoy whatever gifts life held without envying what others had.

Rotea Guilford was also coming by on this Wednesday afternoon. George had finally honored a promise to Guilford by making him the executive director of the Mayor's Commission on Criminal Justice. At about five o'clock the three old friends settled down in the mayor's sitting room to chew the fat and wash it down with holiday cheer.

George's jacket was off as he settled into the comfortable upholstered chair he always took, right in front of the window. Next to the chair was a low table with a telephone console and a big ashtray. Willie and Guilford sat down on the couch, putting their drinks on the coffee table.

George talked for a while about the Dan White situation. Laughingly he told them about the identical letters Dan had been soliciting. "Really bullshit," George said. He also mentioned that the firefighters' union had been by to urge Dan's reinstatement. It was a liberal union and George was counting on their backing in 1979. "I just told 'em," George said, lighting a Marlboro from his second pack of the day, "that there were times when Dan White had screwed me. How could I appoint a guy who would do those sorts of things?"

He had explained to White, George said, that it would be almost impossible to return him to his seat. White, he said, wasn't a bad kid really, he admired the sacrifice he was making in order to provide for his family. He sighed.

Guilford and Willie, both of whom had heard George express concern for the financial wellbeing of his own family, and over having so little time for his own kids, understood what he meant by that sigh. For perhaps the thousandth time George said: "One more term. First I'm gonna rub Quentin's dick in the dirt, then I'm gonna get some things done. One more term and then I'm gonna practice the law, make some money, look after my family." It was by now seven o'clock. The heavy drapes were drawn, the lamps in the sitting room were turned on, George's ashtray was filling up with butts. But George didn't want to go home yet.

Guilford said, "Hey, man, it's getting late, it's Thanksgiving tomorrow, maybe we ought to be hittin' the road."

"No, hey, wait a minute, man," George said. "Have one more." He went to the little kitchen off the study and poured another round. "You know," he said, carrying the drinks back in, "I feel really good, I feel really good about this fuckin' job." He laughed. "I mean, I was out in the limo, you know, the other day, and we passed some cop. You know what the sonofabitch did? He saluted. Howd'ya like that? He fuckin' saluted. Can you beat that?"

It made Guilford feel good to see George happy, to see him full of feeling and wanting everybody around him to feel as good as he did. Willie was happy too. If he appreciated George for any one thing above all others, above his peasant mentality about possessions, above his sense of service, above his wit and his acumen and his earthiness, it was for his schmaltzy sensitivity, because that was what made him incapable of hurting another human being.

"You know, Rotea," George said, "I have made one blatant mistake in my administration." There were tears in his eyes, he was swollen with sentiment. "I'll tell you what it is, too. Quentin wouldn't let me, Crowley wouldn't let me, it would look like they forced me into it. You know what I mean. I'm gonna correct that mistake after the next election. You're gonna be my Chief of Police, Rotea. I guarantee it."

Thanksgiving Day

Dan was up early and spent the morning puttering around the house. He read the *Chronicle.* The first six pages were devoted almost entirely to news out of Guyana, where the stench of the dead men, women and children decomposing under an equatorial sun was keeping authorities at bay. Men wearing handkerchiefs over their mouths and noses would dash in, remove one body from the tangle, and gag.

On page ten Dan came across an item of greater personal interest to him. The story—it had been planted by Harvey, although it did not say so—claimed that Mayor Moscone would probably appoint Helen

Fama to the District 8 seat. Dan clipped it out of the paper and put it on the little desk in his basement den along with other clips he had been saving. He had cut out the snide item about his using the City Hall Xerox machine and a second, by the same columnist, that quoted a Moscone aide as saying "District Eight is redneck country and George doesn't know too many rednecks, especially liberal ones." In the pile, too, was a story that said: "City Hall observers said White, a political unknown before his election, quickly emerged as a hard-line conservative with a pro-development, pro-downtown voting record, as well as antipathy to the city's large gay community." And another from the previous March under the headline: GAY RIGHTS LAW OK'D BY SUPES. Dan had saved a picture of Harvey from when he had been campaigning for his scooper ordinance, pointing at his smeared shoe and laughing. In the haphazard pile were more personal items, too. There was the letter of resignation George had returned to him and which had proved to be worthless; and his treasured clippings, yellowed with age, that documented his father's heroism, the moment of glory in an otherwise ordinary life. All that was piled on Dan's desk on Thanksgiving morning, all that and an editorial from the *Chronicle* which said: "White has only himself to blame for his troubles. If he has any gift at all for self-appraisal, he must be kicking himself."

The editorial writer, who did not sound too sympathetic, had nonetheless hit the nail right on the head. Dan's sense of his own worth was at its nadir again. But as little as he thought of himself, he, better than the newspapers, knew who was to blame. George, who had lied to him and put the squeeze on him. And Harvey, who was butting in where he didn't belong. Ever since he had overheard Harvey on the phone pressuring Jim Lazarus to find against his legitimate claim, Dan had never thought of Harvey without getting that tight, remorseless grin, the grin that was part anger, part mockery and part the hurt of betrayal. Harvey.

Denise, too, had seen the story predicting that the mayor would appoint Helen Fama, and after she read it she called Dan to press the idea of the lawsuit on him. It still seemed to Dan that lawyers had no place mixing in what was really a personal matter: George had promised him his job back, that was the crux of the thing. But Denise was insistent and finally, reluctantly, with a feeling that it didn't matter, nothing mattered, he told her to go ahead and give Bagatelos the green light. He even agreed to come down himself before the hearing the next afternoon. The Fama story had, in fact, finally dashed even Denise's hopes; her optimism by this point was just a front, behind it was the sinking recognition that it was all over. But she was going to go on fighting and she wanted Dan to fight too.

Dan was down, way down. The winter holidays, with all their gaiety and sense of renewal, were only a bitterly ironic backdrop to his despair. He was out of a job—no, two jobs. Three, really. First they had made him resign as a fireman. Then they had cheated him out of his seat. And finally he had decided to stay away from the Hot Potato until this other thing was settled. It was Thanksgiving, but what did he have to be thankful for? With nothing to do, the days were long, very long, there was an abundance of time for thinking; and thinking, to brood. And brooding, to sulk. And sulking, to fix blame.

Usually, when Danny was feeling low, Mary Ann didn't push him, but it *was* Thanksgiving and the entire family was gathering at his sister's house in South San Francisco at three o'clock and she really wanted to go. She couldn't see that it would do him any good to mope around all day, and besides, she wanted to show off little Charlie to the family.

"Oh, c'mon, Danny," she said. "Let's go. We only have to stay a little while. It'll be nice."

Reluctantly, he agreed. He was willing to go for Mary Ann, but he really didn't want to. It wasn't like him to leave the house with a couple of days' stubble, but that's what he did, he went in his old knockaround clothes and in need of a shave. But at least he went. They stayed for a couple of hours and then after the meal they went to visit his mother, who wasn't feeling well enough to come to the holiday meal. Then they drove home, put Charlie to bed, and got into bed early themselves. Or rather, Mary Ann did. She was flying out to Omaha very early Friday morning for a friend's wedding and she wanted to get some sleep.

The good cheer of George's holiday was not unmitigated either. He had been informed that the *Chronicle* city desk had received an anonymous threat to his life. A man had called to say that his brother, a member of People's Temple, had warned that the mayor should have someone with him at all times. "Just please tell the mayor to take care of himself." George called the newspaper himself to find out exactly what had been said. Ever since that woman had come out of the crowd at Leo Ryan's funeral and grabbed hold of him, he had been frightened.

He had told Willie Brown, as a matter of fact, that he was more frightened than he ever had been in his life, and he really couldn't say why. It was probably just the whole atmosphere created by this Jonestown thing, the almost palpable sense of death and destruction that hung over his city.

Friday, November 24

The invitation to the wedding of an old school friend in Omaha had arrived several weeks earlier. Mary Ann hadn't known whether or not to go; she would have liked to, but once Danny resigned and all she didn't know if it was a good idea to leave him alone like that. But Danny had encouraged her. "You should go," he said.

"Do you really think so?"

"This is . . . I know this has been hard for you, it would be good for you, you know, to get away and have a good time for a couple of days." She agreed.

So Friday morning they were up at 5:30 and Dan drove his wife to the airport. When he returned home he went back to bed for another hour, and then when the baby woke up for good Dan fed him, dressed him and dropped the kid off at the house of a friend who did daycare. From there he drove on downtown to meet with Denise and his lawyer, Bagatelos. For the rest of the morning they huddled, planning their strategy for the hearing before Judge Mayer later that afternoon.

About eleven o'clock George called Tom Toomey into his office with a new question: was there any legal impediment to his appointing a federal employee to the vacant seat? Toomey wasn't absolutely certain, but the way George described this fellow's position—without mentioning his name—the city attorney thought it would be okay. Toomey also suggested that the mayor come to the hearing on the restraining order himself, but George said he didn't think that was a good idea, just be sure to let him know what was happening.

Toomey went back to his office to consult with Lazarus and the two men were together when Dianne Feinstein called. She had recently returned from a trip to Tibet where she and her fiancé had visited with the Dalai Lama. People who talked with her at the time found her to be almost uninterested in politics; as one man put it, "spiritual in nature." The board president had come down with a bug in Tibet, and even though she had been back in town for a while she had been laid up and hadn't taken much of a role in what was going on. The one politician in the city whose advice Dan might have heeded, who might have steered him toward a sensible course, had been far, far away. But she had read the city attorney's opinion and wanted to discuss it. During the conversation Lazarus raised another point with her: Dan had told the city attorneys that as far as he was concerned he was still the supervisor for District 8; therefore, he was going to take his seat when the Board convened on Monday, November 27. Lazarus wanted to know how the board president stood on that.

Dianne told him that although she favored Dan getting the seat back—she had, in fact, written a letter to the mayor urging that course on him—she was comfortable with the city attorney's opinion. She understood that if Dan resumed his seat on his own, then any actions taken by the Board were subject to legal challenge.

Right, Lazarus agreed. If Dan insisted on being seated, the city attorneys' office would feel compelled to sue to invalidate any votes he might participate in.

Dianne assured Lazarus that she would recognize whomever the mayor appointed to the vacant seat. Under no circumstances would she recognize Dan.

It was 6:30 when the city attorneys finally trooped down to the mayor's office with the good news that Judge Mayer had turned down the request for the temporary restraining order. He had set a hearing for the following Friday, December 1, on the suit itself but meanwhile the mayor was free to act.

"Okay, that's great," George said. "I'm going to be appointing someone on Monday. You're gonna be surprised. It's not Dan White, it's a good appointment, you'll see."

George hurried home when they had left. He had to change into formal clothes because it was his birthday, his forty-ninth birthday, and there was a five-hundred-dollar-a plate fund-raising party for him that night at the Fairmont Hotel on Nob Hill. George was getting together a war chest for the 1979 election; the days when he refused to accept campaign contributions of more than a hundred dollars were behind him, that much of his populism at least was in the past. He was going to bury Quentin Kopp the way he had dispatched Barbegelata.

Dan ate dinner with the friends who had been looking after little Charlie and got home about nine. A little while later Mary Ann called from Omaha; she wanted to know how things had gone in court.

"Well, the order was denied," Dan told her. But he didn't sound too glum about it. "It's okay," he said. "We've got a hearing set for next Friday. We'll do all right."

Mary Ann picked up his tone and tried to sound cheerful herself. She told him that she loved him and would see him Sunday night.

Dan watched television until he fell asleep. On the late news it was reported that a second layer of corpses, hidden beneath the 500 bodies that had already been counted, had been discovered in Guyana. At least 780 people were dead and they were not through counting.

For Harvey, as for George, Friday was a gala night. His own political prospects were looking divine. Harvey, too, would be up for reelection in 1979. Just that week he had received assurances from Willie Brown that he would serve as honorary chairman of Harvey's campaign, and that meant the Moscone-Burton-Brown forces would finally, at long last, not be opposing him. In addition, Kayo Hallinan, who had finished second in 1977, had agreed to manage Harvey's next campaign. He was, in short, guaranteed another term. He had arrived.

All his life Harvey had loved opera, and this night he was invited to attend a performance of *Tosca* as the guest of impresario Kurt Herbert Adler. Also sitting in Adler's box was Bidú Sayào, a diva whom Harvey had seen perform the first time he had ever attended the opera, when he was a teenager. When he got home, feeling that he was in seventh heaven, he wrote a short note to an old friend in New York.

"Ah," Harvey wrote, "life is worth living."

Saturday, November 25

When Don Horanzy is wearing his eyeglasses he looks thoughtful, but when he takes them off his regular, oblong features have a slightly squashed-down appearance that makes him look like a retired middleweight. He, his wife and their four kids lived in one of the relatively expensive townhouses clustered at the foot of Geneva Towers. When

Horanzy talked about his district, and why it was neglected by City Hall, he would explain that it was "the last bastion of blue-collar America in San Francisco. It ain't sexy. It's working people."

On Saturday morning he drove out to George's comfortable home in St. Francis Wood, at the mayor's invitation. He knew that he was going to be offered the job, and he wanted it. As a supervisor, the long-time community activist told himself, he could really wail, could do all those things he'd been thinking all these years ought to get done. He was as full of high hopes as Dan had been only ten months before.

George came out to answer the door himself. Horanzy had put on a tie but George was dressed casually. Mel Wax and a couple of other people from the mayor's staff were there too. Horanzy heard Gina puttering around in the kitchen.

George outlined for him what he wanted: somebody who would represent the interests of the district, but somebody, too, who was liberalminded enough to go along with what he was trying to accomplish, somebody with a broad view who would be sympathetic to the best interests of the city—projects like the gay community center, or the Officers for Justice consent decree, just to pick a couple of issues at random.

Horanzy, who thought that George was trying to put him at his ease but nonetheless seemed a little frenetic, a little wound up, said he was the guy to fill the bill.

George had one other concern. In light of all that had led to them sitting there, discussing this, did Horanzy think he could make it on ninety-six hundred a year? Because if there was a problem with his being a federal employee he might have to give up his job. If that came to pass, though, George continued, he would appoint him to something like the Air Pollution Control Board, which carried a small stipend. It wouldn't be much, but maybe it would help. If all that could be settled, George said, the job was his.

Horanzy responded that he wanted the job, but he also wanted to talk over the financial angle with his wife one last time. She worked as a nurse, and he figured they'd be okay, but he wanted to check back with her.

"No problem," George said. "Let me know tomorrow."

Saturday evening Ray Sloan drove out to Shawnee Avenue to talk with Dan about what would be happening on Monday; word was out that somebody would be named to fill his seat. Both men had accepted defeat some days back; it had become increasingly obvious that the stuff George was having Dan do—like the petition drive tomorrow that Denise was coordinating—was just a runaround, something to keep them occupied. Dan understood some things about that that Ray didn't, but Dan wasn't talking about the choice George had given him. When he thought about it he felt humiliated, so he tried not to think about it.

Dan's mood was considerably better than it had been on Wednesday and Thursday. Looking after his son agreed with him; that afternoon he had taken Charlie out with him to the store to get some milk and baby food. Being a full-time father for a couple of days kept his mind occupied, and so had the hearing he had attended on Friday. He was pretty active again after a couple of days of malaise, and Ray could see that despite losing the fight DW was, if not exactly happy, then not at least unhappy. He seemed to have come to terms with his defeat; or maybe the mask, the persona, had dropped into place again. More than a week had passed and Ray hadn't caught another glimpse of the Dan White who had appeared that night at the Irish Embassy. Ray had pulled back emotionally himself; they were still a team but they weren't confidantes. Dan was very much the captain again.

They agreed that on Monday morning Ray would go to City Hall and keep an eye on what was going down. Dan said he would stay at home but just in case the unexpected happened, he'd be prepared to speed on down there.

Sunday, November 26

Sunday was the fourth day of the holiday weekend and the city was placid. The zoo was crowded with parents and children and there were more people out for a stroll than there were cars moving on the streets. The morning paper had put the body count in Guyana at 910, and that was the zenith, the story was beginning to peter out. By Monday afternoon it wouldn't even be the top story of the day.

About noontime Sunday, Harvey called a friend of his whose fortieth birthday it was. Harvey told him to come on over, he was going to bake him a carrot cake, but Wayne Friday, who had sampled Harvey's baked goods before, said he'd pass on the carrot cake but how about if he came by for a cup of coffee? While Friday was walking over to Harvey's new apartment Harvey called George. George assured him, as he had the other times they had talked over the weekend, that Harvey would be pleased with the person he was going to appoint. Harvey wanted to know if Helen Fama was going to get the seat, and George hinted she was, but coyly refused to say.

When Wayne Friday arrived Harvey apologized for not having bought him a birthday present. The best he could do was to offer Friday his tickets for the Forty-Niners game.

"If they were opera tickets you wouldn't offer them to me, would you?" Friday teased.

Caught out, Harvey laughed. "The next time I go to the opera, Wayne, you'll go with me. How's that?"

The way things turned out, Wayne Friday would be at the Opera House on Wednesday for Harvey's memorial service.

Sunday morning late Don Horanzy called George and told him it was all systems go. They arranged for Horanzy and his family to come to City Hall Monday morning for the announcement. There would be a press conference at 10:30 and then when the Board convened at two o'clock, he would be sworn in.

George asked his press secretary, Mel Wax, to get out telegrams to all the other candidates informing them that they had not been selected. They drew up a list but Dan's name wasn't on it. Wax didn't think anything about that one way or the other, he figured George would probably call Dan personally to let him know. But George hated to deliver bad news; he didn't call Dan White.

Later that afternoon George and Gina went to the final performance of the year at the Opera House, *La Bohème*. George's enthusiasm for opera left something to be desired; his taste ran more to jazz, melodious jazz. But San Franciscans, or at least the upper crust, its arbiters elegantiarum, fancied their town the Athens of the American West, and the Opera was the crowning jewel in the cultural diadem. There were some things the mayor had to attend, and this was one of them. When Gary Wommack was driving George and Gina home in the limo, George said: "Trust me on this one, Gary. When I'm re-elected we're not going to any of this crap anymore, you've got every weekend off."

George would be going out again Sunday evening but he wanted to take the Alfa. He set it up for Wommack to drive the limo to his own home, and then, first thing Monday morning, to meet him at a garage down in Polk Gulch and ferry him over to City Hall. Gina's station wagon was acting funny and George was going to drop it off to be repaired.

By eleven o'clock Sunday night the mayor ended up where he so often did, in the back room of Vanessi's Restaurant on Broadway, in the red leatherette booth reserved for George and the crowd that always gathered around him. It was an evening much like any other, and by the time he went home there were an impressive number of empty wine bottles on the table.

Mary Ann came up the steps at about seven and unlocked the door. Dan was standing in the living room; he had tidied up the house in anticipation of her arrival. But when she came in full of news, eager to tell him about the trip and the wedding, he didn't move forward to hug or kiss her; with everybody else he put the best possible face on things, only with his wife could he mope like a hurt little boy. Mary Ann took off her coat and started to tell him about Omaha, but he just walked out of the room, back into the bedroom, where he flopped onto the bed. The television was on. Mary Ann followed him and sat down on the edge of the bed and kept talking, but she could see he was down again, he wasn't paying any attention. She undressed and got ready for bed herself; the flight had tired her out and she had to be back at the Hot Potato first thing in the morning, but as soon as his wife got into bed, Dan got out. He told Mary Ann he was going out for a walk. Leaving the house, he headed toward Mission and Geneva streets, about a half dozen blocks away, and bought a couple of books. One was a big picture and text volume by Jill and Leon Uris called *Ireland: A Terrible Beauty*. When he returned home Mary Ann was in bed reading and it was time for Charlie's bottle. When the baby was done feeding Mary Ann went to tuck the baby in for the night. The phone rang.

Dan answered it. Quentin Kopp was on the line. He explained that he had been tied up with a big trial in Marin County and then had been down in Los Angeles for the holiday, so he was out of touch. What was happening?

Dan ran down the business about the temporary restraining order. Mary Ann, listening from the bedroom, was amazed at how normal Danny sounded, even though she knew that inside he was all eaten up.

"I'll tell you," Quentin said, "probably the worst thing I could do is say publicly I support you because if I say anything is white George would say it's black." Quentin smiled to himself at that little pun, which he hadn't intended. "What I'll do is, if somebody else is presented to the Board tomorrow to take the oath, I'll make a motion not to seat him until your lawsuit is settled."

"Jeez, Quentin, that sounds good," Dan said.

The conversation couldn't have lasted more than five minutes, and it wasn't more than fifteen minutes later that the phone rang again. This time the voice was female.

"I'd like to speak to Dan White, please," she said.

"This is he."

"This is Barbara Taylor, of CBS News," she said. "I wonder if you've heard from the mayor regarding the appointment tomorrow?"

"No," Dan said warily.

Taylor had already interviewed Mel Wax. Wax had refused to tell her who was getting the job, but had assured her it wouldn't be Dan White. He told her she could use the information, but not to attribute it to him by name.

"Well, it's my . . . I've been informed by a source in the mayor's office that you're not going to be reappointed and I'd like to do an interview with you about that."

"I don't know anything about that," Dan said. A fucking reporter; hadn't George promised to let him know when he made a decision? And here he gets the word from a fucking reporter. "I don't have any comment."

"Well," Taylor persisted, "do you know if you are getting the seat back? Have you been told anything about it by the mayor?"

"I told you, I don't have anything to say," Dan answered. Barbara Taylor heard him replace the telephone in its cradle and the line went dead.

"Who was that?" Mary Ann called out.

"Nobody, just a reporter," Dan said.

About eleven o'clock Denise showed up at the house to report on the petition drive. She had called a few times during the day to tell him how well it was going. As soon as she walked in Dan told her about the call from Barbara Taylor, and what she had said. Denise said, bitterly, that that's about what you'd expect from George Moscone. Then she picked up a few old campaign posters for the rally that was planned for Monday morning. She had organized a couple of carloads of people to be out in front of City Hall when the mayor showed up, to show support for Dan when she put the petitions into Moscone's hands.

"Guess how many signatures we got?" Denise said.

"Jeez, I don't know," Dan said.

"A thousand! In one day. Now let's see Moscone say there's no support for you in the district."

"A thousand, huh? Mary Ann, did you hear that? They got a thousand signatures for me just today."

Denise left and Dan went back into the bedroom where Mary Ann was still reading.

"Well," she said. "Are you going down there with them in the morning?"

"No, I'm just gonna lie low around here. Denise'll call me and tell me how it's going and Ray's gonna monitor the mayor's press conference."

"That sounds good. I'm going to turn out the light. Are you coming to bed?"

"No," Dan said. "I haven't been sleeping real good. I'd just keep you up. You know, I'll just throw a sleeping bag down or something. I'll be okay."

Dan went back out to the living room. Alone, and faced with the certainty that it really was all over, that this was it, he had been beaten and humiliated, had been lied to by George and stabbed in the back by Harvey, he paced restlessly. He could not bear to join Mary Ann in bed; to take such comfort as she had to offer, when he felt so worthless, so much as if he had let her down, let little Charlie down, let everybody down, was not something he could do. He could rouse his spirits when he had to—on Friday for the court hearing, on Saturday when Ray had come by, tonight for Quentin Kopp and Denise—but from his wife he could not accept succor. His mind was spinning, he knew he wouldn't be able to sleep. He picked up the book he had bought and began to read. After a while he came across a passage about the Easter uprising in 1916:

> The leaders were given a quick secret court-martial and remanded to Kilmainham for execution. Beginning Wednesday, May 3, and continuing through Friday, May 13, they were shot at a rate of one to four a day in Stonebreaker's Yard. . . . They met their end without regret, each making a last outcry of defiance, gently or angered. . . . By these sixteen executions the British had accom-

plished what the rebellion itself had failed to do, and that was to arouse a lethargic Irish people into a rage that would ultimately lead to nationhood.

14
Insurrection

Monday, November 27, 1978

George Moscone's last day on earth was about to begin with a promise he very probably could not have kept.

Babe Zanca came out of his garage, wearing his white smock, to greet George. For a moment they stood discussing the troublesome station wagon. Gary Wommack was already there, waiting in the dark-blue limo, and George gave him the high sign. Babe was assuring George he would have the wagon ready for Gina that evening. It never entered his mind to mention the money George still owed from the last time the car had been repaired. Hell, a lot of people owed Babe money, and he knew that sooner or later George would make it good. Besides, Babe was feeling solicitous because he knew that George's cousin Connie would be buried in just a few hours.

"What in hell you doing here anyway?" Babe said. "Why aren't you up in Guerneville?"

"No, Babe," George said. "Gina and Lee are up there."

The two men walked slowly outside where the tule fog still lingered, continuing their small talk. George could never return to the corner of Broadway and Polk without feeling sentimental. It had been thirty-five years since he had started out there, playing basketball—playground ball, two bits a game, winners out—just across Broadway, and hanging out at Al Lapeyri's joint. Lapeyri's was now just a memory; in its place was Lord Jim's, a singles bar with imitation Tiffany lamps and ferns in the window. A far cry from the old place where the jocks, bookies, horseplayers, newshawks, butchers and bakers of Polk Gulch had lined the long bar and spit into the trough that Lapeyri hosed out on Saturday mornings, way back before the first tequila sunrise had ever been poured. Friday nights George, resplendent in white bucks and sharply creased khakis, had played hearts with the other young blades. Maybe he remembered the night he had borrowed the brand-new Chevy George Pompei's parents had entrusted to their son with the stipulation that nobody else be allowed to drive it. But the young George Moscone, his swan neck cocked and his persuasive powers oiled by the prospect of how his girl would show her appreciation, had somehow fast-talked Pompei into lending him the car. "I swear by everything I'll have it back before midnight," George had promised his reluctant pal. Naturally it was past one when George finally showed up. "Where the hell you been?" Pompei demanded. "My old man'll kill me."

"Don't say anything," George had implored, "but you're covered by insurance, aren't you?" Ten thousand foggy mornings ago.

Babe's garage had been there then and it was still there now but it appeared it might not be around much longer. The landlord was about to cancel the lease and Babe was in danger of losing the business which was the work of a lifetime. As Babe laid it all out, George seemed to fix his whole attention on Babe, who for the moment felt he was the most important person in the world to George Moscone.

George put his arm around Babe's shoulder. "Now listen, Babe, I was born and raised right here and you've been here all the time. We go back, Babe, and the people here need you and we're not gonna let you be thrown out. Trust me on this one, Babe."

"Well, Mayor," Babe said, somewhat abashed, "I don't know. It don't look too good . . ."

"For chrissake, Babe, how many times I gotta tell you not to call me Mayor? We're pals, so you don't have to worry. We'll get this lease business straightened out, I'll get back to you." And with that George took his leave and joined Gary Wommack in the limo and began the drive to City Hall, although they had to turn around and go back when George remembered some paperwork he had left in the station wagon.

If concerning himself with such trivia as Babe's predicament wasn't necessarily using the old noodle, as George himself would have put it, it was nonetheless the essence of his style. His self-indulgence was what usually got him in trouble. George could imagine what somebody like Quentin Kopp would have to say about his promise to Babe: bald-faced political lie, cynical offer made without regard to the public good and in the full knowledge it couldn't be kept; private leases were not within the mayor's purview. Typical George Moscone. And pretty much the same way he had handled Dan White.

George's thoughts turned toward the things he had to do this morning. There were courtesy calls to be made to the other supervisors informing them of his decision to appoint Horanzy, and his remarks for the press conference to be prepared. His promise to Dan had long since been superseded by other considerations.

Back and forth, back and forth, from one end of his basement den to the other, each time Dan paced the length of the room he began at his schoolboy's desk strewn with news clippings and documents detailing his public humiliations and then turned to retrace his steps by the closet where he still kept his service revolver and a box of ammunition on the top shelf. His thoughts traced a groove as narrow and circumscribed as his feet; nearly every object in the room was associated with a part of his life and a welter of memory and emotion. In front of the bookshelves in the process of being assembled was a syncopated windup swing for little Charlie. Mary Ann had dropped Charlie off at the Martinez's before eight, and from there she was going to see their accountant and then go down to open the Hot Potato. On the coffee table was his prized chess set and beside the table on the floor were crates of books he had been accumulating all his life. Other books were haphazardly piled on the couch next to his sleeping bag. He had not slept.

Mary Ann had overslept; she had rushed out leaving the bed upstairs unmade. Rushing to slice potatoes, rushing to get his son to the babysitter. Shame and pity engulfed him. Why were they doing this to him? He had been honest, the people were with him, a thousand signatures. George had promised. Why? He paced from the closet, empty save for the gun on the shelf, back toward the clippings, his long arms hanging. There on the desk was a picture of Harvey, stepping in dogshit. Why was Harvey trying to cheat him out of his job? There was the letter George had returned to him when he had promised. *Promised.*

Among all the news clippings he had saved, and which stared him in the face like a collage of his every failure and humiliation, was not one item that celebrated the triumphs he had known. Not the one that said he had been chosen most valuable defensive player the year he and Falzon had led the police all-stars to the state championship; not a word about his being elected and sworn in; not even the story of his having saved the mother and child from the fire in Geneva Towers, the one that said he, too, was a hero. Only his father's heroism was represented in Dan's private compilation of the public record: Charlie carrying the suicidal minister's son off the Tower, Charlie being presented the medal by Mayor Christopher, Charlie's obituary. His dad was dead, Charlie, who was more of a man than he ever could be. In his consideration of his father, Charlie White still looked as big to him as he had when Dan was sixteen years old and was nothing but trouble to everyone, screwing around in school, not helping enough around the house. His father had done everything right, yet in the end had been left with nothing but a pauper's pension. The rules and regulations had stripped his father's pride by making him choose between humiliation or failure in his duty to his family. The cancer had been God's will, you could not hold the Almighty to blame. But hadn't George Moscone left Dan with the same agonizing choice, humiliation or failure?

The rules and regulations had been used against him, too, cunningly and dishonestly, right from the beginning when they made him quit his fireman's job and put him and his family in a financial bind. The letter of resignation was right there on the desk, George had given it back. But that had counted for nothing in the end. Dan had nothing, they had done it to him, stripped him of everything. He ached with loss, the miasma of his self-pity was bottomless, he was sinking and sinking and his helplessness was almost a comfort. No fireman, no supervisor, no money, no peace of mind, no respect paid to the kind of honest, hardworking man he was, nothing. Back and forth he paced. All his life he had been independent, he had always gambled on himself and on the future, he had never been one of the herd, he had stood up for what was right, he was still standing up for what was right only now he had nothing. He was torn piecemeal by his wounded vanity, he felt as if he could never go back to how things had been. He had been honest and independent and it had brought him to this pass, this nauseating, dizzying, perverse sense of freedom. There was nothing left to lose, they had seen to that. It was not God's will, it was George's. And Harvey's, working against him behind his back, a two-faced faggot snivel. They had *cheated* him out of what was rightfully his, they had killed his good name and his self-esteem. There was nothing more he could lose.

Back and forth, back and forth. From Big Charlie's heroism to little Charlie's swing; from the gun in the closet to the lies and deceptions of George and Harvey. He knew who was to blame. He could see no path to redemption, no way of saving himself, his life was over. Ruined. Dan's thoughts came right up to the edge of an abyss that made his head ache. The phone rang.

He heard the sound from far away as if he were dreaming it, but its summons wrenched him back from the edge. He picked it up. It was Denise, Denise was angry. The mayor, arriving at City Hall in his limo, she told him, had managed to avoid her and Dan's other supporters; they hadn't been able to present him with the petitions. As Dan listened to her he stared absently at the big map of Ireland propped against the wall near the telephone. "He ditched us," Denise said furiously.

Dan jerked himself to a kind of psychic attention, he willed himself to sound normal. Okay, he told Denise, let him know what was happening. He hung up and went back to his pacing and his inescapable reasoning. He was still wearing his bathrobe, he had not shaved since his court date on Friday. He felt worthless, without hope, devoid of the will to act. He wanted to cry. Back and forth from Big Charlie past little Charlie's swing to the gun in the closet. He was truly a lost soul.

Again Denise called, this time to report that not only wouldn't the mayor personally accept the petitions, she had seen Harvey Milk coming out of Moscone's back office door. Harvey had been smiling and she had seen George's hand squeezing his shoulder. For the second time Dan hung up the phone. Harvey was trying to hurt him, hurt him and hurt his family. He had always been honest with Harvey. How could he be so evil? Harvey.

His feeling of humiliation, of degradation, hovered dangerously close to that abyss again, to a moment of pure will. It was what Ed Fortner had seen in the long nights together in the prowl car, that Dan's independence knew, at bottom, no restraints; that he could reason his way to the necessity of any act, and reasoning, feel compelled by duty to do what he must. If Dan's self-pity had been almost comforting because it made him helpless, the rage he now felt, the solid bottom of his quicksand helplessness, was hard and certain. It was all over. *This was it.* He climbed the stairs and went to the bathroom, where he showered and shaved. He dressed in his best suit, a three-piece tan herringbone with light-blue pinstripes; another three-piece occasion. He pulled on his good shoes, lowrise brown boots with buckles and square toes. *This was it.* There was a roaring in his ears. Men had done this to him, he knew who they were and where to find them and what he had to do.

Dan dialed his old office at City Hall and when Robin Wonder answered he told her that he wanted Denise to pick him up at home. A few minutes later Denise returned his call. When she hung up she was excited.

"Dan's coming down, I'm going out there to pick him up," she told Robin. "He wants to give George and Harvey a piece of his mind."

For Harvey, as he rode the bus to City Hall, it was a good morning to be alive. Love, money, work—all the things that really counted— were going better than they had in a while. He was getting over Jack Lira's suicide, thanks in part to Doug Franks; he had arranged a loan to dam temporarily the flood of red ink that was threatening to engulf him, and he was delighted that Dan White would be gone from City Hall for good.

Lira's suicide had changed Harvey for the better, that and the smashing defeat of the Briggs amendment. Some nonsense seemed to be purged from his system; he was less frenetic. Summer and fall of 1978 had been the most grueling, trying time of Harvey's forty-eight years and he had emerged from it a *mensch.*

Money was still a problem but then it always would be for him. He had given up the leased Volvo, but he didn't mind riding the bus. The State Board of Equalization—how long it seemed since he had battled them over a hundred dollars, and winning, began to think about running for office—was having the last laugh; they had garnished his bank account for sales taxes due. His credit card account, woefully overdrawn, had also been closed, and his bank was hounding him for a past due business loan. But this morning his friend and landlord Carl Carlson was going to lend him three thousand dollars which would keep his creditors at bay for a while and provide him with a little extra spending cash. The supervisor needed a new pair of shoes.

Air brakes squealing, the bus arrived at Harvey's stop and he hoisted up his loose-jointed frame and walked jauntily toward the great dome and the elaborately carved and corniced building which was his stage. It promised to be a good day at work. Dan White's resignation couldn't have come at a better time. George had been encouraging him to believe that Helen Fama would get the nod and Harvey had already written her a note of congratulations. The note was in the pocket of his threadbare gray Palm Beach suit. His clothes were dowdy hand-me-downs; the only really luxurious item was his satiny undershorts, and that was his own business.

Harvey walked past the little brigade of pro-Dan White pickets and into City Hall. A short time later he popped in to see George and get further assurances that Dan was out. But George, knowing Harvey to be an incorrigible yammerer who usually spent a part of each morning in the City Hall press room, was careful not to tell him who would be appointed. After that, Harvey descended the broad marble steps beneath the rotunda and headed across the plaza to buy a sweet roll for breakfast. The stumpy, twisted sycamore trees lined the reflecting pool like a picket line of lepers. And then, as if to prove God was in his heaven and life was nothing less than a succession of marvelous coincidences, he bumped into Doug Franks, who worked nearby. The two of them ate breakfast together and Harvey returned to his office.

As she had done on so many mornings during the previous year, Gale Kaufman, Quentin Kopp's aide, went into Harvey's office to join him for an early-morning coffee break. Harvey had opened her eyes in certain ways. There had been the time, for instance, that they were walking together after having heard Gene Washington, the ex-Forty-Niner, make a fund-raising pitch for the art museum.

"Jesus Christ," Gale had said, "that guy is gorgeous."

"Isn't he something?" Harvey agreed with a wicked grin. "Isn't he built?"

It had surprised Gale that Harvey thought so too. She had never talked with a man about what a dreamboat another guy was, and somehow it made homosexuality seem so surprisingly *normal.*

"I'll tell you what," Harvey had said, guessing what Gale was thinking. "I'll bet you ten to one I get him before you do." And he had laughed that nasal, delighted laugh of his.

As Gale walked in, Harvey was on the phone, but he held up a long bony finger indicating it would be just a minute. Gale sat down, studying Harvey. It seemed to her that for the first time Harvey believed he was entirely legitimate.

"So, Harvey, what's going on?"

Pleased as punch, Harvey said, "George told me who he's putting in Dan's seat." The *s*'s at the end of his sentence whistled.

"Tell me who," Gale wheedled.

"No, no, I can't. George made me promise."

"Oh c'mon, Harvey, it's only me, who am I going to tell?"

"I can't, I can't. But it's a good person, it'll work out fine."

"Did you see 'the community' out demonstrating for Dan this morning?" Gale asked him.

"All four of them?" Harvey shot back and they both cracked up. Leave it to Harvey to be irreverent. For a politician his unconscious was perilously close to the surface. Even now, with Dan down and beaten, Harvey had to be cutting. "All four of 'em?" he repeated. He was in *such* a good mood. Carl Carlson's three-thousand-dollar bank check had joined the letter to Helen Fama in Harvey's jacket pocket. He had become solvent and won an important political victory on the same day. Dan was out and the gay community center was in. Gale stood up to return to her office and Harvey followed her into the dim, cool corridor.

"Are you leaving?" Gale asked. It was only an hour until George would name the new supervisor from District 8.

"You've got to be kidding," Harvey said, with a theatrical flourish and a certain rotundity in the way he savored a vowel now and then. "I wouldn't miss today for anything."

The gun, a lethal piece of oiled metal, had five chambers. Dan made sure they were all loaded before he slipped it into the soft leather holster that clipped onto the back of his belt and was hidden by his suit jacket. His handkerchief was already in his pocket. He unfolded it and took down the unopened box of Remington .38-caliber cartridges. The hollow-point shells expanded upon impact. They were snug in their styrofoam slots and there was no way to just shake loose the number he wanted, so he pulled ten extra rounds free. Ten extra rounds, just enough to reload twice. Enough bullets. He wrapped them in his hanky so that they wouldn't rattle around and put them in his pants pocket. He could hear Denise honking her horn from the driveway and as he turned to leave he saw the book he had been reading, *Ireland: A Terrible Beauty.* He tore the front jacket of the book loose, as if he could carry the historical context in which he must act with him, and was folding it in quarters as he walked through the garage, past the heavy punching bag, and out to join Denise in the car. His soul had suffered something in the nature of an insurrection. *This is it.*

As Denise drove, Dan rubbed his palms together. Denise chattered angrily about what had been going on but Dan felt far away and all alone, adrift in his awful freedom. Denise could see he was really ready for action, really ready to lay it on George and Harvey, because he was wearing the suit he wore on special occasions. Dan stared straight ahead, not meeting her eye, squinting. She didn't know, there was no way she could know. Little Charlie, his son, was at the babysitter's and Mary Ann was slicing potatoes. His wife. Denise saw there were tears in his eyes. Dan said, "I'm a man and I can take it. I just want George to tell me face to face. I want to see his face. I want to go tell Harvey, I went out on a limb for him and why is he doing this to me?" Then he lapsed into silence. Ruined his life and ruined his city, killed everything good. He was in the grip of a self-righteous certainty. He saw his moral duty. Its consequences were beyond him.

As they approached City Hall he asked Denise for her key to the supervisors' offices so he could go see Harvey. She gave it to him and when he asked if he could borrow the car later, which he often had done before, she said that would be okay too. Then he leaned forward, ignoring Denise, and rubbed his palms together.

Round and round they paraded through the high-ceilinged anteroom, chanting: "We want to see the mayor, we want to see the mayor, we want to see the mayor."

Fat chance. Gary Wommack and George's other people couldn't see what there was to be gained from letting these Dan White diehards see George. What worried Wommack, who had seen enough real trouble in his time to know that these people weren't going to get out of hand, was that Dan himself might show up and galvanize them. Then there might be the kind of scene it was his job to prevent. So he got on the horn and called down to Dick Weinand, the policeman assigned to the front door of City Hall, and told Weinand to let him know immediately if Dan White showed up. Weinand said he'd keep an eye out. Meanwhile the demonstrators continued to march and chant. One of them was pushing her baby in a stroller.

It was Cyr Copertini who finally got rid of them by signing a receipt for their petitions and assuring them that the mayor would see them. Cyr was responsible for deciding who and what got the attention of the mayor. She was competent, discreet and most of all, loyal. Cyr handed the petitions over to an assistant who put them in the same cardboard box with all the other Dan White correspondence, pro and con.

That was at around ten and George was at his desk, his wonderful desk. The jacket of his grey plaid wool suit, which was well made but well worn, hung neatly on a coatrack. In his pants pocket were a nickel and a dime and in his bank accounts $3,955. That was all the money George had in the world. Maybe he should have practiced the law.

From time to time, as George called the people who had to be told about Horanzy and simultaneously worked over his remarks for the press conference, he tilted back in his chair and looked out over the city he loved, his city. He knew every alley and every precinct of it and noplace and nobody scared him. Take the night he had grabbed Corey Busch and taken him over to some bar on a side street in the Castro that an old pal of his had run when the Castro was all Irishmen and Swedes. They had walked in after midnight and saw right off the clientele had changed. They were the only two men in the joint. Two downtown dudes in suits and the sign above the pool table says FOR WOMEN ONLY. This husky dyke saunters over to them at the bar and says, "You know, you look just like our mayor." George was tickled, she must have thought he was a wayward appliance salesman from Dubuque in town for a convention.

"I am," he says, giving her that toothy grin, which looked slightly lopsided because the left eye closed into a slit but the right eye stayed wide open.

"Well what the hell are you doin' here, then?"

"Having a drink," George said, lifting his glass. "Can we buy you one?"

"Well, I'll be damned," she said, and stuck out her hand. "George Moscone, glad to meetcha. My name's George too."

George's reverie was interrupted when Willie Brown stopped by for a few minutes just after ten o'clock. He wanted to invite George to a party that Wilkes Bashford, the most expensive clothier in town, was throwing on Saturday. The silk tie George was wearing was from Wilkes Bashford; a tie was about the only thing he could afford there. Willie and George made a date to go Christmas shopping together for their families—George loved Christmas shopping, he invariably hummed "Jingle Bells"—and then Willie left. Ever since that business with Sam Conti in North Beach the innuendos and accusations had been unshakable. Somehow it all got stirred up together in the minds of cops and politicians and reporters: George and Willie and Charlie Gain and whores and encounter parlors. But what could you do?

George was accustomed to living with the hatred and the vilification, he had lived with it for years. By becoming mayor of his hometown he had very probably reached his limit. One more term and then maybe never again. Ambition wasn't dead in him, not by a long shot, but it wasn't a spur in his flank either, as it once had been. There was a time when he had glowed, but as he himself put it, "That was when I was a young man and had the good kidneys."

He had seen to it that political power in his town was more equitably distributed than ever before, and what did he get for it? He got a lot of bitter bastards muttering that he was turning San Francisco over to *them*. But *he* was winning; in an hour he would have his sixth vote on the Board. Fuck 'em, they hadn't seen nothing yet. He hunched over his remarks and lit another cigarette.

When his new press secretary, Mel Wax, came in to pick up what George had written and get it to the typist, George jumped up and began to pace. Horanzy seemed like a sensible guy, he said, and maybe now at last he could begin to *govern*. Wax could see that George felt terrific, absolutely terrific.

At almost the same moment that George and Willie Brown were making their plans to go Christmas shopping, plans of a different nature were under discussion by two of Dan's unintentional tormentors—the clerk Gil Boreman and the city attorney Jim Lazarus, who were only doing their jobs—and by the one person at City Hall Dan had always been able to turn to for comfort, Dianne Feinstein.

Back from Tibet, and recuperated from her illness, Dianne had asked Lazarus and Boreman to convene so they could map out their strategy if Dan should follow through on his threat—his stated intention, Dianne called it—to show up at the Board meeting that afternoon and insist on taking his seat. His *former* seat.

The weapons at their disposal to prevent this were the parliamentary procedures embodied in Robert's Rules of Order plus the rulings of both the city attorney and Judge Mayer in denying the request for the temporary restraining order.

The Board President was wearing a white silk blouse with her trademark bow at the neck, which showed off to advantage her stunning violet-blue eyes. She was concerned, her deepest respect went to the process. She agreed with Gil Boreman when he said that he should not, *would* not, include Dan's name when the roll was called. If Dan insisted on casting a vote she would find him out of order. The logic of it was clear: if his name had not been recorded on the roll call, then he wasn't even *there*. And if he wasn't present, speaking in purely parliamentary terms, then he couldn't very well vote, could he, now?

They all three agreed that that was the proper way to handle the situation, but Boreman was still worried. "He's really been acting very irrationally, talking about taking a seat that isn't even his, physically I mean."

"What we want to avoid at all costs is a physical confrontation," Lazarus agreed. "Does the Board have somebody, like a cop, who could remove him if it came to that?"

"Well, there's the sergeant-at-arms." They all laughed at this drollery. The sergeant-at-arms was a doddering supernumerary.

With a certain mirth but earnest concern, Dianne said, "This has the potential to turn into quite a soap opera."

Dick Weinand was on his coffee break and so didn't see Denise drop Dan off in front of the Polk Street door of City Hall just a few minutes before eleven. Denise started around the block toward the McAllister Street well where she had a reserved spot, but when she noticed that her gas tank was nearly empty she turned instead toward a gas station to fill it up so Dan wouldn't have to bother when he borrowed the car.

Dan meanwhile had started up the wide, shallow concrete steps but as he pulled open the door and stepped inside he remembered the metal detector. He couldn't take the gun through the metal detector. Dan didn't recognize the man on duty, so he couldn't be sure there wouldn't be a hassle if he just bypassed it the way supervisors usually did. He turned and went back outside and walked around the corner toward the McAllister Street well. Denise had a key to the side door; maybe he could catch her before she went in. The fog had retreated and was hanging above the telecommunications tower on Twin Peaks but the sun was shining only intermittently.

When Dan went down the ramp toward the well, Denise's car wasn't there and the side door was locked, as always. He paced nervously, wondering what had become of Denise, and after some hesitation, stepped through the open window of a testing laboratory in the basement. An engineer working in the next room heard the noise when Dan jumped to the floor, and looking up, saw a man hurrying past; he hailed him and demanded to know who he was but when Dan identified himself and stammered an explanation, the engineer went back to his work. Dan continued through the basement and found his way up a back staircase that let him out in a corridor near the mayor's office. He was hesitating again outside the double oak doors—he could expect to find Gary Wommack at his desk in the big anteroom on the other side—when a young clerk came out of one of the side doors south of the anteroom. Dan asked her if he could go in that way, and recognizing him, she held the door open until he was inside. He was standing in a narrow, carpeted hallway beyond Gary Wommack's desk. Only Cyr was now between him and George.

The sun outside her window was hidden behind some clouds, making it gloomy in her office, and Cyr was at first aware only of a sudden brightness at the periphery of her vision. She looked up and saw Dan White, looking very nice in a light-colored suit with his hair dry and loose, as if he had just washed it. Uh-oh, she thought, this isn't going to be pleasant.

"Hi, Cyr," Dan said, giving her his best Irish grin, the charmer that never failed with middle-aged daughters of St. James parish. "Can I see the mayor?"

In her usual pleasant, straightforward manner Cyr said, "He has someone in with him, Dan. But let me go check." Not a lie, not really, it was her job to shield the mayor.

"Sure," Dan said. Cyr got up from behind her desk and went through the door to the mayor's formal office, taking care to shut the door behind her. George lifted his dark eyebrows in a silent question. Cyr came toward his desk. "Dan White's here to see you," she told him.

"Shit. How come? How come he's doing this? Well, give me a minute to think about what to do."

George tilted back in his chair and stared into space. Cyr sat down to wait while he made up his mind. Finally George said, "Well, I'd rather not, but okay, just gimme another minute or two. I'll buzz."

"Do you want somebody with you?" Cyr asked. It was the usual procedure.

"No, no, I'll do it myself."

"Are you certain? I could get Mel."

"No," George said.

Thinking that her boss was such a kind man to understand how humiliating it would be for Dan to have a witness to the painful scene to be played out, Cyr went back to her desk and told Dan it would be a few minutes yet.

"That's okay," Dan said. "Well, how are things going, Cyr?" She was uncomfortable and could see that he was too. Under the best of circumstances Dan wasn't exactly a bundle of laughs and so, with her instinctive politeness, Cyr cast around for something to say, to ease the

tension. Her eye fell on the first edition of the afternoon *Examiner.*
Somebody had already scanned it, pulling the sections loose. JAPANESE
DUMP PREMIER, that was the headline, the first in a week about anything other than all those poor, dead people, all that horror of the jungle
sun on bloating corpses. No, Cyr thought, the Japanese premier just
won't do, it's not the moment for foreign affairs. Then, on the front page
of the second section, she saw the picture of Caroline Kennedy at her
twenty-first birthday party.

"Oh, I'm fine," Cyr said. "Would you like to see the paper?"

"No, no thanks," Dan said.

"Well, you're probably right, there's nothing in it anyway unless
you want to read about Caroline Kennedy turning twenty-one."

"Twenty-one," Dan said. "No kidding. It was that long ago? I
guess what's even more amazing is that makes John-John eighteen."
There was an awkward silence. Dan asked if he could have a glass of
water. Glad to have something that would take her away, Cyr went to
fetch the water.

While she was gone, Bernard Teitelbaum—"Horanzy? I've never
heard of him," Teitelbaum had said thirteen days earlier—came in to
use Cyr's phone. Horanzy and his family were waiting in his office for
the press conference to begin.

"Hey, Dan," he said.

"Hey Bernie, how's the backhand?"

"Shitty as usual," Teitelbaum said. They laughed.

Cyr returned with the water and a moment later the mayor
buzzed. Cyr said, "Go ahead, Dan, you can go in now." Dan put the
water tumbler down on her desk. "Good girl, Cyr," he said, and went
through the door. Relieved, she went back to work. She'd keep an eye
on the clock and if it seemed to be dragging on too long she'd ring the
mayor and ask him if he'd had enough.

"How ya doin'?" Dan said to the mayor, walking toward his desk.
His long arms reached almost to his knees.

"Sit down, Dan," George said, nodding toward a chair.

Only this man could save Dan now. He had *promised,* maybe it
was not too late. "What I came for was, I want to know if you're gonna
reappoint me." His voice was rising, he was looking George in the eye.

George leaned forward and rested his elbows on the smooth walnut. "No, I'm not going to appoint you."

"Why?" Dan said. He said it loud, high-pitched. The last signature
had just been put on his death warrant. A flush of shame and dread rose

into Dan's cheeks and his flesh felt stretched tight over his skin, as if his skull were going to burst through. No redemption.

George reached for a cigarette. This was awful. He lit it, dragging greedily. "Well, you know how it is, Dan. I've had a lot of people in from your district saying they didn't want you . . ."

"That's a lie," Dan shouted, his voice rising. "Didn't you see the petitions? A thousand signatures in *one* day. I mean, those are the same people who brought false charges against me, you know that, you're in politics, you know what it's like. Those people, they're the same ones that are doggin' me ever since I've been elected. I've been a good supervisor, *you* know that, I'm honest, I work hard. Those people, they're snakes, they tried to hurt me and hurt my family with their lies . . ."

George could see the kid was in awful shape, puffy-faced and vacant eyed, like he hadn't slept and was holding back tears.

"Weren't you even gonna tell me?" Dan shouted. *Lies, lies, lies,* that's all he heard. He wanted an honest answer. "Why? Why aren't you gonna reappoint me?"

George had heard him out, but enough was enough. There was no point to prolonging this. "It's just a political decision, Dan, like we talked about, and that's that. There's nothing more I can say."

With the hard, hurtful talk blessedly at an end George felt a surge of almost paternal sympathy with the distraught young man facing him. God knows, he understood what it was like to be worried about having enough money for your family. He came around from behind his desk —Dan was still on his feet—and George put his arm around Dan's shoulders. He *touched* him, touched a man who could not even bear to have his wife touch him. Dan could smell him. The casual intimacy, the gesture of comfort, coming from the man who had done *this* to him, was a violation of everything sacred, a profanity. Dan shrank from it.

"C'mon," George said encouragingly, "let's go sit down in back and we'll talk it over. I'll pour us a drink." A drink, what you offered a distraught man. George never drank whiskey during the day, the legacy of an alcoholic father. He began to lead Dan toward the sitting room behind the ceremonial office. "You go back in and sit down, I'll be there in a sec," George said. He stuck his head out into Cyr's office. His deputy Rudy Nothenberg was waiting there to see him and looked up expectantly. George winked, as if to say he'd just be another minute. "Hold my calls," he told Cyr.

Dan sank onto the low couch. The ceremonial office had been airy and light. But the back room was different, heavy drapes and a thick carpet—close, intimate, sensual. The world closed in upon him. George was taking two glasses and a bottle of White Horse down from a shelf in the bathroom where the liquor was kept. *Why's he giving me a drink?* Dan wondered, *I'm not even a drinker.*

George carried the two drinks into the room and handed one to Dan, who put it down on the coffee table without taking a sip. George sank into the big chair under the window, leaned forward, and put his own drink on the same table. He lit another cigarette and inhaled. He turned on that patented Moscone empathy, so sincere and so habitual. "What're you gonna do now, have you thought about it? You thinking about being a fireman again?" The room was narrow, they were not far apart, their knees might have brushed.

Phony, it's so phony. He's the one hurting me and my family, he's the one killing me. Dan jumped up and began to pace. Back and forth, back and forth, Big Charlie, little Charlie, the gun . . .

" . . . your family now?" George was saying. "Maybe we can help out."

Like a voice screaming in his head: *Liar! Liar! Liar! That was it!*

Seeing the stubby barrel of the gun swinging toward him, George began to rise out of the chair and lifted his elbow in an instinctive gesture of self-protection. Dan stepped up close and squeezed the trigger. The hollowpoint slug tore into George's chest and he began to topple forward toward the floor next to the coffee table. Deliberately, Dan moved closer, squeezing the trigger again, the second slug ripping a hole in the back of George's shoulder. Blood began to soak his white shirt. Dan stalked him; the rage released by his act of vengeance made him very clear: way back in his mind the consequences for himself and his family may have flickered like the dimmest of candles. George hit the floor heavily, making the wall groan. Methodically, Dan pursued the fallen body. He set himself carefully, straddling George with one foot planted on either side of his blood-soaked back, leaned down very close, put the barrel of his gun almost up against George's ear so there could be no question, and pumped two more expanding shells into George's living brain. Two droplets of blood, forced out of the cavity in George's head by the expanding gas pressure, spattered against the coffee table beside the untouched drinks. The third and fourth shots had severed the brain stem. There was no need for him to use the fifth cartridge. Dan knew that George was dead.

Promised.

Dan came out of his crouch and backed off from the body. He could see George's electric-blue socks and above them the pale flesh of his ankles. He turned to leave. The lit cigarette was still clutched between George Moscone's fingers, slowly burning a hole in his Wilkes Bashford silk tie.

He was running, his footsteps echoing beneath the rotunda. On the far side of City Hall, Dan put the key he had borrowed from Denise into the lock of room 237, the back entrance to the supervisors' offices. Dick Pabich was just coming by. *What a jerk,* Pabich thought, *still running around here like he's a supervisor.* Dan kept moving, past the open door to Dianne's office. She looked up and saw him: maybe she could head off a physical confrontation at the board meeting. She half rose from her chair.

"Dan!"

He stopped. "It'll have to wait, Dianne." He kept moving. Two doors farther along and on the other side of the little passageway, Harvey was standing in his office, waiting while Carl Carlson finished typing the $3,000 promissory note for Harvey to sign, when Dan stuck his head around the doorjamb.

"Harvey, can I see you for a minute?"

Harvey turned, surprised. "Sure," he said, and followed him the few feet to Dan's old office, which had been cleared out and was empty save for the desk, two chairs, and a bare metal bookshelf. Harvey was smiling nervously. Dan closed the door behind them.

He knows, Dan thought, seeing the smile, *he knows I'm not gonna get it, he was the mastermind.* The office was tiny, as tiny as the closet Harvey had come out of. Harvey perched with an awkward insouciance on the edge of the desk.

"What the hell are you doing to me?" Dan shouted, the enormous retributive force of his rage engorging him again. "Why do you want to hurt my name, my family. You *cheated* me . . ."

Sheepish, frightened by the violence of Dan's outburst, but unable to resist, Harvey smirked. Harvey's sad, plastic, comic face, which had served him so well, betrayed his satisfaction at Dan's loss. Dan freed his gun.

Harvey was rising in fright and exclaiming when the first slug tore apart his bowels. Both his hands came up in front of him, he evacuated, and he started to spin, his long legs crossing. The second wound was

The Act 253

superficial, skimming across his arms and into and out of his chest, but it kept him spinning like a top. His crossed legs tripped him up, and still pirouetting, he began to topple into the narrow space behind the desk. Dan pursued him methodically, the third shot entering his back and the fourth round entering the base of his skull just as Harvey slammed to the floor, a geyser of blood and tissue spattering the wall. Not certain that the fourth bullet had been fatal, Dan wedged his feet under Harvey's body so he could fit between the desk and the wall, leaned over at a ninety-degree angle, put the gun nearly up against Harvey's skull, and squeezed off an insurance round.

He reholstered his pistol and ran out, slamming the door behind him and not noticing the clerks and aides standing in the open doorways watching him.

As Dan was approaching the staircase he passed a city worker he had known for ten years. "Hi, Anne," he said, with his customary good manners, and plunged into the stairwell.

Dianne Feinstein was the first to reach Harvey's body and she could see at once he was dead. She looked up and told Carl Carlson, who was standing there, to call the Chief's office, and Carlson tried but he was sobbing and screaming so Dianne took the telephone out of his hand and said, "Here, let me." Grateful, Carlson ran to a water fountain and swallowed two valium.

Harvey's lifeless body lay bleeding beneath a lovely forest mural, the one Dan and Mary Ann had hung in strips, like wallpaper, back when the world still seemed fresh with hope, so Danny would have something pretty to look at.

Having revenged himself upon the two people who had ruined him and were ruining his city, having done what his awful freedom demanded of him, Dan now sought understanding from God and from his wife. The law would come later.

In the name of the Father, and of the Son, and of the Holy Ghost. Amen. O my God, I am heartily sorry for having offended thee, and I detest all my sins . . . because I fear the loss of Heaven and the pains of Hell.

He knelt alone beneath the slim gold cross suspended high within St. Mary's Cathedral, praying for forgiveness and waiting for Mary Ann, his empty revolver in its holster. For a thousand years murderers had been taking sanctuary in churches, where medieval civil authorities could not, dared not, go in after them. He prayed and he waited.

Dan had run to Denise and got her car keys and driven away from City Hall moments before legions of police cars had descended from every direction. He had turned north, made a U-turn, and doubled back to the pay phone outside the Doggie Diner. The pay phone was a familiar landmark; it was the same phone he had used when he had been assigned to Northern Station. Beneath the smiling ceramic dachshund with its puffy white chef's hat high above the diner on a slim white pole, he had called Mary Ann at the Hot Potato. The number was busy so he dialed an adjacent stand and got somebody to bring her to the phone. Crying, he asked his wife to meet him at the Cathedral. Mary Ann said she would take a taxi and get there as soon as she could. Dan got back into Denise's car and drove up Franklin Street, parking outside a Unitarian church and being careful to lock the car before walking the block and a half to the cathedral.

As news of the killings reached the police, so many of whom had loathed George Moscone and Harvey Milk, scattered cheering broke out on the fourth floor of the Hall of Justice, where the plainclothes inspectors and the brass to whom George had broken his promise had their offices. Inspector Earl Sanders, hearing the joyful ruckus and not yet knowing what had happened, was momentarily puzzled: the World Series was over, and it was months before the Super Bowl, so what were they hollering about?

Mary Ann paid the taxi driver and ran up the Gough Street steps leading to St. Mary's—a frightened woman rushing to stand by her husband. When she found Danny he simply said to her, "I shot the Mayor and Harvey." Mary Ann slumped, every dream and hope knocked out of her by those six words, and they sank down together into a pew. For a moment they were silent. Then Mary Ann asked, "Do you want to speak with anybody else?" Dan was crying again. "No," he gulped, "no, I just want to be with you." His wife held him against her without saying anything. Finally Dan gained control of himself. "Let's walk down to Northern Station now." His head felt better. He felt safe.

They stood—Mary Ann was only two inches shorter than her husband—with their arms around each other, and walked out of the cathedral. "I love you, Danny," Mary Ann stammered. "I'll stick by you no matter what, but please, please don't, please. . . ." She didn't want him to turn his gun on himself, that was the sin for which there was no penance. As they walked down the hill, holding tightly to each other, their heads so close together a casual observer would have seen only a couple of handsome young lovers, Mary Ann slipped her arm under Danny's best suit jacket and rested her large, capable hand on his police revolver.

Dan White in a good suit he bought especially for his campaign.

Mary Ann White and little Charlie outside the courtroom where Dan was on trial for his life.

The Geneva Towers housing projects loom above Visitacion Valley. "There are no picture-postcard views in the faded valley."

Dan, going all out, slides under a tag to score a run in a police-versus-firefighters softball game. On deck: Frank Falzon.

Left to right: The Police All-Stars manager, Frank Falzon, and most valuable player, Dan White, accept congratulations for their 1972 championship season from former Police Chief Donald Scott.

Harvey Milk in the Supervisors' chambers. "Harvey was quick enough to see that his authority came from being an underdog."

George Moscone heads into City Hall for his first day on the job as mayor of San Francisco in January 1976.

Dan White's campaign poster. "A certain glint in his eye that, ambiguous as Mona Lisa's smile, could have been determination or something darker; remorselessness, perhaps."

The Board of Supervisors, 1978. Left to right: Ron Pelosi, Harvey Milk, Carol Ruth Silver, Dan White, Ella Hutch Hill, Quentin Kopp, Robert Gonzales, Gordon Lau, Lee Dolson, and John Molinari. Seated: Dianne Feinstein. Front: the zealous clerk, Gil Boreman.

Terrence McCarthy

Goldie Judge on Leland Avenue. Dan's original campaign manager and later his chief nemesis, Goldie was to Visitacion Valley what Walter Winchell was to all ships at sea.

The Moscone family Christmas card, 1978. George, Gina, and their children in the mayor's office.

Sutro Telecommunications Tower on Twin Peaks, the highest point in the city. Its brooding presence stood for all that had changed in the city of St. Francis.

When Harvey Milk stepped into a pile left behind by a dog to publicize his scooper ordinance, every television station and newspaper in town was there to record the moment.

The notorious photograph of Margo St. James, Police Chief Charles Gain, and Wonder Whore at the 1977 Hookers Ball. "Our savior," Margo gushed.

Dan's campaign manager, business partner, and chief political advisor, Ray Sloan. "Nobody has more cosmic debris than me."

Dan White, San Francisco's own St. Patrick, at 26, showing off his physique and his new shamrock tattoo.

City Hall just behind the Doggie Diner, where Dan White called his wife moments after the killings.

Left to right: Police Chief Charles Gain, Richard Blum, and Dianne
Feinstein leave City Hall under police guard shortly after the shootings on
November 27, 1978.

The bodies of Harvey Milk and George Moscone, wrapped in rubberized body bags,
are put into an ambulance outside City Hall on their way to the coroner for autopsies.

Prosecutor Thomas Norman outside the courtroom during the trial. "He lulled witnesses into thinking of him as a maiden aunt, then sank his knitting needles into them."

Douglas Schmidt, White's youthful lawyer, passes through the metal detector outside the courtroom. An open Midwestern face and a throaty voice full of American verities, like the young Jimmy Stewart.

Police cars aflame during the May 21, 1979, riot at City Hall following the manslaughter verdicts. "Bright balls of heat and light, the siren mechanisms wailing and keening like oxen at slaughter."

Book Two
THE TRIAL

"—and if you're not good directly," she added, "I'll put you through into Looking-glass House. How would you like *that?*

"Now, if you'll only attend, Kitty, and not talk so much, I'll tell you all my ideas about Looking-glass House. First, there's the room you can see through the glass—that's just the same as our drawing room, only the things go the other way."

Lewis Carroll, *Through The Looking-Glass*

1
Before the Trial

Douglas Schmidt arrived at the Hall of Justice for the first day of what the youthful defense lawyer knew would be the biggest trial of his life. He carried a bulging brown leather wedge-shaped briefcase in his left hand the way a plumber carries his tool satchel, like a man with a job to do.

As always, this Wednesday morning the elevators were clogged with a wary mingling of squinting cops, nodding junkies, earring-wearing desperados, a hillbilly girl with her blouse hanging loose outside her jeans and a baby in her arms on the way to the lockup to visit her old man, natty Jewish and Italian lawyers whose haircuts never cost a penny less than twenty-five dollars, and young blacks and Mexicans in bright white tanktop tee shirts carrying those oversize transistor radios that are the attaché case of the Third World. At the third floor Schmidt and his associate counsel, Stephen Scherr, got off.

The courtroom was windowless and bathed in aqueous light, like a fishtank. Separating the judge's raised bench, the attorney's tables and the jury box from the spectators' gallery was a five-foot-high sheet of bulletproof glass with a light-green tint. The security glass, which was nearly two inches thick, was mounted on a waist-high wood railing and topped by a wiremesh screen. Inside the glass, Schmidt set his heavy briefcase on the defense table, and remaining on his feet, rubbed a hand across his cheek and nodded at his opposite number, Deputy District Attorney Thomas F. Norman. Norman was sucking on a coughdrop.

When Schmidt nodded in his direction Norman bowed ever so

slightly, saying, "Good morning, Doug." Into the three words, Norman miraculously managed to cram eight syllables and two complete scales. The forty-nine-year-old chief homicide prosecutor for the city and county of San Francisco was built along the lines of a penguin with a plump, self-satisfied tummy. His hair was kinky and smoothed with pomade into place around a bald spot at the back of his crown. The half-frame reading glasses he now slipped on his nose made him appear punctilious as he glanced over one of several neat looseleaf binders full of his notes and documents. Norman did not carry his papers in a briefcase, but loose and pressed against his puffy chest: Schmidt's papers were his tools but Norman's were the heart of his case.

The spectators' benches were full. In the front row and directly behind the defense table sat Mary Ann, Dan's mother and stepfather, his sister Nancy, and a clutch of uncles and siblings from among the enormous clan. The older men all had seamed napes and the thick, blunt fingers that betrayed years of physical labor. Except for that one bench, the front rows on either side of the gallery were occupied by reporters and courtroom sketch artists. The back benches held the merely curious including, as always, several elderly women of the sagging stockings and floral print dress variety, among whom the dandering Tommy Norman was a particular favorite.

When the hands of the wall clock at the rear of the spectator section showed two minutes before ten o'clock, Dan entered the courtroom through a door beside the judge's bench. His head down, he marched the dozen or so paces from the door to the defense table looking only at his shoetops. His path led him directly toward Mary Ann on the far side of the security glass; three feet short of his wife he swung to the left and took his seat beside Doug Schmidt, who pulled the chair closest to the empty jury box back from the table to show his client where to sit. Dan wore a light-gray suit, a white shirt and a jailhouse pallor. He was not allowed those lengths of material that could readily be used as a noose: no tie, no belt, shoes without laces.

At ten sharp the door on the other side of the judge's bench swung open on its silent hinges and there was an expectant shuffle and mumble in the courtroom as the clerk sang out: "All rise. Department Twenty-one in the Superior Court of the State of California, City and County of San Francisco, the Honorable Walter F. Calcagno presiding, is now in session."

Five months had passed since Dan and Mary Ann had walked down the hill from the cathedral to Northern Station clutching each other. When they reached the station house, Dan, nodding toward his holster and the gun with five empty chambers, and holding his hands wide from his body to show his peaceful intentions, had said to Officer Warren Omholt, "There it is."

Ray Sloan had been on his way from the Hot Potato to City Hall when he heard a news bulletin on his car radio that a supervisor had been shot, and he thought: oh my God, it must be Harvey Milk, it must have something to do with the Briggs amendment. Every block or two there was an update: the mayor's office was being cordoned off, somebody had apparently taken a shot at George Moscone. Ray had begun to wonder if it was a good idea to go to City Hall if there was some nut with a gun loose down there when he missed a light. As he was sitting there he heard the voice on the radio say something, he wasn't sure just what, about Dan White. It was as if there had been an explosion inside his head, momentarily blinding him. *He did it, he did it, he did it* kept running through Ray's mind, and half blind, he made an illegal left turn into Ellis Street against one-way traffic, deserted his car beside a fire hydrant, and ran into Northern Station looking for Officer Paul Chignell. He found him in a back room apparently busy but not unduly distressed. An aged squawk box was blaring away. "Paul," he shouted.

"Relax, Ray," Chignell said, looking up. "We're running it down."

"You don't understand," Ray was beside himself. A look of alarm came into Chignell's pale, freckled face.

"You're not trying to tell me, aw shit, no, don't, you don't mean . . ." Just then, the voice on the squawk box began to broadcast Dan's description. Chignell got very businesslike and hard. "Stay right here," he said, starting away. "Don't talk, don't move unless I tell you to. He's coming here, I know he's coming here." Ray saw other cops running by, one of them was cranking shells into a shotgun. *Oh my God,* Ray thought, *oh my God.* Ray had been joined in the room by a cop he had never seen before. He waited, pacing anxiously.

After Dan had turned himself in, Omholt removed the weapon from his holster, and with Chignell took six live and five expended cartridges from Dan's pants pockets. Omholt checked the chambers; they were empty. The policemen escorted Dan into the assembly room and handcuffed him. Somebody called Homicide. Dan sat and waited with Chignell standing guard over him. He refused to make a statement, but after the brief conversation with Chignell about the book cover in his breast pocket he also asked for a favor. "Paul, would you please . . . don't let the press see my wife." Then he was quiet again.

Ray Sloan knew Dan was there when Mary Ann was shown into the same room where Chignell had made him wait. Her eyes were glazed and she seemed dumbstruck. Ray instantly recalled the look she had given him the night he and Denise had persuaded Dan to ask for his resignation back, the look that had said: what have you done?

Oh my God, what have I done?

Another cop walked in behind Mary Ann and asked her if she'd like a cigarette. Mary Ann said "Yes, please." When the cop lit it for her—Ray knew that Mary Ann didn't smoke and never had—she asked him in a small, flat voice, "Is the mayor dead?"

"The mayor is dead, ma'am. Supervisor Milk is dead too."

Mary Ann didn't respond. The present was a torture and the future unthinkable. Her face turned red and tears filled her eyes. She dragged on the cigarette. Ray moved toward the door to see if he could get a look at Dan, and the cop said to him without any inflection whatsoever, "If you move another foot I'll blow your head off." Nothing personal, just the way cops talk sometimes.

"Why?" Falzon shouted as soon as he stepped into the tiny interrogation room. "I feel like hittin' you in the fuckin' mouth. How could you be so stupid? How?"

When Dan looked up, his blotchy gray skin drawn tight over his skull, there were tears running down his cheeks. "I, I want to tell you about it, I want to, to explain," he sniffled. Falzon's professionalism began to choke off his own riotous emotions. He was going to get the confession nobody else could. "Okay," he said, "if you want to talk to me I'm gonna get my tape recorder and read you your rights and do it right." Falzon fetched his tape machine from his desk and also asked Inspector Eddie Erdelatz, who was still eating his sandwich, to sit in with him. Falzon trusted Erdelatz, they had come up together.

Back in the interrogation room Falzon started the tape rolling. He knew that at any moment he might be cut off by a lawyer who represented Dan. At times during the next twenty-five minutes he heard people moving right up against the door, as if they were eavesdropping or preparing to come in. His sense of urgency, which needed no further stimulation, nonetheless received it.

Falzon began to do his job, asking Dan for his name, which he provided in a firm, clear voice, momentarily gaining control of himself. Falzon recited the Miranda rights. "And having these rights in mind," he said, "do you wish to tell us about the incident involving Mayor George Moscone and Supervisor Harvey Milk at this time?"

Dan's control immediately began to crumble. There was a long pause before he answered, an eleven-second pause during which Falzon watched Dan's tumult surface again in his eyes, black and heavy, the eyes of an old man near death. As if Falzon had been granted X-ray vision, he watched Dan struggle over whether to tell the truth or launch into some politician's bullshit and then, explosively giving it up, Dan said, "I do."

Years of working with district attorneys had taught Falzon that old lawyer's saw, never ask a question if you don't already know the answer. All he really knew was that the mayor was dead and Harvey Milk had been shot. Normally Falzon got his way by being sympathetic up to a point and then boring in, brooking no truth except for his own certainty of what the real truth was. But now, knowing almost none of the facts, swayed by his friendship, hoping against hope that Dan wouldn't lose it entirely and break down, Falzon began cautiously, probing for the facts with which to build his interrogation, treating Dan as if he were fragile.

"Would you . . . normally, in a situation like this we ask questions. I'm aware of your past history as a police officer and also as a San Francisco fireman. I would prefer, I'll let you do it in a narrative form as to what happened this morning if you can lead up to the events of the shooting and then backtrack as to *why* these events took place."

"Well," Dan began, his high-pitched voice strained, "it's just that I've been under an awful lot of pressure lately, financial pressure, because of my job situation, family pressures because of, ah . . . not being able to have the time with my family." He began to sniffle and cry. "It's just that I wanted to serve the people of San Francisco well . . . and I did that. Then when the pressure got too great, I decided to leave."

Dan was providing the same reasons he had used with the press, the same story he had told everybody except for that night in the Irish Embassy when he had admitted to Ray that it wasn't finances at all that had motivated him to quit.

He continued. "After I left, my family and friends offered their support and said whatever it would take to allow me to go back into office, they would be willing to make that up. So since I felt the responsibility of the people that elected me, I went to Mayor Moscone and told him, that I had, my situation had changed, . . . and I'd like to be, retain my seat, to be appointed to my seat. He initially told me that he felt I was the elected representative of District Eight, that I was doing an *outstanding* job, people of District Eight were lucky to have me, and that if it came to a legal ruling he would appoint me, reappoint me," he said, sniffling, "because of the type of person I was. So, with that in mind I tried to set my personal affairs in order, preparing to take my seat. And then it came out that Supervisor Milk"—the name on Dan's tongue was pure venom— "and some others were working against me to get my seat back. . . . He didn't speak to me, he spoke to the city attorney, but I was in the office and I heard the conversation, that he was going to try to prevent me from takin' my seat again. I went back to the mayor, and he told me that he had had some comments made to him that he felt that some of the people in District Eight didn't want me to, to serve, an' I told him that these were people that opposed me in my election, had traumatized my family by taking me . . . pressing charges against me . . . false charges. They put a lot of pressure on me an' my family."

When he mentioned his family Dan began to sob. Falzon laid his hand on Dan's forearm and squeezed it. *Why?* He was sure he hadn't yet heard all the pressures. These pressures, the way Falzon saw it, were the motivation, the reasons why a guy like Dan White had snapped. Very softly, trying to calm Dan, he asked, "Can you relate these pressures you've been under, Dan, at this time? Can you explain it to Inspector Erdelatz and myself?"

Gasping, barely able to speak, Dan said, "Well, it's just that some of these people, just charged me with taking money from big corporations and not recording it but I never did that. I never took money from anybody, but the papers print it. My, my constituents believe it. They, they asked me about it. . . . Two months later the district attorney says they're unfounded but no one hears about it, that the charges are false. But my family suffers. . . ." He was still sobbing, choking out the words.

Falzon decided it was time to zero in. "These meetings that you were having with the mayor, were they all occurring last week or were they going into the weekend, this past weekend?"

"No, I, I hadn't spoken to the mayor since last Saturday," the meeting at which George had given him that awful choice between humiliation and failure. "And he told me that I would have to show some support from the people of District Eight if I was going to be reappointed. I could see the game that was being played, they were going to use me as a scapegoat; whether I was a good supervisor or not, was not the point." He had regained his composure, the narrative was coherent and chronological again. ". . . this was a political opportunity and they were gonna denigrate me and my family, and the job that I had tried to do, an', an' more or less hang me out to dry. And I saw more and more evidence of this during the week, when the papers reported that, ah . . . someone else was going to be reappointed. I couldn't get through to the mayor. The mayor never called me, he told me he was gonna call me before he made any decision, he never did that. An' it was only on my own initiative when I went down today to speak with him. I was troubled, the pressures, my family again, my, my son's out to a babysitter,"—he began to cry again, overcome by self-pity— "My wife's got to work, long hours, fifty and sixty hours, never see my family." He was sobbing and choking.

"Dan, can you tell Inspector Erdelatz and myself what was your plan this morning? What did you have in mind?" Here was a critical question: for murder to have taken place, as it was defined in the law, there must be not the act alone but the *intention.*

"I didn't have any, any *devised* plan or anything, it's, I was leaving the house to talk, to see the mayor and I went downstairs, to, to make a phone call and I had my gun down there."

Falzon did not press the question of intent, he focused instead on the gun. "Is this your police service revolver, Dan?"

"This is the gun I had when I was a policeman. It's in my room and ah . . . I don't know, I just put it on. I, I don't know why I put it on, it's just . . ."

Falzon interrupted. "Where is this gun now, Dan?" It was an injudicious moment at which to interrupt; Falzon had violated two cardinal principles of interrogation. First, never cut off a man who is confessing. Second, a criminal who is stammering and hesitating is buying time, looking for the right words with which to avoid the obvious. But Falzon pounced after the murder weapon. It, too, was a key piece of evidence, and Falzon didn't know that Dan had turned it in at Northern Station. He wasn't paying attention to what Dan had said right after he mentioned the gun, so anxious was he to locate the weapon which for all he knew could be anywhere in the city, tossed over a fence or dropped into a gutter and sure to be stolen. Or maybe Falzon just didn't want his friend to finish the sentence which began: "I, I don't know why I put it on, it's just . . ."

"Where is this gun now, Dan?"

"I turned it in to Officer, ah . . . Paul Chignell, who I turned myself in to at Northern Station."

"You turned yourself in? I wasn't aware of that."

"I turned myself in at Northern Station to Officer Paul Chignell who, who I could trust and I, I knew would do things properly," Dan said. And then he did something quite remarkable, considering his apparent state of upheaval: he returned to his narrative, he picked up his story where Falzon had interrupted it. "An' then, an' then I, I went to the, to the mayor's office."

"You went directly from your residence to the mayor's office this morning?"

"Yes, my aide picked me up but she didn't have any idea, ah . . ." *Idea of what?* "You know, that I had a gun on me or, you know, I was just going to the mayor to, to see if he was going to reappoint me and if not, the reasons why. And I went in to see him an', an' he told me he wasn't gonna reappoint me and he, he was going to, intending to tell me about it. He had some, he told me he had a press conference scheduled and he was going to announce it at the press conference. Didn't even have the courtesy to call me or tell me that I wasn't going to be reappointed. Then ah . . . I got kind of fuzzy, and then, just my head didn't feel right, and I, then he said, let's go into the back room an', an' have a drink and talk about it. An' ah . . ."

"Was this before any threats on your part, Dan?" A curve ball.

"I, I never *made* any threats."

"There were no threats at all?"

"I, I . . . oh *no.*"

Speaking rapidly, trying to keep the momentum going, Falzon asked: ". . . Can you explain to Inspector Erdelatz and myself the conversation that existed between the two of you at this time?"

"It was pretty much just, you know, I asked, was I going to be reappointed. He said no, I'm not, no you're not. And I said, why? He said, well, I've had people in your district say they don't want you, and I, I reiterated that I told him before that these were people that had brought false charges against me and had been doggin' me since I've been in office." Dan was speaking clearly, almost routinely. "And he understood that there are going to be people that dislike you, not everybody was a 100 percent supporter but I told him that oh, you know, an overwhelming majority of the people in my district wanted me as their supervisor, and I told him how a person told me last night that they had on their own gone out with neighbors and gathered over a thousand signatures. A thousand signatures in one day, my constituents, to keep me in office. He knew that and he told me, it's a political decision and that's the end of it, and that's it."

"Is this when you were having a drink in the back room?"

"No, no, it's before I went to the back room and then he could obviously see, see I was obviously distraught an' upset an' then he said, let's go in the back room and, and, an' have a drink . . . But I just kinda stumbled in the back, went, went, went in the back room and he sat down and he was all, he was talking' an' nothing was gettin' through to me. It was just like a roaring in my ears an', an' then um . . . it just came to me, you know, he . . ."

"You couldn't hear what he was saying, Dan?"

"Just small talk that, you know, it just wasn't registering. What I was going to do now, you know, and how this would affect my family, you know, an', an' just, just all the time knowing he's going to go out and, and lie to the press and, an' tell 'em, you know, that I, I wasn't a good supervisor and that people didn't want me an' then, *that was it.* Then I, I just shot him." Very softly, more softly than he had spoken before, Dan said, "That was it. It was over."

Falzon breathed an inward sigh of relief. That was one, now he went after two. "What happened after you left there, Dan?"

"Well, I left his office by one of the back doors an', an' I started, I was going to go down the stairs and then I saw Harvey Milk's aide across the hall at the supervisors' and then it struck me about what Harvey had tried to do and I said, well, I'll go *talk* to him." Once again Dan had regained his composure, he was speaking almost conversationally. "I said, you know, at least maybe he'll be *honest* with me, you know, because he didn't know I had, I had heard his conversation and he was all smiles and stuff and I went in and, like I say, I, I was still upset an' ah . . . then I said, I wanted to talk with him an', an', and just try to explain to him, you know, I, I didn't agree with him on a lot of things but I was always honest, you know, and here they were devious and then he started kind of smirking 'cause *he knew, he knew* I wasn't going to be reappointed. And ah . . . it just didn't make any impression on him. I started to say, you know how hard I worked for it and what it means to me and my family and then my reputation as, as a hardworkin', good honest person and he just kind of smirked at me . . ."—Dan laughed without mirth, and then, dripping sarcasm, said— "as if to say, *too bad,* and then, I just got all flushed an', an' hot and I shot him." Matter of fact. Falzon had done his job.

"And when you left there, where did you go?"

"Well, let's see. When I left there I went into my aide's room and I, an' I took her key to her car, and, and I ran out and I went . . . to where her car is parked . . . and I drove over to the, where did I drive to? I didn't even know what I was doin', and I drove to the, the Doggie Diner . . . and I called my wife and she, she didn't know, she . . ." He began to sob again.

"Did you tell her, Dan?"

"I called up, I didn't tell her on the phone . . . see, she was workin', son's at a babysitter, shit. I just told her, meet me at the cathedral."

"Did she meet you?"

"Yeah, she . . ."

"Saint Mary's?"

". . . she took a cab, yeah. She didn't know. She had known I'd been upset and I wasn't even talkin' to her at home because I just couldn't explain how I felt and she had no, nothing to blame about it . . . she always has been great to me, but . . . I couldn't tell anybody, I didn't, there was just, just the pressure hit me, just, my head's all flushed and it's like my skull's gonna crack. Then when she came to the church, I, I told her and she kind of slumped an' . . . she couldn't say anything, she . . ."

Falzon might have asked what Dan told Mary Ann, but his curiosity was about exhausted: he had two admissions, a murder weapon, and a motive that made sense to him; avenged honor. He would want to question the wife. "Do you know where she is?"

"I don't know now. She, she came to Northern Station with me. She asked me not to do anything about myself, you know, that she loved me and she'd stick by me and not to hurt myself an' then we just walked to Northern Station and went an' talked to Officer Chignell and that's it."

"Is there anything else you'd like to add at this time, Dan?"

Dan started to speak and cry at the same time. "Just that I've always been honest and worked hard, never cheated anybody, or, you know, I'm not a crook or anything an' I wanted to do a good job, I'm trying to do a good job an' I saw this city as it's goin' kinda downhill and I was always just a lonely vote on the Board and tryin' to be honest an', an' I just couldn't take it anymore and that's it."

It was Eddie Erdelatz's turn. Erdelatz spoke slowly, and with more deliberation than Falzon. "Dan, when you went to Northern Station, what did you tell Officer Chignell?"

"I didn't say anything, the police obviously knew. They all knew and I know most of them, I've worked with most of them and . . . they just, you know, checked me out, frisked me and I had the gun and took out my wallet and everything, and ah . . . that's it, I told them, I, I, I wasn't going to say anything."

Falzon's instinct had been right: even though Dan had refused to make a statement at Northern Station, he had spoken to him. Erdelatz said, "Dan, right now are you under a doctor's care?"

"No."

"Are you under any medication at all?"

"No."

"Have you . . . have you carried that gun with you in the past, Dan, since you've been, ah . . . a supervisor, say?" These were important questions, questions that any defense lawyer would also ask.

"I have, because there were some threats on my life, you know, from people that I dealt with before the Board. I never told my wife about it, I never told anybody 'cause it, you know, that's something you don't want to hurt anybody else . . ."

"When is the last time you had your gun with you prior to today?"

"I guess it was a few months ago. I, I was afraid of some of the threats that were made and I had a committee hearing coming up where some of these people were going to appear and I, and I know they had a history of violence and I just wanted to make sure to protect myself, you know. This, this city isn't safe . . . and there's a lot of people running around an' well I don't have to tell you fellows, you guys know that." He was sobbing again.

Sharply, snapping him back, Erdelatz said, "When you left the mayor's office, *Dan,* you proceeded, you say, to Harvey Milk's office?"

"I, I didn't even know if he was there . . ."

"And this, when Inspector Falzon asked you about what had transpired, when you were with the mayor, you mentioned that there was a roaring in your ears, is that right?"

"Yeah, it's just like my head was going to burst, you know, I just . . ."

"Had that ever happened to you in the past, Dan?"

"Yeah, it had, it had when I was under this pressure at home and at night I couldn't sleep. I didn't sleep last night. I wasn't even with my wife, in bed . . ."—sobbing again—"I couldn't sleep, I never even slept. It's just, I don't know . . . it felt like my head was gonna burst."

Speaking slowly, and laying special emphasis on the word "intention," Erdelatz asked: "When you left your home this morning, Dan, was it your intention to confront the mayor, Supervisor Milk or anyone else with that gun?"

"No . . . what I wanted to do was just, talk to him, you know . . . I didn't even know if I was goin' to be reappointed or not be reappointed . . . I was just going down there to talk to him, you know, an' ah . . . why do we do these things? You know, why did I, it, I don't know . . . I never killed anybody before, I never shot anybody . . ."

"What did . . ."

". . . I didn't even, I didn't even know if I wanted to kill him, I just shot him, I don't know."

"What type of gun is that you were carrying, Dan?"

"It's a .38, a two-inch .38."

"And do you know how many shots you fired?"

Dan's response, and the questions and answers that followed, would become critical elements at his trial, where the question of *where* he reloaded would be interpreted and reinterpreted. "Uh . . . no, I don't, I don't. I, I out of instinct, when I reloaded the gun ah . . . you know, it's just the training I guess I had, you know."

"Where did you reload?"

"I reloaded in my office when, when I was, I couldn't out in the hall."

"When you say you reloaded, are you speaking of following the shooting in the mayor's office?"

"Yeah."

"And how many bullets did you have with you?"

"I, I, I don't know, I ah . . . the gun was loaded an', an' I had some ah . . . extra shots, you know, I just, I, 'cause I keep the gun with a box of shells and I just grabbed some."

"Are you referring to some loose . . ."

"Yeah."

". . . bullets?"

"Yeah, yes."

"Inspector Falzon?"

"No questions," Falzon said. "Inspector Erdelatz and I, ah . . . appreciate your cooperation and the truthfulness in your statement." He sounded and felt funereal. "At this time we'll close this statement. It's now 12:30 in the afternoon. Thank you." He switched the recorder off.

It was only about one hundred minutes since Dan had blown George Moscone's brain apart. In his statement he had expressed not a whit of remorse for the mayor's death, nor for his widow Gina and her four fatherless children, nor for Harvey Milk's death, nor even for his city, which he loved and had defiled. When he had cried it had only been for his own plight, or for his wife and son; the taped statement was as self-serving as the acts preceding it.

Falzon, however, in the emotion of the moment, felt that he had extracted a confession to two first-degree murders that would send his friend to the gas chamber. They began the trip upstairs toward the jail. By the strangest of coincidences the uniformed policeman accompanying them, dispatched by his Captain to make sure that what had happened in Dallas to Lee Oswald didn't happen to Dan White, was Sgt. Jay Wallace—the same cop Dan had accused of brutality during an earlier fit of moral pique.

As he escorted Dan upstairs, Falzon was not a happy man. Dan, Falzon thought, must have believed in his heart that Moscone and Milk, for whatever political reasons, had destroyed him as a respected citizen and done grievous harm to his family—had, in short, killed everything of value to him. Therefore he must have felt justified in killing them. Dan, to his own way of thinking, must have believed that he was laying down a sacrifice, like the baseball player who gives himself up to advance the cause of his team. Dan's gun would put in the mayor's chair a person—Dianne Feinstein—who was much truer to his vision of San Francisco, at the same time ridding the city of the people he blamed for destroying the way things once had been. But by making this sacrifice he had ruined himself, his wife and their infant son. Little Charlie would grow up, as Dan had, having to come to terms with a tragedy in his father's life. Dan's idea of a sacrifice, Falzon thought as he walked beside his ashen prisoner, turned on a selfishness so vast and indifferent to its consequences as to be unfathomable.

Slumped beside him, his wrists bound by handcuffs, Dan interrupted Falzon's brooding. "You know," he said as they were walking upstairs to the jail, "in Vietnam you were told to kill people you didn't even know. For your country. For all you knew, those people, they hadn't even hurt anybody."

The bodies of Harvey Milk and George Moscone were wrapped in rubberized bags and wheeled out of City Hall on gurneys. They were taken to the coroner's office in the Hall of Justice for autopsies.

By 3:30, when the afternoon commute was just beginning, the skies were a cold oatmeal gray. The newsboy at the corner of Sixth and Harrison—half a block from where Dan was being held prisoner and right outside a gay bar called the Endup—was having another banner day selling copies of the *Examiner's* extra edition to commuters as they slowed down approaching the southern Embarcadero Freeway toward the working-class suburbs of South San Francisco and Brisbane, Daly City and San Bruno. First Jonestown, and now Dan White, had stirred a rapid trade in the news of death. Traffic moved haltingly under the heavy skies as driver after driver reached out to hand over a quarter in exchange for the paper with the bold headline: MAYOR, MILK SLAIN; DAN WHITE SEIZED. Most neglected to wait for their nickel change. Other people's misfortune being good for their business, the newsboys were having a great run of luck.

Aboard the old surface cars that still clattered along the tracks on Market Street, silence prevailed. The public grieving that had been so common when John Kennedy was murdered had slowly transformed into numbness as Martin Luther King and Bobby Kennedy and George Wallace were felled; and by the time Sara Jane Moore and Squeaky Fromme had declared open season on Gerald Ford in California, assassinations had become a kind of recurring freak show. The passengers on the trolleys did not talk to each other, although there were people who wanted to speak but could not or did not. Very few even read the evening paper; they just sat and stared at nothing, clutching their shopping bags, their briefcases, their noiseless radios.

Silence prevailed everywhere, from Visitacion Valley to the Golden Gate.

Jim Denman, the undersheriff of San Francisco, was at City Hall when the killings occurred and had walked out into the central chamber beneath the great rotunda. People were pouring out of their offices on all four floors and coming to stand at the long balustrades overlooking the central staircase. There were what seemed like hundreds of cops milling around, Denman had never seen so many cops. What struck him most sharply was the silence: he thought it was eerie, like watching a war being fought, but there were no grunts or screams of battle.

Denman was still there when Dianne Feinstein, her knees wobbly, choking back tears, announced what had happened. She was held up by Chief Charles Gain. Under the city charter the board president would act as mayor until the supervisors chose a replacement, but it was a foregone conclusion that she would be chosen to serve out George Moscone's term. Political haggling was impossible under the circumstances. As soon as Denman heard that Dan had been arrested he went down to the jail to take personal charge of the prisoner.

He decided, initially, to house Dan in a cell on the seventh floor outside D block, the psychiatric section, where security was heaviest. Usually the cell was used for suicide cases. Denman was thinking that Dan might suddenly wake up to how unforgivable what he had done was and decide to kill himself, so he ordered a round-the-clock suicide watch. The cell was also isolated from the general jail population. He didn't want any incidents, anybody putting a move on White.

Just about the time he got everything straightened out and ready, Dan arrived. He was fingerprinted, photographed and booked on two counts of murder. Then he was stripped, showered and given an orange jail jumpsuit. He was obediently doing what he was told but Denman could see he was tense, like a taut rope with no play left in it. A lot of the deputies, as awed as the cops had been in Northern Station, gathered around to gawk. A few were glaring, but more were smiling at Dan. One man came up and gave him a pat on the butt. Dan remained unmoved, distant. He showed no emotion at all until Denman escorted him to the telephone in his private office. Dan's voice quavered as he said, "Hi, mom. I guess you heard. How ya doin'?"

Meanwhile, the deputies locked down all the other prisoners and swept the tiers for weapons before they walked Dan down to his cell. Normally the jail is as noisy as the lion house at feeding time, but it too had fallen strangely silent. Dan continued to act Spartan. When the heavy iron door clanked shut behind him, he just walked over and lay down on his bunk, folding his hands beneath his head and averting his eyes from the naked lightbulb. He finally had no more than those stark requirements he had once boasted to Ray Sloan were all he needed.

When Tommy Norman was in the third grade, a boy with the patience to build scale model airplanes, he had sat next to Cappy Lavin, George Moscone's best friend. The first day of school Cappy stared at Tommy Norman, rather penetratingly; then he kicked him on the leg, hard. It was perhaps a prophetic gesture. Tommy kicked him back.

While Falzon had been interrogating Dan White, Norman's boss,

District Attorney Joe Freitas, was flying back to San Francisco from Washington, where he had been meeting with State Department officials about possible charges to be brought as a result of the Guyana massacre. Norman, meanwhile, brushed aside the insistence of the chief public defender that he had standing as Dan White's attorney, but at about 12:15 a lawyer showed up who did have legitimate standing. His name was James Purcell, and in his day he had been counted among the very best criminal attorneys in the city. But now he was close to eighty. Purcell was the attorney for Mary Ann's parents, and they had asked him to help out until they could hire somebody else. When Erdelatz and Falzon came out of the interrogation room, Purcell went in to talk with his client.

"Well?" Norman asked Falzon.

"We have a taped statement." Falzon was laying out what had been said when Purcell returned.

"I just can't understand what happened," the elderly lawyer said, shaking his head. "His mind must have just snapped."

Norman had already gathered, from what Falzon had told him, that the only possible line of defense would be psychological. Trying to disguise his eagerness to counter that, Norman rattled the change in his pants pocket and ever so nonchalantly said to Purcell, "Why don't we have a forensic psychiatrist take a look at him?"

"Hmmm," Purcell said. He went back inside to talk with Dan again, and when he emerged for a second time he told Norman, "You know, Tom, about that psychiatrist, that wouldn't be a bad idea." He looked long and hard at the prosecutor. "Tom, no hired gun."

"Oh no, no, no hired gun." A few moments later, while Falzon and some other inspectors were escorting Dan to the jail, Norman hurried to his office. First he tried Dr. Roland Levy, a psychiatrist on the staff of the University of California's Langley Porter Neuropsychiatric Institute, but Dr. Levy was in class so Norman had to leave a message. Next he was going to call a well-known forensic psychiatrist he had used on a number of other cases, when suddenly he remembered that the man had recently come out of the closet and acknowledged he was a homosexual. Won't do in this case, Norman chuckled to himself. He left messages for a number of other psychiatrists, including Dr. Donald Lunde of Stanford (who, as things turned out, would testify for the defense). Finally, Dr. Levy returned his call and said he would be able to come by and do an examination later that evening. Norman was anxious: if he got a psychiatrist in there fast, before White began to crumble, or before Purcell was joined by another lawyer who might fully appreciate the trap he was setting, and if White got a clean bill of mental health, Norman would have slammed the one escape hatch available.

When Levy finally arrived, he and Norman listened together to the taped confession. Norman realized at once that because Dan had not said he intended to kill anybody he would have to use circumstantial evidence to demonstrate in court that murder had been White's intention. From police interviews that had already been done with Denise Apcar, with the engineer who had seen Dan enter City Hall through a basement window, and from Dan's own taped statement, Norman thought he saw a clear pattern of intention: White had taken his gun *and* extra cartridges, he had told Denise that he planned to give both Moscone and Milk a piece of his mind, he had avoided the metal detector, he had reloaded. Norman asked Dr. Levy to question Dan about why he had climbed through a window to gain entry into City Hall.

About 7 P.M.—eight hours after the killings—Dr. Levy was allowed to interview Dan. During the two hours they talked, Dan explained to Dr. Levy that he had not intended to shoot anyone, that he had reloaded "automatically" before he left the mayor's office, and that he had not used the front door at City Hall because he thought it would "embarrass" the guard at the metal detector to discover his gun.

In the written report he prepared for Tom Norman, Dr. Levy concluded that: "He showed no evidence of psychotic thinking. . . . His overall judgment . . . appeared to be adequate. . . . The defendant shows no evidence of major mental illness either at the present time or previously. . . . With regard to his mental state at the time of the offenses it appears to me that he had the capacity to appreciate the wrongfulness of his behavior and also to conform his conduct to the requirements of the law. . . . I do not think he would be considered legally insane at the time . . . he was able to act with malice and was probably able to premeditate. . . ."

That was quite enough, Norman thought. Let the defense hire all the shrinks it wanted. *His* psychiatrist had seen the defendant within eight hours of the offenses and found him capable of deliberation, premeditation and malice, the three elements of first-degree murder. Norman had tried a hundred murder cases, maybe more, and this was the cleanest and the surest he had ever come across. A dead-bang case.

It was nearly 10 P.M. before Mary Ann and Ray Sloan were permitted to meet with Dan in a visiting room at the jail. The very first thing Dan said, nodding toward a deputy sheriff, was, "Hey, didja know this guy used to play football with me at Wilson?" The team captain, Ray thought, even now, the team captain. Mary Ann and Dan were alone for a while, and then when Ray joined them again, Dan said to him, "Ray, remind them that I gave the first hundred dollars of any supervisor against the Briggs amendment." Ray figured that Dan meant to imply he hadn't killed Harvey Milk because he was a homosexual.

In the days that followed there was a never-ending stream of visitors, even Archbishop Quinn came to talk with Dan. The day after the killings, a dozen immediate relatives showed up at one time to see Dan, all crowding into a tiny room while Jim Denman watched through two-way glass. There were only three chairs in the room, so everybody stood. There was something peculiar, Denman noticed, although at first he wasn't sure what. Then he realized that despite the crowding in the little room nobody was touching. Not one member of his family hugged Dan, or shook his hand, or even patted his shoulder. At first Denman thought it must have been because of aversion from the awful thing he had done, but after a moment he saw it wasn't that at all. Not touching was just normal for the White family. There was no touching, no tears, no shaky voices. Denman wondered if that coldness didn't have something to do with why Dan was capable of killing.

Dan spent most of the days that followed in his cell, seldom stirring. Bail was set at $1 million. He had been brought books by his family and friends, in violation of jail rules, and he read quite a bit. Most of what he was reading were Irish histories and historical novels, things that allowed him to escape from his surroundings to that land which had always represented peace and quiet for him. Dan became quite interested in the life of an IRA martyr named Kevin Barry. Barry was a medical student who was hanged for taking part in a shootout during which six British soldiers were killed. On the day of Barry's execution in 1920, dozens of Irish students and doctors had been aroused to join the rebellion. A street in Belfast was named after the young martyr.

Dan was treated almost as a hero in the jail during the six months before his trial began, allowed special visits outside regular hours, unlimited phone calls, his books. A public health nurse named Jane Halstead watched all this with a bitter amazement. Jane was a lesbian, and she had strong feelings about the murder of Harvey Milk in particular. Every morning between eight and nine she wheeled her big cart stocked with band aids, vitamins, prescribed pills, past Dan's cell. She tried hard to treat him like any other prisoner; she was a nurse, after all, and that was her responsibility.

"How you doing?" she asked. "Do you need anything?"

Invariably Dan replied, "No, I'm okay." He never met her eye. She could tell how wary he was of anything that might turn into a confrontation. But in fact, and despite her strong feelings, she also sensed something likable about him. Compared to the usual machismo of the male prisoners, Dan seemed like a softie. He was so lethargic and withdrawn that Jane suspected he might have been tranquilized, so she checked the medical records and found that a jail doctor had prescribed a daily dose of a strong sleeping pill, Dalmane. The doctor had done something she had never heard of before: he had not entered a date on which the medication was to be discontinued. Dan could take it for as long as he wanted.

Another nurse on the night shift had become fascinated with Dan and most evenings would bring him out of his cell into the medical bay where she would make him tea and allow him special treats—like the chocolate cake she baked for him. When he didn't want to eat the jail food she sent out for roast beef sandwiches for the prisoner. She would also let him use the phone. Every time Dan went into the medical bay the rest of the inmates were locked down; nobody was allowed to move anywhere in the jail when Dan was out of his cell, and that was most every night. The deputies went along with it because a lot of them also treated Dan like a celebrity. They would come by to talk with him in his cell and the atmosphere was always rah-rah. They would jock around and talk about a football game or something like that, and then when they left, Dan reverted immediately into his quiet, withdrawn state.

And cops. A day didn't seem to go by during those first few weeks without some cops coming around, against all regulations, to visit with Dan in his cell. Denman tried to prevent it, but there was nothing he could do. In fact, that very first night, the night of the killings, three cops had bullied their way into the jail against explicit orders and sat alone talking with Dan until it was nearly dawn.

Dan's old friends on the police force and among the firemen set up a lottery to help support Mary Ann and little Charlie. In some parts of the city there were Tupperware parties to benefit Dan's family, and

Free Dan White tee shirts were being sold. The shirts were inscribed with John Donne's famous line: "No man is an island entire of itself."

In the days immediately after the killings Mary Ann had been assigned a round-the-clock police guard—naturally, there had been death threats against Dan's family—and the guards tagged along as Mary Ann and Ray went around town talking to different lawyers, trying to find somebody to defend Dan. It was one of Mary Ann's police guards who first suggested the name of a young criminal attorney who had won a lot of notice for his defense of a Chinese gang member who had taken part in a bloody massacre at a restaurant called the Golden Dragon. Eleven people had been wounded and five killed, most of them innocent bystanders who had just been there to eat dinner. Except for the defendant represented by Douglas Schmidt, all the other gang members had been convicted of first-degree murder and given life sentences. Schmidt's client had been found guilty of second-degree murder and sentenced to twenty-eight years.

Doug Schmidt had been born in the same year as Dan White, 1946, and raised in the town of Alpina on Michigan's Upper Peninsula. Alpina had once been a logging and commercial fishing village but when the white pine was cut and the fish had been caught, it had, like San Francisco, prostrated itself before the almighty tourist buck. During the years of Schmidt's growing up, the most renowned citizen of the Upper Peninsula was John Donaldson Voelker, a justice of the Michigan Supreme Court. Under the pen name of Robert Traver, Voelker had written a national bestseller, set in a fictionalized Alpina, that was made into a popular movie starring Gregory Peck as a smalltown lawyer—*Anatomy of a Murder*. It was just one of fate's mocking riddles that the legal basis for Gregory Peck's successful defense of an accused murderer, and the law that would be used by Doug Schmidt in the murder trial of Dan White, were virtually identical.

Although by 1978 Schmidt had been in San Francisco for ten years, he still had a certain farm boyishness about him, an "aw-shucks" quality that made him capable of blushing and provided him with a disarming courtroom manner. His folks had not been especially well off but their son intended to be. "I'm not interested in being a noted expert," Schmidt would say, "I'm interested in being rich."

He was well on his way. His first law office after graduating from Hastings College of the Law was in a storefront on Haight Street where, as he put it himself, he had picked crap with the chickens. In 1972 he moved his practice to a refurbished Victorian duplex on Union Street, which was known for its swinging singles bars. Schmidt owned six hundred acres in Mendocino County, drove a Corvette in town, and also possessed a station wagon, a pickup truck, a couple of motorcycles and a tractor. He liked to tinker with his machines.

By the time Mary Ann showed up at Schmidt's Union Street office she had talked with five or six other lawyers, but for one reason or another none of them had seemed right. It was so important to get the right lawyer, Danny's life was on the line. She was praying for divine guidance; her faith kept her going. Almost from the moment she met Doug Schmidt she could sense that he and her husband would get along; they even resembled each other: same age, same huskiness, same open, boyish faces and ingenuous manners. In fact, Doug reminded Mary Ann of Dan, of the way he had been before everything happened.

As for Schmidt, he didn't hesitate to take the case. It was a big case and he was vain enough to enjoy seeing his name in the newspapers. And no matter how bad it looked for Dan White, defense lawyers built their reputations on the cases they chose to lose. In addition, he thought that Mary Ann—and Dan, whom he soon met—were nice people. His fee would not be inconsequential, either.

Mary Ann's instinct had been right; Dan and Doug hit it off at once. That very night Schmidt went to the city jail and spent twenty minutes with Dan, and he returned the following day and the day after that. There was a rapport between the two young men, one in so much trouble and the other his possible savior. They were both physical men, and Schmidt brought to the case a sense of challenge that was not unlike Dan's approach to things. For a defense lawyer, Schmidt was politically conservative. When Dan explained the dishonesty of the politicians at City Hall, Schmidt was inclined to agree with his client's view; politics, so far as he was concerned, was a sewer.

One of the lawyer's first responsibilities was to explain the law to his client. There were several justifications or excuses for killing another human being. If you killed in self-defense, or to defend your property or loved ones, or to prevent a robbery or some other felony, those were justified homicides. Dan could see that none of those applied to his situation. Or if, at the time of the killings, you were drunk, or under the influence of drugs, then the homicide might be excused on the grounds that you were incapable of knowing what you were doing. That, too, was inapplicable in Dan's case. Then there was an insanity defense: if you were so crazy that you couldn't distinguish between right and wrong, that might excuse you. Of course, Dan had not been frothing at the mouth. And somewhere between insanity and full culpability was a defense with a contemporary little twist, in line with up-to-date psychological theory: diminished capacity. In layman's language, if at the time of your crime, as a result of mental illness, or stress, or emotional disturbance, you had been unable to fully appreciate the wrongfulness of what you were doing, or unable to control your impulses, then you were guilty not of murder but of the lesser crime of manslaughter. Schmidt laid it all out and Dan understood: something had gone wrong with him, he wasn't responsible. It was arranged for psychiatrists and psychologists to begin probing Dan's psyche to see if they could find evidence of mental illness.

Dan and Mary Ann were well satisfied with Doug Schmidt. Ray Sloan, however, didn't like the guy; he thought he was too young and inexperienced. Ray thought that his appeal was that he was a Dan White clone. "You should be looking for a lawyer, not a friend," Ray advised Dan.

"I *want* Doug," Dan said. "Understand, Ray, it's my life on the line and my choice. And I want Doug."

Schmidt had what seemed like a million things to do to get ready for the trial.

He wanted to keep the district attorney's office tied up with pretrial motions, motions that had no great chance of success: Schmidt requested, for instance, that District Attorney Joe Freitas disqualify himself, and that the judge be removed from hearing the case. He did not, however, ask for a change of venue despite the massive, unfavorable publicity. There was good reason for him to want the case tried in San Francisco. The jury's verdict would depend, to a considerable degree, on their sympathy with Dan White. If Schmidt got the right jury, a jury of people who understood how the city had changed and didn't particularly like it, a jury that didn't have to have spelled out for it stories about black whores and a hundred thousand homosexuals, but could read between the lines, then the battle was half won. So Schmidt wanted the case to be tried in San Francisco, where it would not be just another murder.

And there were fishing expeditions to be undertaken as well. About a month before the trial was due to begin he asked Frank Falzon out to lunch. Falzon had continued as the principal investigator; even though Joe Freitas and Tom Norman knew that Falzon and White had been friendly, they believed they could trust his professionalism, and there was no better homicide cop in town.

Norman was taken aback when Falzon said to him, "I'm going to lunch with Doug Schmidt. Do you have any objections?" Norman didn't like it but he didn't seem to have any choice, either.

"Well, just be professional," he said. "And find out what you can about what the defense is going to be."

Schmidt had already learned from Dan about his long-standing friendship with Falzon, and the mutual esteem in which they held each other. Over lunch, Schmidt confirmed that with Falzon. "What's Dan White's character like?" the defense attorney asked.

"Hey, I don't know any hickeys in Dan White's background," replied the inspector.

The conversation provided Schmidt with some important knowledge. First, since Falzon would undoubtedly be taking the stand to introduce the confession tape into evidence, Schmidt could safely cross-examine Falzon about what kind of man Dan White was without hurting his case. Far more importantly, Schmidt now knew that the district attorney's office had apparently not gathered any information to contradict what would be a key element in the defense case, that Dan White had been a *good man* who had just snapped.

Falzon reported back to Tom Norman about his conversation with Doug Schmidt. "What if I'm asked on the stand," Falzon wanted to know, "what kind of guy Dan White was?"

"What's that got to do with the price of coffee?" Norman snapped. Dan White's background, he assured Falzon, would be inadmissible. As far as Norman was concerned, character wasn't an issue: the man had admitted to pulling the trigger and he hadn't been drunk, crazy or high on drugs. Dead-bang.

Schmidt kept fishing. He could see, just as Norman had, that certain of Dan's actions on the day of the killings tended to suggest *intention:* taking his gun with him to City Hall, for instance, or climbing in the window rather than passing through the metal detector. In January, Schmidt was granted a preliminary hearing from which he had the press and the public excluded. At that closed hearing he called forty-one witnesses, including supervisors and former supervisors who testified that they, too, had carried guns in City Hall. Supervisor Lee Dolson testified, in addition, that he had seen other people enter City Hall through that same window. Schmidt was lining up witnesses who could cast doubt on every link in the circumstantial chain of events that might suggest to the jury that Dan had wanted to kill George and Harvey.

Perhaps an even more important effect of the preliminary hearing was to intimidate District Attorney Joe Freitas, who was a politician first and foremost. Freitas was already campaigning for a second term and he was vulnerable because of the Jim Jones fiasco; it was Freitas who had hired the president of Jones's congregation as an assistant D.A. and then put him in charge of an investigation into voter frauds by People's Temple during George Moscone's 1975 election.

Freitas himself had no background in criminal law; he had personally tried only one murder case and had nearly blown it when he had failed to put an essential witness on the stand. He was mightily dependent upon the advice of Tom Norman in preparing their case. Norman was what was known in the parlance of the D.A.'s office as a lifer, a career prosecutor who knew instinctively and without being told what the different bosses he had served wanted from him. He did not have to be told, for instance, to go easy on politics. Norman was aware that Freitas's career was on the line. And Norman was, as well, a gentleman of the old school, concerned that the posthumous reputation of George Moscone not be besmirched. Norman had, in fact, assigned a detective within the district attorney's office to look into the "George Moscone stories" and had learned that many of the rumors about George's personal life were true. He was bound and determined that none of that would come out during the trial.

Tom Norman's prissy manners and Joe Freitas's political concerns played right into Schmidt's hands. And Schmidt was doing nothing to discourage speculation in the press that he would try the case, as one article put it, "on a broad spectrum of social, political and ethical issues." He even included State Senator John Briggs, the anti-gay crusader, on the list of potential witnesses he might call at the trial. Schmidt was using mirrors to create the illusion that he was ready to try the case on the issue of political character, to put the city politic on trial. It was a game the district attorney's office wanted very badly not to play.

Doug Schmidt always made a point in preparing his cases of gathering his proposed instructions to the jury at the outset. He wanted to know at every step exactly where he was headed. If the judge incorporated the modifications he proposed, and if the instructions—the applicable law the judge would read to the jury before they retired to arrive at a verdict—fit perfectly around the evidence that had been presented, then his client's chances were that much better.

From Dan's taped statement, and from interviews with Mary Ann, with Dan's mother, with his sister Nancy, and with Denise Apcar, Schmidt gleaned that Dan had been subject to "down moods," and further, that on the day of the killings he had had all those funny symptoms, like the ringing in his ears and the feeling that his head was going to explode. It certainly sounded like a case could be made for diminished capacity. Along with his associate counsel, Stephen Scherr, Schmidt had early on researched and prepared instructions to fit their basic line of defense, and to provide as well that on November 27 Dan had been in the grip of an "irresistible impulse." Most fortuitous of all, though, in laying the legal foundation for the defense, was the precedent in a case known as *People* v. *Berry.*

A man named Albert Berry had strangled his wife after she taunted him repeatedly about her other lover, offering and then withdrawing her sexual favors to her husband over a considerable period of time. At Berry's trial there had been only two defense witnesses, Berry himself and a psychiatrist, Dr. Martin Blinder. Dr. Blinder had testified that the repeated provocations by his wife had whipped Berry into a frenzy, a heat of passion which he was powerless to control. The trial judge had refused to instruct the jury on the law as interpreted by Dr. Blinder, but the state supreme court had found the trial judge in error and Berry's conviction for first-degree murder had been overturned. Dr. Blinder's argument in the Berry case could equally well be applied to the political provocations of George Moscone's broken promises to Dan White. One problem with this line of defense would come if the D.A. asked the judge for an instruction to the jury explaining that heat of passion must, under the law, arise out of a sudden quarrel and not belatedly as revenge or punishment. Schmidt fully expected Norman to incorporate that standard line of legal reasoning into his case.

Still and all, *People* v. *Berry* opened up, as Robert Traver had put it in *Anatomy of a Murder,* "beautiful rolling vistas of lovely law and instructions. Boy oh boy."

Schmidt was as ready as he ever would be.

2

A Jury of His Peers

Judge Calcagno, a North Beach Republican of the old school, tucked his judicial robe under him and sat down. It was, in fact, a choirboy's robe. The clerk declared, "Be seated." Calcagno scanned the crowded courtroom in which not one person knew about the pain in his stomach, the malignancy, and nobody would.

"It is now my duty," he said, clearing his throat, "to select a jury, a fair and impartial jury."

Tommy Norman felt the familiar tingle as the first twelve potential jurors filed into the box. No matter how many times the ritual began, he never failed to feel this stirring, part anxiety but mostly the thrill of being in the arena. The world outside, outside the *pit,* as he thought of it, simply vanished. He barely noticed that Doug Schmidt was on his feet, his arms folded around his chest, paying his respect to the jurors, as he sat peering over his half-frame glasses.

Norman liked to do his *voir dire* fast, trusting to his instincts; the juries he had selected in hundreds of cases had returned verdicts that gave him one of the best conviction rates in the state of California. Twelve ordinary, honest people, that was all he deserved and all he wanted, ever.

Four of these first twelve would survive the process of challenge and elimination: Irene Dewey, the middle-aged wife of a bank branch manager, who lived about a half mile from Dan and Mary Ann's house on Shawnee Avenue; William Wald, two months retired as a printer of tax forms for the Internal Revenue Service; Darlene Benton, the daughter of a sheetmetal worker and herself an underwriter for Hartford Insurance Company; she had lived all of her thirty-three years in those San Francisco neighborhoods that lay south of downtown; and George Mintzer, who would be selected as the jury foreman, a selection that did not please the defense lawyers.

It was hard to tell about Mintzer. Schmidt had no objection to him, he fit certain requirements they were looking for. He had served in the army during the Second World War and so was familiar with guns and probably wouldn't be shocked by their use. He was of a certain age, and where he lived, only a block away from Irene Dewey, was the right kind of neighborhood. Mintzer, though, had been in the city for only five years, transferred there by the Bechtel Corporation, for whom he did cost estimates, mostly on power plant designs. A Jew, with a big, soft body and a face like schoolteacher-turned-comedian Sam Levenson, there was an ironic smile playing around his intelligent eyes. There was no telling, but he might be a closet liberal.

Though for entirely different reasons, Schmidt and Norman were each challenging jurors who gave indications of liberalism.

Norman did not want opponents of the death penalty hearing a capital case. Capital punishment was an issue that for the prosecutor had as many sharp edges as a razor ribbon. To begin with, Norman wasn't bloodthirsty; he accepted the death penalty with no problem but he didn't embrace it with the fervor that some did. His boss, Joe Freitas, was in fact an opponent of the death penalty and didn't relish the idea of standing for election in November while pleading for a punishment which contradicted his own views. But, on the other hand, Freitas and Norman didn't really have too much to worry about in that regard in San Francisco. It had been the only county in the state to vote against capital punishment in the last election, and among courthouse cognoscenti it was a given that San Francisco juries didn't gas even the most heinous, socially unredeemed killers. So in fact Norman might have allowed some death penalty opponents, as long as they weren't doctrinaire, onto the jury without any probable loss of advantage. But— and it was a big but—because the murder trial of Dan White was as much a political as a judicial event, it would *look* bad, look like the D.A. wasn't really trying to throw the book at Dan, if they let somebody who was admittedly against capital punishment onto the jury. They had to be challenged, even though that meant bumping liberals, the kind of people who might have been partisans of George Moscone or Harvey Milk. And that, in turn, meant risking a jury more sympathetic with

White. The political consequences for Freitas of a manslaughter verdict were too awful to even contemplate, but Tommy Norman had assured him this was the best case for first-degree murder he had ever tried, and so Freitas and Norman agreed that challenging death penalty opponents was the better course, judicially and politically.

Schmidt and his associate counsel, Stephen Scherr, had no such tortuous hesitations about eliminating jurors who were homosexuals; there would be no homosexuals on Dan White's jury of peers. When George Riley, a young man with short, dark, curly hair and a neatly trimmed moustache was being questioned on *voir dire*, Schmidt asked him: "Have you ever supported controversial causes, say homosexual rights, for instance?" Reilly replied, "I sign anything that comes along at Eighteenth and Castro, I'm not very discriminating that way." Riley was excused by the defense.

When Schmidt asked Felix Amato whether he had any homosexual friends and Amato answered, "Being gay myself, yes, I have homosexual friends," Amato was also bumped. Pretty soon the gay weeklies began to refer to Dan White's "all-heterosexual jury."

(Outside the courtroom a TV reporter asked Amato for an interview. Amato shrugged. "Oh well," he said, "there's nothing like coming out to your boss on TV. You have to do it sooner or later, I guess. Okay."

A reporter standing nearby who had been a friend of Milk's said, "Harvey must be happy about that, wherever he is.")

Schmidt and Scherr had done a lot of talking about what kind of people they wanted on the jury, and had a profile of the ideal juror. The perfect juror would be somebody working class—that was very important to them—preferably Catholic, conservative and older than fifty. The men should be familiar with guns and the women with those sympathies a mother feels for a good boy in big trouble. While Schmidt did the *voir dire*, Scherr sat at the defense table, shuffling yellow index cards they had prepared on each member of the jury panel, watching for the subtle clues conveyed by an expression or a gesture, and sometimes whispering a suggestion to Schmidt. Scherr looked like he had once been a prodigy, someone who had worn a sliderule on his belt in high school and had been president of the chess club. He and Schmidt had never worked in tandem before, but they were finding that their abilities meshed quite easily. The handsome, disarming Schmidt, with his simple eloquence, would handle the pleading, while Scherr, with his fecund, scholarly mind, handled the law motions and rode shotgun, covering Schmidt's flank.

By the lunch recess on Friday, April 27, there were seated in the jury box six more people who had so far passed muster with both sides. Grayce Jackson was unmarried, a retired saleswoman of wholesale beauty supplies whose wavily coiffed white hair and bright red lipstick gave every indication that her vanity was intact. Helga Soulie had lived all her life in San Francisco and her father, brother and son-in-law were all cops. Patricia Powis was a secretary for an insurance company. She had three kids. Barbara Costuros and her husband, who worked at the county jail, were native San Franciscans. Her favorite television show was "Quincy," and the first thing she read in the newspaper was "Dear Abby." Nelson Bermudez and George Connor had certain similarities. Connor had grown up in the Excelsior, in District 8, and Bermudez lived there now. One was a mechanic and the other a printer. Tommy Norman liked them both because he figured they might identify with what he thought of as younger thoughts, with George Moscone-type thinking.

Norman, Schmidt, and Judge Calcagno were all keeping score on printed jury lists as prospective jurors came and went. Outside the security glass, in the first row behind her husband, so was Mary Ann, who today was wearing the Dianne Feinstein look, a white blouse with a bow at the neck. Norman still had remaining to him twenty-two of his twenty-six preemptive challenges—for which he needn't offer reasons—and Schmidt only one less, when Richard Aparicio, in seat number eight, began to undergo *voir dire*.

Aparicio said that he was a retired policeman, although the truth was that he had been a patrol special, a merchant-employed beat walker licensed by the police department and generally known in San Francisco as a "door rattler." Both Norman and Schmidt like the idea of having a cop, or a close approximation, on the jury. Aparicio had the bluff, perhaps overly earnest manner of a self-conscious go-getter.

"Do you believe Dan White killed George Moscone and Harvey Milk?" Schmidt asked him.

"Yes, I do," he said, as had every potential juror.

"Do you have an opinion as to why?"

Aparicio hesitated, concern registering on his wide, red face. Like all the others on the panel he had watched the two days of *voir dire* on a closed-circuit television hookup from an assembly room upstairs, and was aware that nobody had answered that question affirmatively.

"Yes," he finally said. "I have certain opinions, um, yes, I mean I'm not . . . yes, I do."

"And what are they?"

"Well, I'd say it was social and economic pressures," Aparicio responded. Schmidt's heart must have sunk; the answer was too good to be good. In the months since the killings, "pressure" had become the catchword used by those people, and there were many, who sympathized with what had driven Dan White into the abyss. It had begun with a headline the day after the shootings: WHAT MADE WHITE GO ON RAMPAGE?, the *Examiner* had asked. The answer in the subhead, quoting Supervisor Lee Dolson, who had visited Dan in jail, was: Ex-Cop Was a Casualty of Pressure.

"Could you put that opinion out of your mind?" Schmidt asked.

"Yes, yes, I could."

Tommy Norman put on his half-frames and studied the yellow legal pad on which he had been jotting notes. He leaned over and whispered for a moment with Frank Falzon, who would sit beside him for the entire trial.

"Mr. Norman," the Judge said expectantly. It was Norman's turn for a challenge.

"The People pass, Judge," Norman said. He liked to do it fast, and his instinct was that these twelve people were a hanging jury, the kind he always worked with, the kind he knew.

Now it was Schmidt's turn. Looking at the same panel that satisfied Norman, he saw a jury much like he and Scherr had hoped for but never expected to really get. Nine of the twelve had lived in San Francisco for twenty years or more and knew firsthand what had changed. There were more Catholics than non-Catholics, and four of the women were old enough to be Dan's mother. If you had to guess you'd say that only one or two at most might have voted for George Moscone. They were a pretty representative sample of the new San Francisco working class, a pretty good cross section of the kind of people who felt oppressed and neglected by the political system: housewives and clerical workers for insurance companies and banks and corporations, a mechanic and a couple of printers and the wife of a jailhouse employee. Most of them had spent the better part of their lives in the faded stretches of poor and modest neighborhoods south and east of Twin Peaks. And then there was Aparicio, and it only took one strong advocate to hang a jury. That was how Schmidt had beat Norman the only other time they had gone against each other in a murder trial: his advocacy had produced not one but two hung juries.

Schmidt leaned over and whispered into Dan's ear. Dan's head was slumped forward, but Doug put an arm around his client's broad shoulders and reassuringly squeezed his left shoulder, the one with the shamrock tattoo.

"The defense passes, your honor," he said.

"Very well," said Judge Calcagno, with his index finger resting lightly on his lips. "It appears we have a jury."

"We will now commence the trial," Judge Calcagno said when he assumed his seat on Tuesday morning, the first of May. He turned to face the jury. "You made an inquiry to me yesterday about the taking of notes. Let me just give you a warning about taking notes because many of us can't take notes as fast as we hear the evidence . . . so don't get so involved in note taking that you are missing the balance of the case, and that is the end of the sermon.

"With that, Miss Clerk, please read the information to the jurors."

"Ladies and gentlemen of the jury," began the clerk, "this is the information in the case now pending before you:

"In the Superior Court of the State of California, in and for the city and county of San Francisco, the People of the State of California, plaintiff, versus Daniel James White, defendant.

"Action Number 98663. Count one: Daniel James White is accused by the district attorney of the city and county of San Francisco, state of California, by this information, of the crime of felony, to wit: Violation of section 187 of the California Penal Code, committed as follows: That said defendant on or about the twenty-seventh day of November, 1978, did willfully, unlawfully and with malice aforethought murder George R. Moscone, the duly elected mayor of the city and county of San Francisco, California.

"Use of firearm allegation: It is further alleged that in the commission of the above offense said defendant, Daniel James White, personally used a firearm, to wit: a .38-calibre revolver.

"Count two: The defendant, Daniel James White, is further accused by the district attorney of the city and county of San Francisco, state of California, by this information, of the crime of felony, to wit: Violation of section 187 of the California Penal Code, committed as follows: That said defendant, Daniel James White, on or about the twenty-seventh day of November, 1978, did willfully, unlawfully and with malice aforethought murder Harvey Milk, a duly elected supervisor of the city and county of San Francisco, California.

"Use of firearm allegation: It is further alleged that in the commission of the above offense, the said defendant, Daniel James White, personally used a firearm, to wit: a .38-calibre revolver.

"And the defendant, Daniel James White, has entered a plea of not guilty to each of the charges and allegations contained in this information."

Judge Calcagno faced the prosecutor's table, where Tommy Norman had been joined this morning by the sleek, silver-haired District Attorney Freitas, who would not appear in court again until the last day of the trial, and by Frank Falzon, who was sitting no more than three feet from Dan, at the defense table. "Mr. Norman, do you desire to make an opening statement at this time?"

"I do, Judge."

"All right, you may proceed."

The counsel for the People stood at his table, which was the nearer to the jurors, whose eyes were all fastened on him. He hitched his trousers up a notch.

"Your Honor, members of the jury—and you are the jury now." His dainty hands quietly laid his glasses on the table in front of him. "I am Thomas F. Norman and I am the assistant district attorney. Members of the jury, you have heard the information read to you, I'm sure that you generally know what this case is about." His tongue clucked against the roof of his mouth. "The statements that I make at this particular time to you are, as His Honor indicated, not evidence. They are simply an outline, briefly, of what I expect the evidence in this case is going to show, which will support these charges."

Norman took the jury rapidly through the sequence of events beginning with Dan's resignation, his attempt to regain his seat, George Moscone's exercising his "duly sworn" authority to choose whomever he wished to fill the vacant seat, right up until the morning of the twenty-seventh.

"Mr. White," he said, "before leaving his home, armed himself with a .38 Smith and Wesson revolver which is commonly called a Chief's Special. The gun was loaded when he took it, put it in a holster, strapped it in his belt."

Norman followed Dan to City Hall, through the basement window, up the stairs to Cyr Copertini's desk, and finally, "into a back or private office, almost like a lounge."

Except for the scratching of the reporter's pens and the artists' pencils the courtroom was still. You could sense Norman's supreme confidence as he continued. "They sat down. The mayor poured Mr. White a drink, poured himself a drink, neither of which was ever consumed through the intercession of other events which immediately followed." His voice fell and rose from syllable to syllable, sometimes chalky, the next moment reedy.

The two men had a short discussion, Norman told the rapt jurors. "Mr. White drew out his .38 special revolver and he fired two shots into the mayor's body." The foreman, Mintzer, and the secretary, Patricia Powis, both flicked their eyes toward and away from Dan, who sat rigidly, his eyes fixed on nothing. He was so pale he looked green. "After the mayor fell to the floor disabled, he then discharged two more .38-calibre special rounds into the mayor's *head,* on the right side, about the area of the right ear, at very close range, which were not unlike *coup-de-grace* shots." Norman, his hands folded on his tummy, savored the Frenchified phrase like a deliciously evil bonbon. It was so nicely suggestive of an execution. He continued.

"Mr. White then reloaded his pistol with some of the rounds that were in his pocket, and entered the main hallway." White, he told them, ran across City Hall and found Supervisor Milk. "Now, Mr. White and Mr. Harvey Milk were politically dissimilar to each other, having substantially different views," Norman said, passing over the distasteful and the dangerous as lightly as a feather duster. "The two of them went into the office. The door was shut. A shot was heard, and Harvey Milk was heard to cry out, "Oh, no." He took three shots to the body and when he fell to the floor he was shot twice in the back of the head."

Dan White ran out of the building, Norman explained, and within an hour "surrendered himself."

"Members of the jury," he concluded, hitching his pants again, "that, briefly, is what I expect the evidence in this case will show, which I expect, at the conclusion of this case, will support the charges of murder in the first degree which have been alleged here. Thank you very much." Norman's presentation had been direct, low-key but strong in both tone and content; his conclusions as inevitable and indisputable as death—death for Dan White in the gas chamber at San Quentin.

It was Doug Schmidt's choice now whether to make an opening statement as well. He might have waited until after the People had concluded their case, but wasn't it better to immediately admit the offenses—they could not be denied, at any rate—and thus take the wind out of Norman's sails? Mightn't the jury be very nearly bored by the repetitive recitals of proof of offenses already admitted? And wasn't it better to create some sympathy with Dan, and to frame the questions as Schmidt wanted them to be considered, at the outset?

"All right," said Judge Calcagno, "Mr. Schmidt, do you desire to make an opening statement at this time?"

"I will make an opening statement," Schmidt said, rising and nervously wiping his left hand across his cheek.

"Very well."

Schmidt wrapped his arms around his husky chest. To appear honestly unafraid of the truth was the key to his strategy. He turned his open, Midwestern face toward the twelve strangers in the box.

"Ladies and gentlemen, the prosecutor, Mr. Norman, has quite skillfully outlined *certain* of the facts," he began. "And I think for a proper understanding of what did happen on November twenty-seventh it will be necessary for all the facts, all the truth, to be presented here, and rather than putting out some of the facts that I believe will support some theory of the defense, I intend to present all the facts, including some of the background material that will show not so much *what* happened on November twenty-seventh, but rather *why* those tragedies occurred."

Schmidt walked out into the arena in front of the judge's bench. Behind his rimless glasses his clear, blue eyes sought contact with a juror's.

"I believe that it's important for two reasons. One, that the people of the city and county of San Francisco deserve to know all the facts. Second, perhaps more importantly, for a *closer* understanding of what did occur on November twenty-seventh. . . . It's not disputed that Dan White did, indeed, shoot and kill George Moscone, and I think the evidence is equally clear that Dan White did shoot and kill Harvey Milk . . . Daniel White gave a statement to that effect.

"You might ask, why is it necessary to have a trial, and the answer to that simply is not so much as to *what* occurred on the twenty-seventh, but the facts as to *why* that occurred, and I think that when all the facts are out the charge of first-degree murder simply will not be supported here, and it's simply not what happened. . . . The issue in this trial is properly to understand why that happened."

Having posed that tantalizing question, that psychological thriller, and having brushed aside the killings themselves as indisputable, Schmidt now brought his protagonist onto the stage. The audience of twelve, his chosen audience, was following his every word.

"He was a native of San Francisco," Schmidt began, in the past tense, subtly directing their attention to what had become of the once vital man sitting at the defense table. Dan stared straight ahead toward a blank pressed-wood wall, appearing almost tubercular, somebody who had once been big and now had shrunk. There were knots of worry and incomprehension around his pale forehead and eyes. "He went to school here, went through high school here. He was a noted athlete. He was an army veteran who served in Vietnam, and was honorably discharged from the army. He became a policeman and later transferred to the fire department. He was married in December of 1976." Grayce Jackson, the retired beautician who was juror number twelve, looked toward Mary Ann, pale and strained on the outside of the security glass. "And he fathered a child in July 1978. Dan White was a good policeman and Dan White was a good fireman.

"In fact," Schmidt continued, pacing, "he was decorated for having saved a woman and her child in a very dangerous fire. But the complete picture of Dan White was not known until sometime after these tragedies occurred. Good people, fine people with fine backgrounds, simply don't kill people in cold blood, it just doesn't happen." He paused to let that sink in, it was the nub of his case: if the jury didn't buy that they wouldn't buy the defense. If you closed your eyes and listened to Doug Schmidt you heard the twang of the pinewoods and farmlands of the Upper Peninsula, you heard the throaty sincerity of the young Jimmy Stewart portraying all the classic American virtues, the Norman Rockwell virtues.

Schmidt's hand passed nervously across his cheek again. "The part that perhaps went unrecognized, and certainly went unrecognized until it was too late, was the fact that Daniel White was suffering from a mental illness. He had been suffering from a mental illness since the time of his early manhood, and it's a disease like any other disease, perhaps not as easily diagnosable as a broken leg or arm, but far more devastating to the person, and the disease Daniel White was suffering from is called depression, sometimes referred to as manic depression, and sometimes simply as depression. It's *not* a feeling that perhaps you and I have experienced, wherein one is depressed over certain turns of events or disheartened by something that has happened, but this is a clinical change that occurs within the man's body, and it's diagnosable and substantiated as a disease.

"I don't think Daniel White was particularly insightful as to what his underlying problem was . . . he was an idealistic young man, a *working-class* young man. He was deeply endowed with and believed very strongly in the traditional American values, family and home." Schmidt looked at the jury: these were things they understood, that they believed in too, were they not?

"I think that he could be classified as almost rigidly moral, but above all else, he was an honest man and he was fair, perhaps too fair for politics in San Francisco. He trusted people. . . . Dan White came from a vastly different lifestyle than Harvey Milk." Eighteenth and Castro sported briefly on the grave of Holy Redeemer parish. "Harvey Milk was a homosexual leader and *politician,* and Dan White, though they were from vastly different lifestyles, thought to befriend Harvey Milk after becoming a member of the Board of Supervisors. And he tried to be tolerant, yet protective of the issues that *his* constituency felt were important, and those issues were the traditional values of family and home." Dan White was, Schmidt repeated, "a working-class man, with no political prowess, with no connections."

All the facts, Schmidt had promised, the whole truth. Law professors and courthouse cynics agreed: use the truth whenever possible. He had given the jury, so far, a good man, a working-class man, a man not unlike their husbands or themselves, surely? A man with faults that were perhaps the excesses of virtue—lack of insight, rigid morality—and with a hidden flaw; a man who came to City Hall hoping only to do good. And now he offered them a tragic undoing.

"The irony is," Schmidt said, "that the young man with so much promise, in seeking the job on the Board of Supervisors, actually was destined to construct his downfall." The words and the cadences were in the collective mind of every English-speaking person, even those who could recite only a single line of Shakespeare: "For Brutus is an honorable man/So are they all, all honorable men."

Schmidt described how Dan had been forced to give up his job as a fireman, how Mary Ann had become pregnant, how their income plummeted and despite that, how they mortgaged their new home and went into debt to invest in the Hot Potato. "He started spending long hours, because he wanted to give one hundred percent to his constituency, and yet he wanted to give one hundred percent to his family, and one hundred percent to his new business endeavor, and there simply aren't that many hours in the day.

"The stress continued to build. He was having some difficulty coping . . . some difficulty understanding that in politics one does not always vote one's conscience, rather one votes on occasion because it's expediently and politically sound, and it's a process of compromise, basically. Then, in the summer of 1978, he went into one of those depressive episodes which was triggered by the chemical change of his underlying mental illness. He tried to keep himself physically well and in shape, but the symptoms of sleeplessness and various changes and the stressful factors aggravated the underlying mental illness, and so it was a never-ending spiral of stress." Dan, he told them, resigned.

"In that resignation he cited financial difficulties, but that was a thinly veiled excuse. That resignation actually said that Dan White simply *was not coping* with the job as a supervisor because of all the stress applied to him . . . through politics in San Francisco, through his financial condition, and all his personal problems, together with the underlying mental illness, he simply was not coping. . . . I think he was desperate at that time, and something was wrong with him."

He had the deep attention of all twelve jurors, they were hanging on every word as he wove his tale, as he recreated his client's desperate state of mind, and the events and elements that had conspired in his desperation.

Schmidt began to describe how, under that pressure, Dan had asked George Moscone to reinstate him, and how the mayor had returned the letter—actually put it in his hands—and said he would return his seat to him. And how that had not been true. How Moscone changed his mind but never told Dan. And how, finally, on the morning of the twenty-seventh, Dan left his house to confront the mayor.

"He had no intention at that time to harm anyone, much less to kill the mayor or Harvey Milk," Schmidt continued. He paced restlessly now, quick with conviction. "As he went to City Hall he took a .38-calibre revolver with him, and that was not particularly unusual for Dan White. Dan White was an ex-policeman"—looking at Aparicio, the door rattler who called himself a cop, and at Barbara Costuros, whose husband worked in the jail—"and as a policeman one is required to carry, off-duty, a gun, and well. . . . I think it's common practice.

"And additionally," Schmidt said, "there was the atmosphere created by the Jonestown People's Temple tragedy, and I think it will be shown that that was tied more to the liberal elements of San Francisco politics and not so much to the conservative elements."

Sitting beside Tom Norman, District Attorney Joe Freitas had one hand elegantly resting on his hip under his beautifully tailored pinstripe suit. He remained expressionless.

Schmidt described how Denise had dropped Dan at City Hall and then went to fill the gas tank, and how Dan, impatient to speak to the mayor and without his keys, had climbed through the window and finally was closeted with George Moscone. "Moments thereafter shots rang out in the mayor's office, and Dan White, as was quite apparent at that point, had cracked. The underlying mental illness and stress factors due to the fact that he hadn't been notified, and the sudden emotional surge that he had in the mayor's office was simply too much for him, and he cracked."

It was the notion at the root of the entire system of laws and punishments: that beneath the socialized surface of every individual was a thrashing beast on a tight leash, and that society itself was just a veneer, a neatly mowed lawn beyond which lay the jungle. Pushed far enough, who would not crack?

"He shot the mayor, reloaded his gun, basically on instinct, because of his police training, and was about to leave the building at that point, [when] he saw somebody that he believed to be an aide to Harvey Milk. . . . In the same state of rage, of emotional upheaval having cracked this man, ninety seconds from the time he shot the mayor, he shot and killed Harvey Milk.

"Given those facts, I believe that the theory of the People as to first degree simply is not supported . . . I believe you will agree that the mental illness and stress and emotion of that moment simply broke this man, and this was not a deliberate, premeditated killing.

"Thank you." Schmidt went back to the defense table and sat down beside his client, who continued to stare straight ahead, never looking at his lawyer or the jury, seeing only the blank blonde wood wall and an American flag with gold tassels, if even that.

"Counsel," said Judge Calcagno to Norman, who would present the People's case first, "rather than commence with the witness now, we will take a break. I think we will take the morning recess for fifteen minutes and then you can resume with your first witness."

On the far side of the security glass reporters with afternoon deadlines rushed for the telephones. Inside the glass, where despite the legal niceties a savage, primitive battle had begun over Dan White's life, the Judge turned his attention to the jurors in whose hands the decision rested.

"Let me admonish, ladies and gentlemen of the jury, not to discuss this case among yourselves nor with anyone else, nor allow anyone to speak to you about the case, nor are you to form or express an opinion until this matter has been finally submitted to you."

The twelve judges of the facts, some nodding, were led into the jury room by a tall, ramrod-straight black bailiff.

3
Omissions

"Doctor Stephens, will you please tell the members of the jury and the court your occupation."

"Yes, counsel. I am the chief medical examiner/coroner for the city and county of San Francisco." Boyd Stephens immediately went to work with a pinky digging at an itch inside his ear. Dr. Stephens, whose job it was to poke and cut the enduringly still, was himself kinetic, constantly scratching or tugging at some part of himself. He wore glasses with heavy black frames that seemed almost a natural feature of his thick, Germanic face with its fleshy lips and a nose like a half-full ink bottle, growing squatter and darker near the bottom.

Tommy Norman, his right hand softly jangling his loose change, his head poised like a turkey's, began to ask the questions that would "qualify" Dr. Stephens as an expert. It was always a pleasure for Tommy Norman to examine a pathologist. His knowledge of anatomy, absorbed in his father's surgery, was extensive. Sometimes, in fact, Norman regretted that he had not done what his father had wanted of his only child and become a doctor himself; doctors, after all, saved lives, whereas Norman's profession required a more dolorous duty of him. Methodically, the prosecutor went about eliciting Dr. Stephens' background and training in anatomic, clinical and forensic pathology, what the coroner himself called "the morbid sciences."

"Doctor, inviting your attention to Monday, November twenty-seventh, 1978, in the morning time, did you have occasion to officially respond to the City Hall, which is generally located in this city and county at Polk Street and McAllister Street?"

"Yes, counsel, I did." Dr. Stephens interlaced his fingers, noticed a speck of dirt under a nail, picked it loose, knit his fingers together again.

One step at a time, Norman led the coroner into George Moscone's back office, pausing to introduce a diagram of City Hall into evidence.

"Would you just walk to the diagram."

"Yes," said Dr. Stephens, turning toward the judge. "If I may step down."

"Yes," nodded Judge Calcagno. "There is a pointer right there, Doctor."

"I have one, a pathologist is always prepared." And indeed he was. Dr. Stephens had taken the stand believing that the key question in the case was whether the killings had been one emotional, continuing event, or whether they had been planned and completed in stages. To answer that question as a pathologist, he had scrutinized the death scenes inch by inch with a microscope, had analyzed the bullet paths and sequences, had sifted and pored over the evidence day after day. This morning he had brought with him to court a pair of mannequins he would use to demonstrate his professional conclusion that both killings had been deliberate, aggressive actions with follow-through. The mannequins were in the witness room, ready when they were needed. Relying on evidence and deduction, it was the coroner's legal charge to tell the jury, if he could beyond a reasonable doubt, what had happened in those two offices where the mayor and the supervisor had been killed. During pre-trial conferences he had told Norman that in his opinion the killer was following his targets, that the evidence indicated that the acts had not been a spontaneous frenzy, where the shots were fired so rapidly the killer didn't even know what he was firing at. No, in these cases the evidence showed beyond a reasonable doubt very deliberate motions. Dr. Stephens was prepared.

Now, at Norman's request, Dr. Stephens pointed out to the jury the location of the mayor's office in City Hall on the diagram. "I entered this area of the mayor's study and from the doorway could see a body located towards the east end of the room."

Norman approached the witness with the quiet purposefulness of a floorwalker in a very fine shop, and handed Dr. Stephens six photographs from which the coroner identified the room and the body of the mayor.

"By the way, Doctor, was Mayor Moscone dead?"

"He was dead upon my arrival."

It took Tommy Norman, with his customary thoroughness, sixteen questions to get Dr. Stephens from George Moscone's body to Harvey Milk's, including waystops at the diagram where the coroner made a variety of *x*'s and dotted lines in red pen. The red pen, like the pointer, he had brought with him. Boyd Stephens had testified for Tommy Norman many times over the years.

"Did you see anything in that office that's marked 'DW'?"

"Yes, counsel. The body of a man was in that office."

"Did you learn the identity of that man who was in the office?"

"I recognized the individual, counsel."

"Who was that person?"

"That was Mr. Milk. Harvey Milk."

It was like a slow bicycle race, in which he who finishes last wins. Dr. Stephens scratched an eyebrow. For his court appearance he was wearing a business suit, and not, naturally, the white smock he sometimes wore in his lab with the little color pictures of Elmer Fudd, Mickey Mouse, Donald Duck and his nephews Huey, Dewey and Louie.

At the defense table Doug Schmidt listened but did not take notes. Norman had Dr. Stephens identify the photographs of Harvey Milk's body and the criminal scene. The jury would be shown the black-and-white photographs of both victims but not, at Schmidt's insistence which was upheld by the judge, the more lurid color versions.

Dr. Stephens described how the second body had also been taken to his laboratory, and how it, too, had been subject to an autopsy. In the photographs shown to the jury, both men were naked, their eyes were closed and their mouths open. The pattern of minuscule powder fragments, called tattooing, was clearly visible covering the right side of George Moscone's head.

"Doctor, how do you distinguish a gunshot wound of entry as opposed to a gunshot wound of exit?"

"Counsel, there are many ways of doing this. Some are very accurate. Some are less so. Experience, of course, plays a large part. In many of the cases involving skin, gunshot wounds of entry have a characteristic finding around them called an abrasion collar. It's a scraping-like effect produced as the bullet punches into the skin. . . . This is most suggestive of an entry wound, although I would tell you it's not absolute for entry. The exit wounds tend not to show abrasion unless they have another feature called buttressing. They tend to show a more ragged pattern. . . . In addition, if the bullet strikes bone there may be fragmentation in what's called coning, which is similar to a BB hitting a plate glass window."

Under Norman's guidance, Dr. Stephens described the paths of each of the bullets that had inflicted wounds in Harvey Milk.

"Now, Doctor," Norman said, folding his hands over his tummy, "with respect to the two bullet wounds of entry into the right back of the head . . . who shaved the back of the head, if you know?"

"I shaved the back of the head, counsel. . . . I examined that area carefully for foreign material. I examined it microscopically or with a magnifying lens."

"Now these two wounds to the back of the head, were they wounds of entry in your opinion?"

"The wounds in the back of the head are both wounds of entry, counsel."

With every question and response, Norman was directing the jurors' attention to what, exactly, had been done to these men in the photographs.

"Do you have another photograph there, particularly the next one in order, which is a closer view of the wounds to the back of the head?"

"Yes, counsel."

"Hold that up, please, Doctor. . . . Doctor, did you remove any bullets from the body of Harvey Milk?"

"Yes, counsel, I did."

"How many bullets did you remove from the body of Harvey Milk?"

"I recovered four bullets from the body of Mr. Milk." A fifth had passed through the body and been found on the floor.

Judge Calcagno harumphed softly. "Whenever you feel it is an appropriate time, we will recess for lunch."

And so, with Harvey Milk on the autopsy slab, and the bullets that had killed him secured in small brown evidence envelopes, a two-hour break was taken for lunch.

"Doctor, were you able to form an opinion with any medical certainty . . . as to what the medical cause of death of Harvey Milk was?"

"Yes, counsel."

"Would you explain that to the members of the jury."

"Yes, the cause of death was the multiple gunshot wounds, and most specifically, gunshot wounds involving the head, particularly the bullet that passes through the base of the brain, into the area called the brain stem. This wound, specifically, is one that would cause instant or nearly instant death."

Turning to face the jury, Norman asked Dr. Stephens, whose tongue was loosening the remains of lunch from between two teeth, to describe the sequence of the five bullets that had struck Harvey Milk.

The coroner began with the three wounds to the body. "The wounds to the head, in my opinion, counsel," he continued, "are received by the supervisor when he is on the floor . . . and already incapacitated by previous wounds. I believe, in addition, the wounding sequence is very rapid, a matter of seconds."

There was one more sequence of questions begging to be asked regarding which wounds were fatal, but Norman now turned his attention to the autopsy on George Moscone. At the defense table Schmidt and Scherr exchanged a quick glance.

Under Norman's prodding, the coroner now repeated the entire chain of proof for the death of George Moscone: the number of bullets, their paths, the identification of the photographs of the scene and the bodies, the bullets. The hands on the wall clock at the rear of the courtroom seemed hardly to be moving. Stephens identified Dan's gun as being compatible with the markings on the bullets, and explained how by analyzing the powder fragments in George Moscone's face he had been able to determine that the gun had been held very close to the mayor's ear when the last two bullets were discharged.

"Doctor, based on your visit to the scene in the mayor's office, where you found Mayor Moscone's body, and you looked at it, and other observations made by you in connection with the autopsy, were you able to form any opinion as to the sequence of the wounds occasioned to George Moscone's body?" Norman hooked a soft, white hand under his jacket and rested it on his hip.

"Yes, Counsel."

Turning away from the witness, Norman swept his small, round eyes—under which were dark, sad circles—over the courtroom, as if he were searching for somebody or something, but focused well above the heads of the spectators on the far side of the green tinted glass. "Would you explain that to us, please."

As he had with Harvey Milk, Dr. Stephens described the shots entering the body first. "The wounds of the head," he concluded, "were received when the mayor was already on the floor incapacitated."

"And Doctor, based upon your autopsy, and again your education, your skill, training, experience, were you able to form any opinion with reasonable medical certainty as to what the medical cause of death of the late George Moscone was?"

"The cause of death is multiple gunshot wounds. Two of these wounds, specifically, could cause the mayor's death rapidly. One of these in the lower right chest passes through the liver and produces extensive injury to that organ, and also produces other damage. With our trauma system, he might have survived that wound. The two wounds in the head passed through the brain stem. Both of these wounds, in my opinion, would be compatible with instant death. So it's a matter as to which of the wounds produced actual death. . . ."

At the preliminary hearing in January, from which the press and the public had been excluded by the defense, and the transcript of which remained sealed, Doug Schmidt, preparing himself for the worst that could come out at the trial, had asked Dr. Stephens: ". . . can you give us an opinion as to which of the bullet wounds would have caused death as to Mayor Moscone and then as to Supervisor Milk?"

In that closed hearing, for which there had been no jury, Dr. Stephens had replied that both victims would very probably have survived their other wounds except for those final, hollowpoint shells fragmenting and expanding within their brains. In other words, that Dan had made absolutely certain that both the men he shot died.

But now, before the jury, Norman didn't continue to question the coroner, to elicit that same damning testimony which so strongly suggested a purposeful execution. He felt that he had been as thorough as need be, that there was no way the jury could have missed the cold-blooded nature of the acts. And anything he had missed he could always pick up on redirect when Doug Schmidt was finished questioning the coroner.

"Your witness," Norman said to Schmidt.

Schmidt shook his head. "I have no questions of Doctor Stephens," he said.

"Sir," said Judge Calcagno, "you may leave."

A bailiff took the microphone off Boyd Stephens, and he started toward the door behind which were the unnecessary mannequins. He felt as if he hadn't even testified, that the jury had not learned from him any more than that the two men had died from gunshot wounds. The jurors, he thought, must believe that his testimony was of virtually no significance if Schmidt didn't even want to question him. He looked at the earnest, open-faced defense lawyer, who had spent so many more hours with him preparing his case than Tommy Norman had. Dr. Stephens looked into Doug Schmidt's disingenuous blue eyes, and knew that the jury would never hear another word about what had actually, physically occurred when Dan White had been alone with George Moscone and Harvey Milk; because the coroner alone was legally qualified to speculate about that, he alone could have testified that they were deliberate acts, acts that were completed with a vicious finality. Tommy Norman had not been thorough enough and Doug Schmidt, who was conceding that the acts had taken place, was not going to give him a second chance. In the nonchalant silence of the young defense lawyer the coroner saw genius in action.

The crones in the back benches of the spectators' gallery were waiting for Tommy Norman to pounce, the way he always did when the moment was propitious. They knew how softly the homicide prosecutor with the old-fashioned manners and the widow's peak lulled witnesses into thinking of him as a kind of maiden aunt, and then, when they let down their guard, sank his knitting needles into them.

But since it was Norman's turn to present his own case, not to attack his opponent's, they would have to wait. On Tuesday afternoon and Wednesday morning he put several witnesses on the stand who might have testified about the appealing personal qualities of George Moscone, or about the political conflicts that had existed between the liberal mayor and his accused killer. Cyr Copertini and Rudy Nothenberg, the deputy mayor, had known and loved George Moscone in their different ways. And although the character of the deceased was not within the bounds of allowable testimony, there are many ways to suggest it. Every lawyer knows that juries try victims as well as defendants. To remind the jury about George Moscone, Norman might, for instance, have asked his widow and his children to sit some days on the outside of the security glass, where Mary Ann's taut, anxious presence was so palpable. But he didn't. He thought that was smarmy. "What would it prove?" he asked himself. "That there's an empty place at the dinner table?"

Nor was he desirous of getting into the character of George Moscone. The possibility that if he invited a witness to eulogize the late mayor, the defense might somehow introduce some of the less savory aspects of his character, tied the hands of the prosecutor. In Tommy Norman's theory of the case—and a dead-bang case it was—there was no room for politics, or for sex, whether heterosexual or homosexual.

With Cyr Copertini, Norman restricted himself to asking about the events leading up to Dan White's coming to the mayor's office on November 27, and about the conversation between them while White waited for the mayor. Then Norman turned her over to Schmidt.

"Would you like to take a break or anything?" Schmidt began.

"No, I'm fine."

"Mrs. Copertini . . . was there any apprehension you were aware of with regard to the People's Temple incident?"

"Concern."

"All right. Then I would take it that was concern for the safety of individuals at City Hall, is that correct?" It was a tenet of the defense that Dan had taken his gun with him in part because of the dangerous atmosphere in the city. Schmidt moved to a different tack: ". . . Mrs. Copertini, would it be fair to say . . . that the mayor did not really want to see Dan White?"

"I'd say that he was uncomfortable about it . . . yes."

"In fact, you told [Dan], perhaps, he had someone with him?"

Mintzer, the jury foreman, gave a brief, softly ironic grin. He took the point: Dan White had been lied to up until the very last moment.

"I had said that earlier," she replied. But Schmidt was already moving on. "Was there any personal animosity between George Moscone and Dan White?"

"I would say there was empathy," she answered.

"As a matter of fact, they got along pretty well?"

"As far as I know."

"Thank you, ma'am. I have nothing further."

On Tuesday afternoon and Wednesday morning, Norman called three witnesses with whom he continued to build the chain of circumstance every bit as carefully as he had built model airplanes when he was a boy: Carl Carlson, who had been typing Harvey's promissory note when Dan had arrived on the morning of the twenty-seventh; the engineer who had seen Dan in the basement after he came through the window; and the clerk who had held open the back door to the mayor's office. Then it was Rudy Nothenberg's turn. Nothenberg was thin as a toothpick. As he took the witness chair he buttoned his jacket, which had wide lapels, perhaps as an acknowledgment of the formality of the inquiry. Norman had the deputy mayor tell the jury of seeing Dan run out of the mayor's back office and a few moments later, finding the mayor in a pool of his own blood.

"You may examine," Norman said.

Schmidt had only a few questions. In answer to one of the last, describing the moments before George Moscone was shot down, Nothenberg said: ". . . I was waiting . . . the mayor stuck his head out of the office. . . ."

Schmidt ran his palm over his cheek. "Did he do anything or say anything?"

"He did not say anything to me. . . . He winked at me and then withdrew back into his office."

"All right," Schmidt said, placing himself between the witness and the jury, so Nothenberg had to look in that direction. "By winked, could you demonstrate for us what he did?" The lawyer wanted the jurors to see George's cavalier gesture made while Dan waited for him in the back room, betrayed and distraught.

"He smiled and blinked his eye," Nothenberg said.

One more time so the jurors couldn't miss it. "Winked his eye?"

"Right . . ."

"I have nothing further," Schmidt said, and resumed his seat beside Dan. On the stand Nothenberg had avoided looking toward the defendant. Now he angled a glance his way and saw only a characterless, stupid, graceless cipher. He had hoped, somehow and rather vaguely, for a sign of dignity, but there was nothing in Dan White's visage to redeem the dead weight of the loss. He left the courtroom overwhelmed by futility.

Dan refused to meet Nothenberg's eye, he refused to meet anybody's eye. For five days now, ever since jury selection had begun, Irene Moreno, a court reporter, had been playing a possum game with the defendant, who stared straight ahead, blank as a cigar store Indian but far more intense. All of a sudden she would lift her eyes from her stenorette, but not once had she succeeded in catching him looking at a witness, or the jury, or the lawyers.

Dan just sat there, his hands on his knees, at ease rather than at full attention. At times his head tilted ever so slightly left toward Doug Schmidt. Once he had wiped his sweaty palms on his trousers. But all the *life* to be seen was Schmidt's, who moved huskily around the arena when he examined a witness, who rocked on his heels and cosseted his chest when he asked questions, who seemed somehow winning when he bumbled and repeated a question, somehow mildly buffaloed when he didn't question a witness at all, as he hadn't the coroner.

Francis Moriarty, who was covering the trial for the *Washington Post,* suspected that Dan's lack of affect in the courtroom was a cunning gesture. On a hunch, over a cup of coffee in the basement cafeteria, Moriarty asked White's other attorney, Steve Scherr, if he played chess, and when Scherr said he did, Moriarty asked the defense lawyer if he had played with Dan.

"In his cell, yes," Scherr said. Instantly the same image occurred to both men: Dan's apparent shellshock as he sat in the courtroom superimposed over him concentrating on a chessboard, plotting his moves.

"Just once," Scherr added, blushing. The reporter and the lawyer smiled at each other; they were quick-witted and enjoyed the verbal fencing that was a skill demanded by both their professions. Scherr's smile was inward-dwelling and faint. Moriarty's had a certain glint. Scherr kneaded his nail-bitten fingers.

"I've backed myself into a corner now, haven't I?" he said.

Out of sight of the jury, in the jail, Dan's behavior was rather normal. He was reading, exercising every evening, visiting with his family and friends.

Since the trial began, in fact, the nurse Jane Halstead noticed an upswing in Dan's mood. He liked to talk to her about his dreams and about the Irish novels and histories, liked to talk about dreamy, faraway things. But she noticed, too, how carefully he watched what was going on around him; it particularly struck her one day when she was dealing with somebody in the psych wing, which bordered on Dan's cell, and apropos of nothing, he spoke to her. "Jane, you're a real good nurse," Dan said. *He knows my name,* she thought, *I'll be damned.*

But that was out of sight of the jury. When he was in court, he neither moved nor looked, but hung his head just a bit so the pale nape of his neck showed as he stared into the middle distance. He was a man devoid of a personality. His lawyer, meanwhile, who was exactly the same age, and who Mary Ann had noticed at once was so much like Danny, kept his vital, down-home personality very much on display. Looking from one to the other, it was not difficult for a juror to imagine that the apparently broken, empty shell of the man who was on trial for his life had once been so very much like the man who pleaded for him now.

4

Madam Mayor

Tommy Norman glided toward the witness as if his hips were fragile. "Good morning, Your Honor."

"Good morning."

"You are the mayor of San Francisco?"

"Yes, that is correct." Dianne Feinstein had worn her glasses to court. In the startling, artificial light of the courtroom not a line was visible in her face, as if the forty-five-year-old former Stanford Quad Queen had defied aging by a formidable act of will. Nor was there a single lacquered hair out of place. The blouse with the bow at her neck was white, the skirt and sweater jacket, cranberry. Twenty-four eyes in the jury box caught and held her.

"Mayor Feinstein, may I ask if you are acquainted with the gentleman who is seated at the defense table here, who is Daniel James White." The syllables of the name—three alone in W-h-ite—rose and fell in succession, breathy as a clarinet.

"Yes, I am."

"Calling your attention, now, to Monday morning, November twenty-seventh, of last year, were you in your office some time at approximately around eleven o'clock?"

"It had to have been, oh, probably around nine-thirty, because I was, because I received a phone call from the mayor about nine o'clock, perhaps a little before, at my home."

"Was that phone call you received from the late Mayor Moscone in connection with any appointment that he was likely to make on that day to the Board of Supervisors?"

"Yes, it was."

"Mayor Feinstein, now bringing us up to a little later in the morning, did you have occasion to see Dan White . . .?"

"Yes, I did."

"Will you tell the members of this jury where you were and where Mr. White was, and just indicate what observations you made."

"I was sitting in my office," she began. "We had been working on the parliamentary procedure to prevent a problem from taking place, because Don Horanzy was to be sworn in at eleven thirty . . . (and) . . . if I were to . . . find Dan White and talk with him . . . I felt I could talk him out of taking his seat . . . I was sitting in my office with my door open.

"My staff . . . had told me that Mr. White had gone to the mayor's office to make a last-ditch appeal, and then would come to see me directly thereafter. So I was waiting for him to come in the door, and I was sitting at my desk, and I heard a door open, and I saw him enter, and I said, 'Dan,' and he said something to the effect of, 'Just a moment,' or, 'I have something to do first,' and went by very rapidly . . .

"And I heard him go down the hall, and I heard the door close. It was a very short period of time . . . and I heard the unmistakable shots.

"Directly after the first one I thought he didn't, knew he wasn't going to be reappointed and he shot himself, and I, then I heard the additional shots, and I knew that something was wrong, and I heard several shots. I couldn't be precise about the number because there was a pause in between them, and I knew I had to move, and I was trying to force my brain and my body to function together and move out of the chair, and I had gotten out of the chair and was approaching the door of my office when I saw Dan leave, and I said, 'Dan,' and he went right by, and the door closed.

"I . . . smelled gunpowder, went down the hall, saw that the door to Harvey Milk's office was closed. I opened the door, and I saw his body, and I tried to get a pulse, but I could not, because of the blood, and I felt he was dead. . . ."

In the jury box Darlene Benton, of an age and a background much like Dan's, was struggling to keep her face under control. Richard Aparicio, the door rattler, was studying Mayor Feinstein intently.

"Mayor Feinstein . . . was it in Harvey Milk's office?"

"No, it was Dan White's office, I'm sorry."

Norman now changed the direction of his questions, trying to head off Doug Schmidt at the pass.

"Mayor Feinstein, had you ever carried a concealed firearm?"

"Yes."

"When was that that you carried a concealed firearm and pursuant to what?"

"I had had several threats from the New World Liberation Front terrorist organization. . . . A bomb had detonated at my house which had approximately two pounds of water gel construction explosive in it. . . . I also had fifteen bullet holes put in a beach house that my husband and I owned, and the threats were continuing, and with that in mind, I applied for a concealed weapon permit."

"You had a permit issued you legally by the chief of police of San Francisco to carry a concealed firearm by a person, didn't you?"

"That is correct."

"Thank you very much, Your Honor." Norman returned to his seat.

Judge Calcagno asked, "Any questions, Mr. Schmidt?"

Schmidt ambled toward the witness box. In his throaty twang, he asked: "Mayor Feinstein, you mentioned that you first met Dan White after the election in '78."

"That's correct."

"At that time you were carrying a firearm; had you ever mentioned that to Dan White, that you recall?"

"No."

"Do you know whether any other members of the Board of Supervisors past or present carried or kept firearms at City Hall?"

"I'm only aware of one."

"Who was that?"

"The former chief of police, Supervisor Al Nelder."

Schmidt moved on.

"Would it be fair to say [Dan] was politically inexperienced at the time he took his seat?"

"Objection," Norman said. "I think that is calling for an opinion and conclusion." The prosecutor knew where *that* line of questions could lead—right to praise of White's character.

Judge Calcagno ran an index finger over his lips. "Ask the witness whether or not she felt that he was. Change the form of the question and I will allow it."

"Did you feel that he was?"

"I felt that Dan was new to the process . . . Dan White and I had lunch from time to time, discussed various problems and issues, and I tried to provide as much help as I could."

"Did you feel, generally, that he was somewhat idealistic?"

"Yes," she answered, at the same time Norman was yelping, "Objection, that is vague."

"Overruled," said the judge.

"Go ahead," Schmidt said.

"Yes, I felt that Dan had very strong ideals. He had always worked very hard, and he took the process very seriously, and we talked about it from time to time. Also, we had light moments, and shared humor, as one does."

"Initially, would it be fair to say that it was a bit of a frustrating experience for Dan White, and perhaps for anyone, being new to that type of job?"

"That is correct. The Board is a frustrating experience to everyone."

"Would it be fair to say you were shocked to realize that he had resigned from the Board?"

"Yes. . . ."

Schmidt had Feinstein describe Mayor Moscone's initial willingness to reinstate Dan, the return of the letter, the legal impediments.

"Now," said the lawyer, "returning to November twenty-seventh, 1978, when you saw Dan White, could you describe for me his appearance, and I know you saw him only briefly, but describe it the best you can recall."

"Yes. He came in the office very rapidly. His jaw was clenched, and he, as sometimes happens, his hair had fallen slightly over his forehead," Dianne said. She sounded wistful. "And he was pale, and otherwise, there was nothing unusual that I perceived . . ."

"You had talked to Mayor Moscone that morning, correct?"

"Correct."

"And he indicated to you that Dan White was not going to be reappointed?" Schmidt asked, his arms wrapped around his chest.

"That's right."

"Did he indicate to you at any time what he had told Dan White in regards to the reappointment issue?"

"No, that issue did not come up."

"In any event," Schmidt said, half facing the jury, "he did not mention that he had called Dan White?"

"No . . . that was one of the reasons I was trying to reach him, I thought I would soften the blow . . ."

"Given that you knew Dan White quite well, would it be your opinion that the man you knew was the type of man that would have shot two people?"

Norman was howling, the broken capillaries in his cheeks were flaming. "Objection as calling for an opinion and conclusion and specu-lation." There was *no* way that was allowable.

"Overruled," said Judge Calcagno.

"No," said Mayor Feinstein. "It would not be my opinion."

Doug Schmidt had just accomplished what Dan White could never master: he had turned the rules to his own advantage, and the woman who was made mayor by Dan's gun into Dan's first character witness. *Good people, fine people, with fine backgrounds, simply don't kill people in cold blood, it just doesn't happen.*

"I have nothing further," he said.

5

Keep the Press
Away From My Wife

Pandemonium in the corridor outside the courtroom. Two pool reporters were being allowed to sit inside the security glass, as if it were a foreign land, and the man from the *Chronicle* was reporting to his ink-stained brethren that he had seen a tear fall from Dan's eye while Dianne Feinstein was testifying. The scene in the corridor was not unlike the floor of the commodities exchange in a bull market.

"Did he wipe it away?"

"No."

"How many tears?" another reporter shouted.

"How far did they run?"

"Were they cascading?"

"One eye or both?"

"Which eye? Which eye did you say it was?"

"Tommy Norman told somebody he saw it fall onto White's cuff."

"It was his first sign of emotion, right?"

"Did it roll all the way down his cheek and drop off?"

During the lunch recess one courtroom artist had another pose with his hand to his eye, wiping away a phantom tear. He had missed the moment itself, as had practically everybody in the courtroom, but he wanted to make sure he got the hand right. His rendering—of a tear he had not seen being wiped away by a hand that was not Dan White's —went out over the wire.

That tear became the biggest newsbreak of the trial so far. Both local papers had it in their leads on Thursday. It had appeared, according to the man from the *Chronicle,* when Dianne Feinstein had said: "I heard the unmistakable shots. Directly after the first one, I thought he didn't, knew he wasn't going to be reappointed and he shot himself."

Five months after he had killed George Moscone and Harvey Milk, Dan still wept only for himself.

6

Looking Through the Glass

It promised to be a long afternoon; Norman had seven witnesses on call. Tomorrow he would put on the ballistics expert and have Falzon play the confession tape and cross the finish wire. He planned to hold back the psychiatrist, Dr. Levy, for rebuttal, after the defense had presented its case.

First to take the stand was Patricia Byrne, a policewoman assigned to the legal department.

"Officer Byrne, have you at my instance and request examined [the] records to determine whether there is an official permit issued by the chief of police to a Mr. Daniel James White of 150 Shawnee Street, San Francisco, California, to carry a concealed firearm?"

"Yes, I have."

"What have you found in that regard—if anything?"

"I find no permit."

"Do persons who were once on the police force . . . and who have resigned their position, do they have a right to carry a concealed firearm on their person?"

"No . . ."

"Thank you very much." To Schmidt: "You may examine."

Schmidt stood but remained at his table.

"Just very briefly. Miss Byrne, you have examined all the files with regard to concealed weapon permits issued to the public, correct?"

"That's correct."

Schmidt blinked. "How many are there outstanding presently?"

"None," replied Officer Byrne.

He hesitated: in other words, every private citizen in the city wearing or carrying a pistol was doing so illegally; it was no big deal. "I have nothing further."

"You are excused, Miss Byrne," said the judge. "Call your next witness."

"Warren Omholt."

The young policeman entered and the clerk administered the oath. "Do you swear to tell the truth, the whole truth, and nothing but the truth?"

"I do."

Norman led him through Dan's arrival at Northern Station. "When you took the weapon . . . this .38 special, did you examine it to see whether it was loaded?"

"Yes, I did. It was unloaded."

Norman twirled his half-frame glasses slowly. This was something he wanted to be sure the jury absorbed; he would come back to it in his closing argument. If the gun had been empty when White surrendered, then he hadn't reloaded "on instinct" or any other way after he had killed Harvey Milk. And that was strongly suggestive, was it not, that Dan White was a man who had set out to do a certain job, and having accomplished it, did not need to reload again.

"But when you say it was unloaded, Officer Omholt, did you open the cylinder?"

"Yes, I did."

"And when you opened the cylinder did you find there to be any loaded cartridges, or spent cartridge casings . . .?"

"None."

"Then we can understand that when it was opened there were five completely empty cylinder holes?"

"That's correct."

Well satisfied, Norman had Omholt identify the live and spent cartridges he had taken from Dan's pockets, and turned the witness over to Schmidt, who immediately asked Omholt to repeat that Dan had turned himself in.

"And he was accompanied by a woman?"

"Yes, sir."

"Do you see that woman in the first row?" Schmidt nodded in her direction and Mary Ann stood up, as the jury turned like a single twelve-headed entity to look at her.

"I don't know if I would recognize her again if I saw her or not," said Omholt.

Schmidt faced the jury and folded his arms across his chest. "Why don't you come down and take a look."

Omholt came down into the arena.

"Looking through the glass at the woman standing: is that the woman that was accompanying Mr. White?" In the sympathetic portrayal Schmidt hoped to create, Mary Ann would provide the denouement—this moment was staged foreshadowing.

Mary Ann's arms hung at her sides. Beneath her makeup she looked peaked. The green tint of the glass gave her a sickly pallor as Officer Omholt and the jury stared at her. Mary Ann was a true victim, suffering for love. Inside the glass, in the hothouse atmosphere of the arena, was dry exposition and dead meat. There the rule of law prevailed, exacting a heartless dispassion. But Mary Ann, pale and prayerful where she remained just outside the glass—how could the jurors react to her with anything but their hearts?

"As I recall," said Officer Omholt, "she looks very familiar."

Schmidt nodded again, and Mary Ann resumed her seat, tucking her skirt under her with one large hand, its nails painted a demure pink. Grayce Jackson, the retired beautician, continued to stare in her direction.

"I have nothing further," Schmidt said.

The afternoon droned on with talk of guns and bullets and descriptions of a dazed Dan White surrendering himself. Several of the jurors began to squirm in their seats. A few minutes after 3:30 Judge Calcagno released them.

The jury was led to the two vans that had been rented for them and driven the mile or so to the Jack Tar Hotel where they were sequestered, cut off from all the familiar faces and routines and smells of home. They were ordinary people thrust suddenly into a critical role in this most extraordinary event. The newspapers they were allowed to read had all references to the trial neatly clipped out. For entertainment there were card games, television (with a bailiff present so they wouldn't be exposed to a news report), and the movies they were taken to en masse in the vans. Their real worlds, their usual worlds, receded rapidly in their isolation, and in the face of their solemn obligation. They ate and moved and gossiped together, twelve strangers never able to talk about the one thing that was most on their minds. In this curious, vivid interruption of their lives only what transpired inside the glass was real, for these few weeks only that would truly matter. Perhaps the lawyer who best understood them and most effectively entertained and moved them would carry the day.

As the jury was arriving back at the motel, Doug Schmidt, carrying his heavy briefcase, was waiting for an elevator on his way out of the Hall of Justice when he was approached by a reporter who asked him whether it troubled him at all that if he did his job well enough society, the city, might be ill served.

"Society doesn't have anything to do with it," Schmidt said. "Only those twelve people."

7

Man Among Men

Like all detectives, Frank Falzon had on-duty clothes and testifying clothes. Thursday morning Falzon put on his best dark-blue suit. It was a special day and he was bringing the family along for his hour in the spotlight. His wife had never been to a trial before, and his son Daniel, who was seventeen, wanted to go because he had aspirations to be a policeman or a lawyer. Debora and David, who were sixteen and fifteen, went too. They left the house quite early, when the mist was still upon the green hills. In the quiet of the early morning the Marin County suburb, where it was said close to half the residents were policemen, looked safe and sound and decently prosperous. Before eight o'clock the Falzons drove into the tunnel with the rainbow painted on its lip and when they emerged down the hill, ahead of them was the Golden Gate, its graceful strength a monument to the best men could do, and beyond it, across the glassy bay, huddled the magical city. The city where Falzon earned his living by being very good at catching murderers.

Falzon got his wife and kids settled into seats in the spectator gallery and sat down with Tom Norman, waiting to be called. The confession tape was in a bulky brown evidence folder that he placed on the table in front of him. He wasn't nervous but he was concerned. Tommy had not seemed to take it seriously enough when Falzon had asked him, after his lunch with Schmidt, what would happen if the defense attorney questioned him on the stand about the kind of man Dan had been. In the detective's view, policemen, firemen, soldiers were the real men, and Dan had been exemplary. Falzon would have to tell the truth, his entire self-esteem rested on sticking to his word. Tommy had assured him that he could prevent the questions from being answered, that he had recent case law all ready to cite. But Mayor Feinstein had already been allowed to answer similar questions. Falzon thought that Tommy was some kind of genius, but maybe he was too accustomed to winning, maybe he was dangerously arrogant.

Beside him, Tommy Norman was wrapped up in his own thoughts as the jury filed into the box. The prosecutor had taken the jury one inch at a time through the events that braided a noose around the pale neck of Daniel James White, and this morning, with the taped statement, he would yank it tight. Norman had listened to the tape again and again, listened to White admit to shooting and killing both of his victims. The tape, recorded only an hour after his crimes, showed his powers of cognition, his clarity of thought. It had been suggested to Norman that rather than play the tape he use a transcript, but no, he had to play the tape, he couldn't afford to use a transcript and then have Schmidt play the tape; that would look as if he were trying to hide it. True, White had whimpered and stammered and sounded pitiable. But whom did he pity, when did he whimper? Only when he spoke of himself, his family, his plight. When he had spoken of George Moscone and Harvey Milk he stopped whimpering, noticeably, singularly. Tommy trusted that any thinking, analytical person could hear the absence of remorse. The prosecutor sighed. He rubbed a speck of dust off his black wingtips and sneaked a glance at the jury.

Falzon, his woolpad hair freshly washed, his watery blue eyes very private, was settling now into the witness seat with his brown evidence folder and his tape recorder. Tommy stood and approached him; from the moment they had come across each other outside Northern Station just after the killings, they had worked this case as a team. The prosecutor had Falzon identify himself, took him over the circumstances leading to the taping of the statement.

"Now, Inspector, with respect to this case, and this statement, you tape-recorded it?"

"That is correct, sir."

"Do you have a cassette of the tape recording? And I am referring to the original cassette."

"I do."

"Where is it?"

"It's contained within one of the case folders."

"May I see it?" Falzon handed it over. "Your Honor, may this be marked as People's number fifty-four?"

"So ordered," said the judge.

Tommy asked Falzon, "Has the erasure been punched out so that we don't inadvertently erase it?"

"Yes, sir."

"Is the tape recording an accurate reproduction of everything that was said?"

"It is."

Norman turned toward the judge. "The People at this time move the tape recording into evidence."

A glimmer of amusement was in Judge Calcagno's eye. "Well, if you're going to play it, then why don't you play it?"

Chidingly, Norman responded, "I think it has to be in evidence before it can be played."

Falzon inserted the tape into the recorder and brought the microphone down close to the speaker. He pushed the play button and there was a loud whirring over the public address system as the tape began to spin. Then Falzon's voice: "Today's date is Monday, November twenty-seventh . . ." Loudly, very loudly, so that the disembodied voice of the seemingly spiritless man on trial filled every molecule of the courtroom, Dan White's tape-recorded voice began to talk, and then began to cry.

On the bench Walter Calcagno was pleased with the clarity and high quality of sound. It was he who had suggested to the homicide division that they soundproof their interrogation room and buy better tape recorders. About a year ago they had done what the judge asked and now Dan's sniffling, piteous voice reverberated clearly in the courtroom. "Well, it's just that I've been under an awful lot of pressure lately, financial pressure, because of my job situation, family pressure because of ah . . . not being able to have the time with my family. . . ."

The tape rolled and Dan admitted the killings and he cried and Norman, watching the jury, saw something which took him entirely by surprise: wet eyes. Oh no, he thought, this is turning into a disaster.

On the tape Falzon's voice asked, "Is there anything else you'd like to add at this time?"

Dan's strained, cracking voice replied, "Just that I've always been honest and worked hard, never cheated anybody, or, you know, I'm not a crook or anything an' I wanted to do a good job, I'm trying to do a good job, an' I saw this city as it's goin' kind of downhill an' I was always just a lonely vote on the Board and tryin' to be honest, an', an' I just couldn't take it anymore," he sobbed, "an' that's it."

In the jury box Darlene Benton and Grayce Jackson were crying openly, and Barbara Costuros was wiping the tears out of her eyes. Aparicio and Helga Soulie and most of the others looked as though they had been poleaxed. The irony was gone from Mintzer's face.

The tape stopped rolling. You could feel the cathartic release of emotion in the courtroom, invisible, intangible, yet profound and unmistakable as a sudden calm in the midst of a storm.

Tommy Norman could hardly believe that the enormity of the crimes to which Dan White's disembodied voice had been confessing would not have weighed more than the emotionalism, but then a failure of imagination had plagued him ever since he had agreed to empanel this jury, so like the people who had voted Dan into office. His pride and his certainty about the strength of his case had made him arrogant, and arrogance reduces even smart men to stupidity and carelessness. He had never appreciated how this case was different from all the other murder trials he had argued and won, how this defendant was not just another poor or colored sociopath whom the jurors wanted removed from the streets of their city, or gassed to death, as badly as he did. It had always been the prosecutor's presumption that as the lawyer for the People he automatically shared a certain affinity with the twelve men and women in the jury box. As he watched the jurors sniffling and drying their eyes while Falzon removed the tape from the machine and replaced it in the evidence envelope, Norman's certainty was floundering. Doubt gnawed at the underpinnings of his mastery, frightening him. Even though the jurors surely abhorred the killings, they were people very much like those who had responded so deeply when the handsome young candidate, the man who did not have to explain that he was with them because he was *of* them, had exhorted his followers: "You must realize there are thousands and thousands of frustrated, angry people such as yourselves waiting to unleash a fury that can and will eradicate the malignancies which blight our beautiful city."

Moved by the stammering, tearful voice on the tape, they were now receptive to, were in fact in need of, explanations. How could this have happened? Like Falzon on the day of the killings, like Doug Schmidt in his opening statement, they wanted to know *why* Dan White had killed the mayor and the supervisor. So far Norman's case had not answered that most humanly sympathetic of questions.

Judge Calcagno called the morning recess.

* * *

Doug Schmidt began to cross-examine Falzon. First he would cover the business of reloading on instinct, and then he would establish Falzon's good character before he got to the more important issues.

"Inspector Falzon, are you trained regarding the reloading of a firearm in a stress situation, a situation of danger?"

"Yes, sir . . . this training . . . it begins when you enter the police academy."

". . . did they teach you anything regarding keeping a firearm loaded?"

"Basically, the training at the police range consists of stress situations, how to respond, how to react instantly, in order to save your own life. This would be timed situations, wherein you fire your revolver, you then unload your revolver, reload and fire again . . ."

"This is part of every policeman's training, is it not?"

"Yes, sir, it is."

Schmidt asked Falzon when he had most recently fired his gun in line of duty, and Falzon recalled the night he had killed the fleeing robber who had shot at him.

"Would it be fair," Schmidt asked, "to say you were acting with your police training in mind, under that situation?"

"I can honestly attribute my police training and the Man Above for the fact that I am sitting here today."

"Inspector Falzon, you mentioned that you had known Dan White in the past, prior to November twenty-seventh, 1978?"

"Yes, sir, quite well."

"About how long have you known him?"

"According to Dan, it goes back to the days we attended St. Elizabeth's grammar school together, but we went to different high schools. I attended St. Ignatius and he attended Riordan." Unbidden, Falzon continued. "He walked up to me one day at Jackson playground, with spikes over his shoulders, glove in his hand, and asked if he could play on my . . . police softball team, and since that day Dan White and I have been very good friends. . . ."

"You knew him fairly well, then, is that fair?"

"As well as I knew anybody, I believed."

"Can you tell me, when you first saw him on November twenty-seventh, how did he appear physically to you?"

"Destroyed. This was not the Dan White that I had known, not

The Trial 323

at all." Falzon looked toward Norman, waiting for an objection. He was telling the truth, and the longer he did that the more he would betray the prosecution's case.

"Destroyed in what respect? What did you notice particularly about his appearance or—"

"Totally unlike Dan White, the man I knew *prior* to Monday, the twenty-seventh of November 1978, who was a man among men . . ." Tommy Norman's ears were burning, he could not believe what his chief investigator was saying. *A man among men.* The whole thing sounded rehearsed to him. Could that be true? Falzon kept talking. ". . . he was . . . what I described as a hustler, a fellow that did not know how to stop. He had tremendous drive, ambition. That day I saw a shattered individual . . ."

Schmidt was ready now with the most important question he had for this all-important witness. He wanted to get Falzon to describe Dan's state of mind; it bore directly on the question of intent, and the absence of intent was to a diminished-capacity defense what unbleached flour was to white bread.

"Knowing, with regard to the shootings of Mayor Moscone and Harvey Milk, knowing Dan White as you did, is he the type of man that could have premeditatedly and deliberately shot those people?"

"Objection," said Norman, "as calling for an opinion and conclusion."

"Sustained."

"Knowing him as you do," Schmidt persisted, "have you ever seen anything in his past that would lead you to believe he was capable of cold-bloodedly shooting somebody?"

"Same objection." Norman was on his feet.

"Sustained."

"Your Honor," said Schmidt, walking to his table, "at this point I anticipated that there would be some argument . . . and accordingly I have prepared a memorandum of what I believe to be the appropriate law."

"All right," said the judge. "Do you wish to lodge it with me?"

"Fine . . . maybe we can have the jury recessed."

When the jury was gone, Calcagno laid out the position of the court. "I have no quarrel with your authorities, but I think the form of the questions that you asked were objectionable. . . . If you asked the questions as they are indicated in the case law, then I have no objection to those. . . . Ask the first question as to his observations, what he knew about it, his conditions, before you ask that question."

"Perhaps I'm not following the court. I thought that I had established that foundation . . ."

"You are asking this witness whether he is capable of forming a premeditated killing, and I don't think that that is a proper question at this time. . . . Get the facts from this witness. I will let you get those facts, whatever they are."

"All right," said Schmidt. "We'll try that."

"Are we all set for the jury?" Judge Calcagno asked. He looked at the prosecutor, who had so far remained silent. "Or do you want to make any statement, Mr. Norman?"

"I haven't heard any question right now, and so . . ."

"All right," said the judge. The jury, led by a bailiff, filed back into the box.

"Inspector Falzon," Schmidt said, "Again, you mentioned that you were quite familiar with Dan White. Can you tell me something about the man's character . . . prior to November twenty-seventh, 1978?"

"Objection as being irrelevant and vague."

"Overruled . . . you may answer it."

"The Dan White that I knew prior . . . was a man who seemed to excel in pressure situations, and it seemed that the greater the pressure the more enjoyment Dan had. . . . Examples would be in his sports life, that I can relate to . . . for the first time in the history of California there was a law enforcement softball tournament . . . he was named the most valuable player. . . . At the end of the tournament, a dinner was held, the umpires were invited, and one individual had umpired baseball games for over thirty years, made the comment that Dan White was the best ballplayer he had ever seen participate in any tournament in South Lake Tahoe . . ."

Falzon described Dan telling him he was running for supervisor. "I said, 'How are you going to do it, Dan? Nobody ever heard of Dan White . . .'

"He said, 'I'm going to do it the way the people want it to be done, knock on their doors, go inside, shake their hands, get to know them on a first-name basis, let them know what Dan White stands for . . . Dan White is going to represent them. There will be a voice in City Hall . . .'"

"Given these things that you mentioned about Dan White, was

there anything in his character that you knew of him, prior to these tragedies of the twenty-seventh of November, that would have led you to believe that he would ever kill somebody cold-bloodedly?"

"Objection, irrelevant—"

"Overruled."

Tommy Norman felt as if it had started to rain on him, pour. He flushed and his voice got angry and squeaky. "Let me state my grounds for the record."

"Overruled," repeated the judge.

"Thank you, judge." Dagger-point sarcasm. "It's irrelevant, and calling for his opinion and speculation."

"Overruled. You may answer that," Judge Calcagno said to Falzon.

"Yes, Your Honor. I'm hesitating only because there was something I saw in Dan's personality that didn't become that relevant to me until I was assigned this case.

"He had a tendency to run, occasionally, from situations. And I just attributed it to his own righteousness, his own high degree, that he put upon himself, over pressure situations, that he needed to get away. I saw this flaw and I asked him about it and his response was that his ultimate goal was to purchase a boat, just travel around the world, get away from everybody, and yet the Dan White I was talking to was trying to be involved with people, constantly being a fireman, being a policeman, being a supervisor. He wanted to be helpful to people and yet he wanted to run away from them.

"That did not make sense to me. Today, this is the only flaw in Dan's character that I can cite up here and testify about. Otherwise, to me, Dan White was an exemplary individual, a man that I was proud to know and be associated with."

"Inspector, I have one last question. Did you ever see him act out of revenge . . . the whole time you have known him?"

It was the first time that word *revenge,* ticking like a timebomb beneath the entire defense premise that Dan had acted in a heat of passion, had been mentioned in court. The case law was specific. The "irresistible impulse" that could make a killing manslaughter instead of murder might be provoked by any high-wrought emotional state except for revenge.

"The only time Dan White could have acted out in revenge is when he took the opposite procedure in hurting himself, by quitting the San Francisco Police Department."

"Thank you, sir," Schmidt said, and sat down.

Tommy Norman was livid. The change jangled madly in his pocket. What was he supposed to do now, discredit his chief investigator, the man the jury had seen sitting beside him and consulting with him every day of the trial?

"Inspector Falzon, you regard yourself as a close friend to Mr. Daniel White, don't you?"

"Yes, sir."

"Do you regard yourself as a *very* close friend of Mr. Daniel White?"

Falzon would not have his honesty impeached. "I would consider myself a close friend of yours, if that can relate to you my closeness with Dan White."

"Of course, you haven't known me as long as you have known Mr. Daniel White. Have you, Inspector?"

"Just about the same length of time, Counsel."

"Was the Dan White that you knew, and you have testified about, and whom you know now, a person who could express the emotion of anger?"

"I have never seen it, except for one time prior to today's date in court. I had only seen Dan White express anger once, and it was only verbally." Falzon was referring to the time Dan had slammed the toilet booth door after they had lost the ballgame to the fire department.

"Have you ever heard any reports about him in regard to the active expression or acting out of anger?"

It was a measure of the thoroughness of Falzon's investigation that, under oath, he was able to reply, "No, sir," even though Dan had been a young man notorious for his temper and his willingness to fight, and more than one politician would have been willing to testify to what they considered his bullying, overbearing ways.

"Do you feel that Dan White felt he was being dealt with less than fairly, perhaps treacherously, by the late George Moscone?"

"My opinion?"

Well, of course he had been free enough with his opinions up until now. "Yes," Norman said.

"Yes, sir, I do believe that was Dan White's thinking."

"Do you feel that he also felt that the late Supervisor Harvey Milk was somehow acting to thwart or prevent his appointment to the Board of Supervisors by the late George Moscone?"

"Yes, sir," Falzon said, adding gratuitously: "And the investigation proved that to be true."

Norman checked his anger. He could not be treating his own investigator as a hostile witness, especially not with Falzon's family in court. At any rate, it didn't appear to *him* that the best first-degree murder case he had ever tried was going to rise or fall upon Frank Falzon. "Thank you," he said.

"Just very briefly," Schmidt said, rising again. "Inspector Falzon, it was no secret that you had been friends with Dan White, isn't that correct?"

"That is correct, sir."

"And if you didn't have the ability to be objective about this case, there were people that had the authority to have you removed, isn't that correct?" Tommy Norman, for one.

"Most definitely. The investigation was handled no differently than any other case I've ever worked on."

"You haven't done Dan White any favors in this case, have you?"

"None whatsoever."

"I have nothing further," the defense lawyer said. When he sat down his broad shoulder rested against Dan's.

Falzon took his tape recorder and his evidence envelope and walked back to his seat beside Tommy Norman with his customary muscular purposefulness. The last, the most important double play ever had been turned, and Falzon had spoken not a single untrue word.

8

The People Conclude

Norman called one last witness for the prosecution, a bearish criminologist who took one and a half hours to provide the jury with a single gruesome fact: George Moscone and Harvey Milk were killed with shots to the head from a range "not closer than six inches . . . [and] not further than a distance of eighteen inches." Norman had ended with the coup de grace, those shots fired into the brains of the fallen men in the classic, downward-leaning posture of the assassin, or the executioner; that gesture which said so much, and about which his case had explained so little.

In three days he had sworn and examined nineteen witnesses, but he had concluded without ever describing where, exactly, Dan White had reloaded after he had killed George Moscone. And that absence of fact suggested others: George Moscone had been absent from the prosecutor's case, as had Harvey Milk. The *smirk* Dan had mentioned in his confession—that arch, mocking, defensive expression, the very emblem of homosexual style—that was the only image that had been introduced of the man named Harvey Milk. The two living, breathing human beings who had been dispatched by Dan's gun had not been evoked in the windowless courtroom inside the green-tinted glass. And if there had been no victims, in a sense, neither had there been a clearcut motive provided for the jury. Neither personal hatred, nor political antagonism, nor moral outrage, nor—and this was the loudest of all the silences—revenge.

The judge called the noon recess and as the jury was filing out,

Schmidt leaned across the gap between the two tables and said, "Tom, can we see the judge, just briefly?"

"Well, sure."

They caught Calcagno just before he went out the door to return to his chambers. As they walked up he was saying to a bailiff, "Take Dan upstairs."

Tommy's eyes met Calcagno's and sparks flew.

"You mean *the accused,* don't you, Judge?"

At three o'clock the lawyers were through for the day. Tommy, as he did most afternoons, went into Joe Freitas's big office on the third floor of the Hall of Justice, perhaps a hundred yards from the courtroom. With his boss, Tom Norman, the good lifer, was obsequious.

"How are things going?" Freitas asked. "Are you satisfied with the progress of the case?" The D.A., who was finding time to campaign in gay bars, had not appeared in court since the opening arguments.

Norman told him what had happened with Falzon.

"He said *that?*" Freitas muttered. "What were you doing?"

With all the acid suggestiveness at his command, Tommy Norman answered, "Objecting."

Afterward, Tommy took a long walk, mulling over the case. He couldn't get it out of his mind. So many things were boxing him in. There was his politically-minded boss, whose concerns prevented him from exploring the political enmities, and his own squeamishness about George Moscone's private life, which constrained him from exploring Dan's character for fear of opening a can of worms.

He would not agree with the observation that he was suppressing information, neither in an evidentiary nor a psychological sense. Nor did he consider, of course, his own failures of imagination. And now, already hemmed in by his boss and his own shortcomings, there was Falzon. In a very real sense Tommy was all alone with the biggest case of his life. After his walk he called his father, who was eighty-three and whom he checked on almost every day. He cooked and ate a light dinner and then went back to work on the miter-jointed cabinets he was making for the kitchen of his new home, executing them in white oak so they were elegant as could be. The careful work was a sort of gift for his fiancée. As soon as the trial was over they would be married.

After a while Marilyn came over. They talked and Tommy told her how the judge had called the defendant "Dan."

"Maybe the judge feels a little sympathy with Dan White," she suggested. Whenever she had been able to get away from her own courtroom—she was a stenographic reporter whom Tommy had met during an earlier trial—she had sat in watching her future husband's big case.

"You know," she said, "I think he's being a little tough on you."

He sighed and nodded his head. Tommy Norman was in love.

9

Very Close and Warm

There was an excited hubbub of anticipation among the spectators and reporters queued up to pass through the metal detectors and the pat-down on Friday morning to hear the first of the defense witnesses. Each of the bailiffs who pat-searched every person entering Department 21 had a distinctive style. The chunky blond bailiff was gruff and palsy; the tall one with the beard, who this morning was reading a *Village Voice,* had surprisingly soft hands—his touch, as he searched for hidden weapons, was almost seductive.

The members of the press regularly assigned to the trial had already broken down into cliques. The reporters for the gay weeklies sat together, bristling, as did the sketch artists, who were all apparently easygoing. The women dispatched by each of the local network affiliates *never* sat together but were joined by subliminal radiations. The men from the dailies wore sport coats or suits and took notes on stenographic pads which fit inside their jacket pockets. The fellow from the *Washington Post,* whose name was Moriarty, had a fierce black-Irish moustache and a catechismal point of view; he sat with the magazine writers from *Rolling Stone* and *Playboy,* who wore jeans and did not shave every day. This morning, as they took their regular seats, almost to a person they opened their notebooks and wrote: *Mary Ann—tartan suit.*

By this time Doug Schmidt had had a cup of coffee or a meal with most of the reporters, and had disarmed them all. It was a part of his plan—because he left as little to chance as possible—to avoid press conferences but rather to cultivate reporters individually or in small groups, and to feed each of them exclusive tidbits. The man from the afternoon *Examiner,* who needed feature and analysis material, was told about the importance of the jury instructions and the precedent-setting case, *People* v. *Berry.* To one of the television women who was especially interested in human interest angles, Schmidt confided that he liked macho movies such as *Destry Rides Again* with Jimmy Stewart, and wanted to enlarge his land holdings. He let drop to the man from *Time* that he had done "pretty good" in the seven or eight murder trials he had handled, and when pressed, admitted that he had in fact won acquittals or hung juries in every case except for the second-degree conviction in the Golden Dragon massacre. Schmidt told the reporter from *Rolling Stone* that "I'm not much of a scholar, as probably could be gleaned." When the writer responded by saying "Aw shucks," Schmidt made a fist and swung it in a short arc and blushed.

The legal strategy of Schmidt and Stephen Scherr in presenting Dan's case involved a variety of tactics. First, they would try to create reasonable doubt about every link in the chain of circumstance Norman had constructed to indicate a murderous intent on Dan's part. The defense would, in addition, call friends, family members, and fellow policemen and firemen to establish Dan's character as a working-class hero, and to testify as well to his moody, withdrawn, even quirky behavior prior to the killings. Psychiatrists and a psychologist would diagnose his mental illness and conclude that he had not had the capacity, in the grip of a depression and under great pressure, to act with intent. The success of their legal strategy depended on Judge Calcagno adopting their proposed modifications of the jury instructions, so that the facts as they presented them through their witnesses, and the law as the judge interpreted it for the jury, would make a perfect fit.

Denise Apcar was the first defense witness called. She had on a feather brooch and a simple string of pearls. A high color in her cocoa-butter cheeks gave sign of her nervousness. ". . . He was a very serious . . . very optimistic person," she said, describing Dan's attitude toward his duties. "He wanted to do the best job he could."

"How did Daniel White and Harvey Milk get along, generally?"

"As a matter of fact, they were good friends in the beginning, they liked each other personally very much."

". . . How did Dan White and George Moscone get along?"

Denise shifted in her seat and straightened the lapels of her white blazer. "They shared common interests in athletics, which always gave them something to talk about. They were personal, uh, they were friends in a casual way, and there was absolutely no animosity between them."

"Now, you mentioned that he was hardworking initially . . . Did there come a time when that seemed to change a bit?"

"Yes, I think it started as early as March of 1978. . . . He became frustrated with the job quite early. He was having difficulty . . . adjusting to the political process . . . and he became moody and withdrawn, and started to come much less, started to cancel meetings, just basically depressed a lot."

"Did you notice anything about his health habits or diet that was irregular?"

"Yes," Denise said. "He would ask me to buy him candy a lot during lunch breaks and board meetings and at recess, and he ate a lot of candy, and he would eat doughnuts, junk food, sugar drinks."

"Was that unusual?"

"It was very unusual. When I first met him he said he never wanted anything but milk, never drank, didn't smoke or drink coffee. . . . He always ate very healthy foods."

It has often been remarked that a criminal trial is a dramatic form, and indeed, there are many similarities, not the least of which is that everything which preceded the raising of the curtain is unknown to the audience, in this case the jury, which is asked, as all audiences are, to willingly suspend its disbelief until the last act. They had no way of knowing that Dan had eaten a steady diet of junk foods when he was in uniform, nor that even now a jail nurse was bringing him ice cream and candy bars he insisted on every night.

"Now," said Schmidt, rocking on his heels and encircling his chest, "did there come a time later in 1978 when you noticed his mood alter again or change, or in any way become different?"

"Yes, it just became worse. From March on . . . he was withdrawn, he wasn't happy, and he wanted to do so much, and he couldn't do a hundred percent . . . he was so frustrated . . ."

"Did you ever notice the time during the later summer meetings that he did go to, that went well or poorly?"

Denise glowed. "There was one meeting in which he came off very, very well. He was just a dream."

Tommy Norman's ears perked up at Denise's tone and he scribbled a note on his yellow legal pad.

The lawyer began to bear down on the lies which Dan had been told. "Did the mayor express himself with regard to whether or not he would reappoint him if a reappointment became necessary?"

"Right. I have forgotten. He did say *that,* in his press conference. That if it became legally necessary . . . he said that in unequivocal terms . . ."

Denise recounted how the mayor had backed away from that promise and asked Dan to show support in the district, and how the letter-writing campaign and the petition drive had been organized.

"Did the . . . mayor's office ever make a statement at that time as to the number of letters that were coming in, or anything such as that?"

"Yes, they did," Denise said sharply. "They said that thirty letters had been received and that was all."

"Do you believe that . . . they were in excess of that?"

"Well, I was well aware that there were over three hundred letters."

"Within your personal knowledge, were you aware that the mayor told Dan White, at any time, he was going to *notify* him before he made a reappointment?"

"I recall, at one time, Dan White saying to me—"

"Objection," said Norman.

"That *is* hearsay," acknowledged Judge Calcagno.

Schmidt said, "It goes to the state of mind."

"Then she can answer," the judge said, ". . . but the question can be answered with either a 'yes' or a 'no,' and you can pick it up from there." Calcagno turned to the witness. "Do you recall ever obtaining, to your own knowledge, any indication as to whether or not Dan White was going to be notified as to whether or not he was going to receive the appointment?"

Norman was miffed by this little law lesson for the benefit of Doug Schmidt.

"Yes," said Denise.

"Did he tell you why he . . . thought he might be reappointed?"

"Well, the mayor had *told* him . . . and Dan always felt that a person was going to be honest when they said something . . . he believed it up until the end."

Schmidt led Denise over the events of the final weekend and on into the morning of the twenty-seventh of November.

"Did he . . . mention that he was going to talk to Harvey Milk?"

"Yes, he did," Denise said. There was an audible gasp in the courtroom, on both sides of the glass. In his confession Dan had said that he only thought of seeing Harvey when he had spotted his aide across City Hall after George Moscone was already dead, and Denise's answer directly contradicted that. It raised the specter of a cold-blooded assassin who had begun to concoct an "I just went crazy" alibi immediately after his crimes. But Schmidt knew something that the jury and the reporters didn't: on the afternoon of the killings Denise had given the police a statement which included this aspect of the conversation in her car. It would appear far more in keeping with what Schmidt had told the jury in his opening statement—that he wanted *all* the facts out, that his was a dispassionate inquiry into the question of *why*—to draw out this revelation himself, rather than leave it to Norman, who was certain to make it appear as if it had been concealed, and thus doubly damning.

"Was there any indication in the car that he was going to do anything violent that day?" It was the best Schmidt could do to soften the effect.

"No."

After a few more questions he turned Denise over for cross-examination. From Tommy Norman's very first word to the witness, the crones on the back benches heard the delightful clatter of their favorite's knitting needles.

"*Miss* Apcar?" Never had an unmarried state sounded so licentious.

"Correct," she said.

"During that period of time, all together through which you had known him, up to and including the twenty-seventh of November, you regarded him, you told us, as a friend?" Four syllables in fuh-ur-en-d. "Is that right?"

"Most definitely."

"Did you regard him as a good, close friend?"

"Yes, I did."

"Are you acquainted with his family?"

"Yes, I am."

"Do you know his wife?"

"Yes."

"Have you visited in his home often?"

"Often."

"Did he visit in your home?" His manner was insinuating, spellbinding. There was in his questions a tantalizing suggestion of compromise.

"Never."

Norman's small eyes again sought out some middle distance at the back of the courtroom, well above the heads of the people on the far side of the glass. He hooked one of his soft hands under his jacket and rested it on his hip. "I take it that you feel very close, and very warm, to Mr. White."

"Yes."

"Miss Apcar, do you believe that he was depressed because he was somehow a little disappointed with the activities of his colleagues on the Board of Supervisors?"

"That's fair, yes."

"Do you feel that there was any disappointment felt by him and entertained by him not having achieved certain objectives no matter how hard he tried?"

"On occasion, yes."

Tommy Norman hitched his pants. The Dan White he was painting with his deft questions was a crybaby and a quitter. Now he asked Denise to describe Dan's reactions when George or Harvey had broken their word to him. "Tell us what he said about Harvey Milk in that regard."

"Just surprise, bewilderment . . . that kind of thing."

"Did Mr. White appear to be disappointed at this type of behavior?"

"Yes, he did."

"Would you say he was shocked by this type of behavior?"

"Yes."

"Would you say he was *offended* by this type of behavior?"

"I, I think I would say that."

"You have to keep your voice up, ma'am," Judge Calcagno said.

Norman pushed ahead, eventually reaching the morning of the twenty-seventh, and George Moscone's arrival at City Hall while Denise was leading a picket line.

"Did you feel that the mayor was trying to avoid you?"

"Most definitely."

Norman had her describe going upstairs to the mayor's office and seeing a grinning Harvey Milk emerge, and George's hand on his shoulder.

"Did you tell Mr. White that you had seen Harvey Milk come out of the side door of the mayor's office after you had been informed the mayor was not in?"

"Yes, I did."

Finally he asked Denise about the ride to City Hall. "When he got into your car, did he do anything that appeared unusual to you? . . . Would you favor us with some of these things, please?"

"Well, he was just blowing into his hands and rubbing them, like he was cold, like his hands were cold . . . he acted very hurt, yes. He was, looked like he was going to cry. He was doing everything he could to restrain his emotion."

"Did you ever describe him as acting 'all fired up'?"

"Yes, I—I believe I said that."

"Did you ever say he was going to 'really lay it on the mayor'?"

"It's been brought to my attention I said that, yes."

"Now, did you ever say, referring to Mr. White, that Mr. White really wanted some action?"

"Well, I probably said that. I was very nervous."

"Of course, when you made those statements, that was, *Miss* Apcar, that was on November twenty-seventh, at about forty minutes after noontime, wasn't it?" Once again, satisfied that his point had been made, Tommy Norman rested a hand upon his hip and clucked.

"B-a-r-b-e-g-e-l-a-t-a." George Moscone's most bitter political enemy spelled his name for the court reporter.

"Good afternoon, sir. Were you ever on the Board of Supervisors . . .?" Schmidt asked.

"Yes, I was."

"Did Denise Apcar ever work for you as an aide?"

"Yes, she did."

"Now, during that period of time, were you ever subjected to any threats on your life or wellbeing?"

"On at least twenty-five to forty occasions . . ."

"In fact, your house was bombed at one time?"

"Yes, it was."

"Did you ever keep or carry a gun at City Hall?"

"Yes, I did."

"Did you experience any particular pressure once you were on the Board for that first time?"

"Yes, I did. Enough to have a heart attack after being on the Board for eight months."

"Did you attribute that to the pressures you had from the job as a supervisor?"

"My doctor told me it was total frustration and shock—I came out of a business that deals heavily in money, in the real estate business where people are not exactly honest, buyers, sellers and realtors, and I had been pretty toughened to the business world, having been older and around.

"When I got into politics I was in my late forties, and I was used to cheaters and liars and that sort of thing, and I could take it in the business world. But when I got into politics, I couldn't take it.

"It was just too much for me . . ."

10
Best Terms Possible

On Friday afternoon Schmidt called Ray Shine and two of Dan's firemen friends, Don Frediani and Jim Sullivan. It was Sullivan who had introduced Dan and Mary Ann. Frediani told the jury about Dan: "He'd always have his milk."

Shine recalled how Dan had saved his life when he fell overboard in the rough waters of the Potato Patch. Schmidt questioned him about Dan carrying a gun.

"Do you recall any specific incidents that he was carrying a gun?"

"The exact date escapes me," Shine said. "However, it was at a Giants baseball game last summer, a night game, with the Philadelphia Phillies, and they were playing with the Giants."

"What did he tell you at that time?"

"He stated that he occasionally carried the gun to some of his board meetings at City Hall."

"Do you recall where you had this conversation with him?"

"Yes, we were sitting in box seats, along the third-base line of Candlestick Park."

"Did you ask him why he was carrying a gun?"

"He explained, he stated that certain radical groups had threatened him . . . and that the degree of the potential for harm to him was so great that he carried the weapon as protection to himself."

"And that group was?"

"The White Panther Party."

"The White Panthers had a shootout with the police, had they not?"

"Yes, they had," Shine said.

On cross-examination, Norman concluded by asking: "Could I say, Officer Shine, that given your feelings of close friendship to Daniel White, that you would like to see Daniel White dealt with at least less harshly . . . in connection with these proceedings?"

"Well," Shine allowed, "I think it would be fair to say that I would like to see justice dealt to Dan on the best terms possible."

"Thank you," the prosecutor purred.

When the last witness of the day took the stand—fireman Jim Sullivan—there was another exchange about guns.

"Lieutenant Sullivan, you are an ex-police officer. Have you ever carried a gun?"

"Yes, I have."

"Since that time you were a police officer?"

"Yes, I have."

Norman was quick to follow up.

"May I ask you, Lieutenant, do you regard that as unlawful, to carry a concealable firearm upon your person, mindful of the state of California law as it is in that regard?"

Sullivan fixed Norman with a cheerless stare. "Mr. Norman," he said, "on occasion when I do happen to carry a concealed weapon, the necessity of doing so outweighs the consequences . . ."

For the first time since the trial had begun, Richard Aparicio, the door rattler who called himself a cop, smiled. Sullivan was excused.

"Would that be the sum total of your witnesses?" Judge Calcagno asked Doug Schmidt.

"Yes, Your Honor, that's all I managed to put together for today." For a moment he seemed almost inept. It was only 3:15.

11
Killer Cupcakes

The first day of the second full week of the murder trial was beginning. "Are you presently employed as a nurse?" Schmidt asked the witness.

"I am," said Dan's sister Nancy Bickel. She had the same broad cheeks and bulky body as her big brother.

"A registered nurse?"

"Registered nurse."

"During the time that you visited Dan and were close to him, did you ever notice any peculiar behavior on his part?"

"I did."

"What did you notice?"

Bits and pieces of what she had been prepared to say came tumbling out: "Well, he would always not go to the family, uh, well, I would say his moods were, just for a period of time where, you know, he wouldn't want to come out . . . you know, he would just . . . spent a lot of time in bed."

Schmidt prompted her gently. "When he was in these moods, would you go see him, go to visit him?"

"I would, usually, just to drop in, and most of the time he would talk to me briefly, then . . . I could get the hint he wanted me to go, and I would."

"Did you notice any changes in his health habits, anything such as that?"

". . . I noticed . . . during these periods, he called me sometimes to go out and get lunch for him, and gave me a specific list of what to get, like hardroll sandwiches, Cokes, Twinkies, candy bars, stuff like that."

Tom Norman thought the junk food testimony was just delectable. "Of course," he said during cross-examination, his eyes on nowhere, "your *mother* served a balanced diet, did she?"

"Yes, she did."

"With respect to those foods that you have suggested and told us he ate—Twinkies, I think you said?"

"Chocolate cupcakes."

"How often did you see him eat these chocolate cupcakes, for example?"

"Every other month. I don't remember how often he had the depressed moods, but . . . that is one thing he did, when he was in his depressed moods, was to eat the junk food."

Norman jangled his change. "Did he drink"—pause— "*Cokes* at that time?"

"Yes, he did."

"Mrs. Bickel, are you telling us that you are *equating* his depression with the ingestion of chocolate cupcakes . . .?"

"What do you mean by 'equating'?" Dan's favorite sister asked. "That *is* what I noticed when Danny was way down in those moods, that he ate that kind of food, didn't eat that, you know, when he wasn't depressed. He used to drink a lot of juices."

"You have been a nurse for *how* long now?"

"I was a licensed vocational nurse for four years. I just recently passed my registered nurses board."

"*Thank* you for coming today."

12
Some Difficulty

Schmidt had seemed more adept as a cross-examiner than as the architect of a defense case; his witnesses were for the most part repeating each other's testimony. Another cop friend of Dan's took the stand, and Mary Ann's best friend, Loretta Maret, and Ray Sloan, who had gone into hiding from the press right after the killings and had been referred to in one story as "a mysterious figure." One witness, a private investigator by the name of Harland Ansel Minshew, who was the proprietor of Forensic Investigations and Analyses, testified for only about five minutes.

"Now, Mr. Minshew," Schmidt said, "you were contacted by my office and asked to go to City Hall . . .?"

"Yes, sir."

"Pursuant to my request, did you walk from the private office of the mayor, in a fairly rapid pace, to . . . room 237?"

"Yes, sir, I did."

"Describe for me your findings."

"Walking at a rapid rate, I timed it . . . and it took me forty seconds."

"Nothing further," Schmidt said.

One reporter whispered to another, "What the hell was that all about?" and the second man shrugged.

It was only five minutes to eleven on Tuesday morning when Schmidt said to the judge, "Your Honor, I seem to have some difficulty determining the lengths of witnesses."

"Excuse me?" Judge Calcagno said.

"I say, I seem to have some difficulty in determining how long witnesses are going to take because I have run out of witnesses for this morning."

"All right." Judge Calcagno ran a finger across his lips. He looked down toward his papers and adjusted his glasses. "We heard from six persons."

"Yes," Schmidt said, wiping a hand across a cheek. "They went a little faster than I thought. I apologize for wasting time."

"All right. Can you get the [next] witness in at one-thirty?"

"Actually . . . I don't think so."

"All right. Well, we will reconvene at two o'clock."

Over lunch several reporters were talking, and they all agreed it looked as if Dan White were on his way to the gas chamber unless his young lawyer could produce more than sisters and cupcakes, doughnuts and stopwatches.

13
Rule of Law

Marty Blinder is very short and very smart. His broad forehead is burrowed with lines, his eyes pop froggily, and he bites his fingernails. Dr. Blinder lives in a big home which commands a Marin County hilltop. In the valley below is the town of San Anselmo. For a time, the psychiatrist was the mayor of San Anselmo. He likes to go out with attractive women taller than himself.

Steve Scherr had been Blinder's intermediary during his sessions with Dan, and Blinder met Doug Schmidt for the first time during the lunch break on Tuesday. He accepted the lawyer's apology as his due: the handsome, manly Schmidt said he was sorry for having been too busy to get together earlier, but he had read Blinder's report and the doctor seemed to need his assistance less than anybody else. Blinder got the impression that Schmidt was slightly in awe of him.

Once on the stand, he lounged. It took nearly ten minutes for him merely to recite his degrees, his advanced training, his accomplishments and publications, the journals he edited, the medical schools and hospitals with which he was associated, and his expertise as a forensic psychiatrist.

"You mentioned the term 'forensic psychiatry.' Explain briefly what the field of forensic psychiatry is, first of all."

"Forensic psychiatry is a subspeciality of psychiatry concerned with issues dealing with the relationship between law and psychiatry," Blinder said, "based on the happy assumption that there is a relationship." That got a little smile of acknowledgment from Mintzer, who would be selected by the jury as its foreman.

Though the private practice he maintained was prospering, Blinder found it to be somewhat cloistered. He needed the satisfaction he got when a jury delivered a favorable verdict, and he could tolerate that certain amount of ambiguity about his role which led some other psychiatrists, such as Dr. Thomas Szasz, to call men who sold their expertise as Blinder did, "hired liars."

"You mentioned," Schmidt said, "that there are uses and abuses of psychiatry. What would be the abusive form of psychiatry, in your opinion?"

"Well, I think the courts, at least some aspects of the courts, tend to place psychiatry in a position where it doesn't belong, where it becomes simply the sole arbiter between guilt and innocence, in certain kinds of crimes, whether or not a man is insane. I think psychiatry has a lot to contribute to these judgments but that these judgments are more than psychiatric judgments, and I do not think they should be equated."

He touched his face lightly and continued. "I think it's also a tendency in the stresses of the adversary system to polarize psychiatric testimony so that a psychiatrist finds himself trying to put labels on normal stressful behavior, and everything becomes a mental illness, and I think that is an abuse."

In forensic circles Blinder was not known for committing that particular abuse; his specialty was diminished capacity cases. It was his testimony in *People* v. *Berry* that had been cited by the appeals court in overturning the first-degree murder conviction of Albert Berry for having strangled his wife Rachel with a telephone cord. Dr. Blinder had entered the case after Rachel's death, of course, but in his testimony he had described her as a depressed, suicidally inclined girl whose self-destructive impulse had led her to provoke rages of sexual jealousy until her husband killed her. Dr. Blinder had testified that this provocative behavior on the part of the dead woman had consummated her unconscious desire for suicide.

He was also known as a spellbinding storyteller, and now Schmidt invited him to tell the jury what he had learned of Dan White during their three jailhouse sessions.

"Mr. White," he said, "spent all his life in San Francisco. He described his father as a warm, loving man whom he respected greatly but whom he missed because his father was out of the home a great deal, attending to his job as a fireman . . . he hungered for more contact with the man, and in fact, when he died, when Mr. White was seventeen, he felt that as one of the greatest losses of his life. Mr. White's words to me were: 'I never had a chance to know him and now I never would.' And he continues to speak about wishing that his father would be proud of him. . . .

"He described his mother as an unemotional woman, solid like a rock, who raised her nine children properly, more out of a sense of duty, more from her head than her heart."

Mrs. McHugh's face, where she sat beside Mary Ann on the far side of the glass, was composed.

"It seemed to him," Blinder said, scratching his scalp, "that no matter what he did it was never enough in the family, who were demanding of him, expecting him to do more, and he seemed to feel he was always criticized, indirectly or directly. He grew up, to use his words, 'feeling different from the group I wanted most to be accepted by.'

". . . As a consequence he learned pretty much to keep not only his behavior to himself, and thoughts and feelings to himself, but since he spoke his mind and was slapped down, he learned to keep his own counsel, keep his feelings inside. . . ."

Blinder was warming to his story. He knew it behooved him to be articulate. "He was brought up as a strict Catholic, and as a youngster he took parochial instructions, and believed literally what the Bible says, that this is the way the Bible says it, and by golly, this is the way it is. And he tried, perhaps more than most people in his parochial classes, to live up strictly to the teachings of the Church, and as a consequence, as he got a bit older, and began to measure the literal teachings of the Church, and see the realities of everyday living, he began to find that the Church teaching is ridiculous, wherein it is a sin to eat meat on Friday, a sin to masturbate, and his efforts to live up to the letter of the Catholic law led him to reject it, because it seemed to him too extreme."

Dr. Blinder described how Dan had joined and quit the police department to roam "à la Jack London," and how he had rejoined and quit again after the incident of the Shy Fox; how he had joined the fire department and come to the aid of the probies who were being unfairly washed out in his estimation. "In '76 he married a schoolteacher, and was somewhat ambivalent, not about this woman, who is the best possible wife, but about assuming marital responsibilities. But again, there was family pressure, that this was expected of him. And whether he wanted to be a free agent or not, he was going to get married and do the proper thing."

Dr. Blinder described Dan's election campaign. "Paradoxically," he said, "this victory served as a catalyst for the tragic events that occurred on November twenty-seventh, 1978."

"Doctor," said Schmidt, "at this juncture, having reviewed the background material that you have thus far, did it become evident to you that there was an underlying mental illness of some sort in play here?"

"I'm not so sure, Mr. Schmidt, that I would elevate it to the threshold of illness, but certainly there were a number of problems of an emotional sort pressing on Mr. White that were of great relevance here . . . in a sense, Mr. White has been in conflict all his life.

"On the one hand, he wanted to be something of a free spirit and follow his feelings, but at the same time, was exquisitely sensitive to family and middle-class pressures, obligations, that he prove that he can do the right thing, the social, acceptable thing, and do them well, and be a policeman, fireman, be a husband, be a father, and retrospectively he might have been happier if he had just gone along and traveled around. . . .

"And he always kept his own counsel, as he put it to me:"— referring to his jailhouse examination—" 'All my life I have been able to handle any problems by myself. If the going got tough, I just dug in harder.' Although he added, rather grimly: 'I guess this time it didn't work. The harder I dug in, the deeper I got. I had been in stress before as a policeman and soldier, but never broke, but I guess this time things got too much for me.' " Blinder brushed his lips with his knuckles.

"In other words," Schmidt said, "the factor in there, the overall question of Mr. White's personality, mental status, is the fact that he has depression, perhaps as many as a half dozen a year?" He was trying to bring Blinder to a point of legal significance.

"*Is* the fact that he's had depression, perhaps as many as half a dozen per year, each lasting four to five days, often without any apparent trigger," Blinder agreed. In his written report the psychiatrist had called the episodes "bouts of despondency," but on the stand he picked up Schmidt's word—depression.

"During these spells he'd become quite withdrawn, quite lethargic. He would retreat to his room. Wouldn't come to the door. Wouldn't answer the phone. . . . And during these periods he found that he could not cope with people . . . any confrontations would cause him to kind of become argumentative . . . whenever he felt things were not going right he would abandon his usual program of exercise and good nutrition and start gorging himself on junk foods, Twinkies, Coca Cola.

"Mr. White had always been something of an athlete, priding himself on being physically fit. But when something would go wrong he'd hit the high-sugar stuff. He'd hit the chocolate and the more he consumed the worse he'd feel, and he'd respond to his ever-growing depression by consuming ever more junk food. The more junk food he consumed, the worse he'd feel. The worse he'd feel, the more he'd gorge himself." Blinder spoke with a certain cultured thickness.

Blinder described Dan taking office, being forced to give up his job as a fireman, the pyramiding financial pressures. "Another source of continuing pressure on Mr. White, and this is somewhat subtle, is the fact he got married, and he had ambivalence about getting married. He was always extremely cautious when approaching apparently congenial members of the opposite sex." That would have surprised Alma had she heard it. "He has always been very wary of situations where strong feelings are likely to emerge. And of course that included marital relationships. Always kept his feelings in check. And though he feels he has an excellent marriage, even his wife has never been a confidante. Even his wife had never really shared in his feelings. . . ."

Mary Ann was sitting at the edge of her seat, her chin resting on her palm, looking terribly interested, as if hearing things about her husband for the first time. A few feet in front of her, but on the inside of the glass barrier, Dan stared blankly at the courtroom wall, the gold-tasseled flag.

"His most profound and proximate stress, though," Blinder continued, "was attendant to his position as San Francisco supervisor. Mr. White found City Hall rife [with] corruption. With the possible exception of Dianne Feinstein and Harvey Milk, the supervisors seemed to make their judgments, their votes, on the basis of what was good for them, rather than what was good for the city. . . . Supervisor Molinari voted against a ballfield tax exemption because he didn't get the right tickets—"

"Doctor," Schmidt interrupted, "we decided not to mention any names with regard to specific supervisors and that sort of thing."

Blinder was momentarily taken aback. It sounded to him as if there had been a stipulation, a handshake agreement between the attorneys, sanctified by the judge. Schmidt really should have mentioned it to him earlier.

Jim Woods, the *Examiner*'s experienced trial reporter, reacted as Blinder did, and underlined what Schmidt had said: *decided not to mention any names*. Now *that* explained a lot that had been puzzling him. He thought that if he ever did write a book about the trial (at least five reporters were contemplating books or film scripts), he'd begin right there; all the deficiencies in Norman's case made better sense if there had been some sort of secret agreement.

"*I* thought it was *extremely* interesting," Norman said jovially, drawing a laugh.

"Would you tell us," Schmidt said, ". . . all of these stress factors and any others you are about to point out, how that fits in with the mental status . . .?"

At City Hall, Blinder continued, Dan "was continually defeated. So finally he decided that since he couldn't play the game their way, his best bet was simply to quit. He and Mary Ann were so busy they hardly saw each other. He was run down in the press.

"Lack of activity and all this junk food caused him to gain twenty pounds while he served on the Board." Blinder was fleshing out the case. He described how Dan had quit, changed his mind, and finally realized that he would not be reinstated. "But now, getting very depressed about the fact that he would not be reappointed, he just sat there before the TV, bingeing on Twinkies. He couldn't sleep . . . virtually no sexual contact at this time. He was dazed, confused, had crying spells, became increasingly ill, and wanted to be left alone. Mrs. White reports to me that at this time sexual contact, which had been as often as three times a week, came to a complete halt."

It was impossible to tell from looking at Dan, whose expression and rigidity never changed, what agonies these intimate revelations were costing him. The man who kept his own counsel was not only having his deepest privacies invaded, but even more mortifying, having them put on display for his mother, recorded by the press.

Blinder described Dan's sudden decision to go to City Hall on the twenty-seventh of November, and the killings, which he said Dan had committed as if he were in a dream. "And I would suspect that if it were not for . . . all the tremendous pressures on him the weeks prior to the shooting, and perhaps if it were not for the ingestion of this aggravating factor, this junk food . . . I would suspect that these homicides would not have taken place. . . . I feel that all of these pressures sufficiently discombobulated him that he didn't have his wits about him. And I think that these factors would play a substantial part in impairing his ability to premeditate. . . . Based on the information that I have, Mr. Schmidt, his capacity to harbor malice would be significantly affected by these . . . powerful pressures upon him."

"I understand," the lawyer said. "Lastly, doctor, you have indicated in outlining the material that you went through briefly here, that there were certain provocative episodes with regard to the reappointment. Within your expertise, was that type of provocation the type of provocation that would arouse some passion in a person, not necessarily arouse some passion in the ordinary, reasonable person so that he would kill, but simply arouse that passion?"

Blinder, too, understood. His next answer was the most important he would give.

"Yes," he said. "I think that any man, even one not carrying all the special burdens that Mr. White carried, I think that any man, even one for whom reappointment did not hold that very special significance that it did for Mr. White, would be aroused to tremendous emotions and tremendous passion, emotion and passion which might serve to short-circuit some of the mental processes necessary for premeditation, malice, intent and so on. And certainly in the case of Mr. White, I think it's common sense that these pressures would have a profound effect upon him and indeed move him to an unaccustomed state of passion."

Schmidt had gotten what he needed from the witness. The judge would not now dare to fail to incorporate the jury instructions covering heat of passion and irresistible impulse. The last judge who had discounted Marty Blinder's testimony about heat of passion had been reversed by the state's high court. Now, if the jury only followed what the judge must, of necessity, tell them to do, you were looking at manslaughter. "I have nothing further," Schmidt said. "Thank you, sir."

Judge Calcagno called for the afternoon recess. At 3:15 Dr. Blinder resumed the stand and was approached by the prosecutor.

"Good afternoon, Doctor Blinder."

"Mr. Norman." Twenty times and more it had been Tommy Norman's dubious pleasure to cross-examine Marty Blinder. Blinder, he felt, would have had even him diminished if the fee were right. Norman held the psychiatrist's report in his hand.

"This data," he said, ". . . was it such to you, doctor, that you could say that he suffered from an articulable mental illness?"

"I'd have to say I'm not sure."

"Did he seem, Dr. Blinder, to express any remorse?"

"Yes, he told me that he was particularly upset about the Moscone family. He remembered what it was like to lose his own father, and that was, of all the terrible things he did, that was perhaps the worst. Deprived this family of their winner and their father."

"Did he tell you, at any time, that he felt sorry that George Moscone had lost his life as a result of his act?"

"I don't think he said that specifically, no."

"I take it, then, that he did not include George Moscone in that sorrow?"

"Not that I can recall."

Schmidt wrote himself a note on his legal pad.

"With respect to Harvey Milk," the prosecutor continued, his voice ranging across scales, savoring syllables, "did you ask him if he felt sorry that Harvey Milk was dead and that he had caused it?"

"No," Blinder said, touching his face. "I did not specifically ask that question."

"Mr. White, as you have described him, doctor, is a man whose background you said was of Catholic religious persuasion. Would you say that his attitude toward life . . . was rigid?"

"I'm not sure I understand your question."

"Well, did he have and entertain specific philosophies toward the way life should be lived and acted out in a rigid sense?"

"Yes, he did."

"Did he regard things, Doctor, would you say, as either right or wrong?"

"Yes."

"Was he the type of person, based upon your material . . . and the interviews, who was able to compromise his feelings between right and wrong?"

"Not very readily, no."

"Do you believe, Doctor, that he found the Board of Supervisors . . . a frustrating experience because of the give-and-take-nature of bringing about legislation?"

"Yes, I think that's a good chunk of it . . ."

"Do you believe . . . that he felt very strongly repugnant to that way of bringing about legislation or doing business, as the case may be?"

"Yes. He felt it would be immoral."

"Did you say *immoral?*"

"Yes."

A half hour and several dozen questions later, Norman asked: "Dr. Blinder, when he left home on the morning of November twenty-seventh, at that time did he have the capacity, in your opinion, to form the intent to kill George Moscone?"

"Possibly."

"He had the capacity at that time to form the intent to kill Harvey Milk . . .?"

"Possibly."

"Well, Doctor, at that particular time did you feel he had that capacity to reason out the following, perhaps it's an oversimplification, but: 'I am going to kill George Moscone for what he has done'?"

"Yes, I think it would be possible for him to do that. . . . I don't think he would. I think that's at war with the way Mr. White is put together . . ."

"Doctor, when you say that you think that it's possibly at war with the way he thought, it's difficult to know what he thought, or to look into a person's mind to know just what they are thinking at a particular juncture, isn't it?"

"That's right."

"It's almost impossible, isn't it?"

"It's impossible to know. The best you can do is know how a person usually thinks, and then apply that information to a particular moment."

Norman jangled his change. "When he and the mayor went into the room adjacent to the mayor's office, where the mayor offered him a drink, then made some inquiry . . . about the plight of his family, doctor, do you feel at that time he was capable of knowing that if he pointed a gun at the mayor and that if he discharged it that in all likelihood it would kill the mayor?"

Blinder scratched the side of his head vigorously. It was the kind of question he enjoyed toying with. "Yes and no," he began. "I think he certainly walked into that office in possession of that basic information. But knowing something is more than simply possessing a piece of information. You have to have it accessible. It has to be part of your awareness . . . without that, it's possible to know something and not know it. Just like you might meet somebody who you know very well . . . but suddenly at that moment . . . you can't think of his name. . . . You know but you don't know."

"Doctor," Norman sneered, "isn't it kind of *basic* that the pointing of a gun which is loaded at another human being, and the discharge of it, is likely to bring about death . . .?"

"Yes, that's certainly basic. Just as basic is the name of a friend. . . . It is possible to lose your grip on basic information if you are sufficiently emotionally discombobulated."

"Doctor, can we say that, in your opinion, it's possible that he could have premeditated and deliberated and formed malice?"

"Anything is possible, Mr. Norman . . ."

When Norman was finally finished with Dr. Blinder, Schmidt took over again for redirect questioning, and then Norman, and finally Schmidt again. So it was quite late in the afternoon when, in his response to a question about Dan's attitude toward the legislative process, Marty Blinder said of Dan White: ". . . and certainly, he considers himself the very embodiment of the rule of law."

In his four hours of testimony Blinder had contributed only one strong element to the legal defense, and that was the basis for jury instructions covering heat of passion and irresistible impulse. Tom Norman, in fact, was pleased with the way it had gone. Blinder, he thought, had been so equivocal that he had very nearly been a prosecution witness.

But something subtle and indefinable had happened while Marty Blinder accounted for Dan White, as Tuesday afternoon ran its course and was swallowed up by ennui in the windowless courtroom. For the first time since Doug Schmidt's opening statement to the jury a week earlier, the silent, immobile man whose presence was like a question mark punctuating the meting out of justice had, through the vehicle of the psychiatrist's gift for words, become quite humanly understandable.

14
Crazy

Dan's cell was only a few feet away from the psychiatric tier in the city jail on the top floor of the Hall of Justice. Every nook of the jail is noisy but where the crazies are kept it is bedlam. Because Dan was a celebrity in the incarcerated world where most everybody had done something bad but he had done the biggest, baddest thing of all, the psychiatric inmates would wander right up to the gate of their tier and shout across the short distance separating them from Dan in his solitary cell. Jane Halstead, the nurse, had begun to notice that Dan treated the crazies just the same way the deputies treated *him*.

When one of them would begin to babble at him, Dan would turn on a winning smile. "Hey, how ya doin' today?" he'd chirp. "How's it goin'?"

Dan, the deputies, the crazies—it was, the nurse thought, a real case of see no evil, hear no evil, speak no evil. Rah rah rah, sis boom bah.

Tuesday evening Dan had a visitor who did insist on making him consider what he had done: Dr. George Solmon. No other psychiatrist had played a more significant advisory role in the formation of the defense strategy than Dr. Solmon. He had already interviewed Dan three times, but after Marty Blinder's testimony about Dan's lack of remorse, the lawyers had called Dr. Solmon and asked if he couldn't go over that ground again that night, prior to taking the witness stand in the morning. It was emotionally important for the jurors to believe that Dan deeply and painfully regretted his wrongdoing. Even remorse, though, if it existed, did not necessarily suggest the presence of repentance.

15
Mind Over Matter

Doug Schmidt never touched on the subject of remorse during his direct examination of Dr. Solmon, who was a dark, apparently nervous man, given to wrinkling his brow and mumbling to himself before answering questions.

In relation to the psychiatrists and the psychologist who would occupy the witness stand from Tuesday afternoon until Thursday afternoon, Schmidt made himself out to be something of a bumbler and a stumbler after truth. "In your conversations with me," the lawyer asked at one point, "did you discover that I was not particularly attuned to psychiatry and mental states and what we believe make people do things, and cognition, and all of those phrases?"

"I think that you probably know less about psychiatry than I know about the law, let's put it that way," the doctor responded.

"Precisely my point," said Schmidt.

Schmidt never asked Dr. Solmon even one question about remorse, and on cross-examination, seeing a chance to drive home the point he had made with Dr. Blinder, Norman fell right into the trap.

"Well, Doctor," the prosecutor asked, "did he ever say to you in so many words: 'I feel sorry for George Moscone, for having done this to George Moscone'?"

"He didn't feel sorry for Mr. Moscone because he was dead. You can't feel sorry for somebody who is dead. He said, yes, he did say he was sorry he had done it, in so many words."

"Doctor, do you feel that those feelings of sorrow, expressed by him to you, were feelings of sorrow that he has put himself in, and his family in, the plight that he finds himself in now?"

"I don't think that is the only reason, no. I think he feels sorry for the act that was committed."

"Doctor, did he ever express to you that he was sorry that he had shot and killed Harvey Milk?"

"Yes."

This was not going at all the way Norman had anticipated; for a moment he himself was discombobulated. He had already learned from Dr. Solmon that the psychiatrist had visited with Dan the night before, and had he been thinking a little faster he might have asked if the sorrow was discussed then, or if the subject had been suggested to Dr. Solmon by Doug Schmidt, but instead Norman said: "In saying he felt bad about what he had done, do you feel, Doctor, that that embraces in some substantial part [his] plight . . .?"

"Well," said Dr. Solmon, twisting his gold bracelet, "interestingly enough, I might be more worried about his self-destruction if he were not punished at all by society. He is a very self-punitive person.

"For example, if he was acquitted, which is not an issue in this case, of total acquittal . . . I would worry that he might commit suicide, because I think that because of his guilt he would punish himself very severely . . . he has . . . certainly been miserable . . . a total acquittal might be very dangerous."

Schmidt, very pleased with the exchange, kept his face expressionless. His strong, jutting chin was virtually identical to Dan's, except it did not have the cleft.

During his direct examination of Dr. Solmon, Schmidt had asked the psychiatrist about Dan's character, and the psychiatrist had more or less agreed with Dr. Blinder.

". . . [he] had, basically, I think, a conflict of identity . . . he was never able to integrate into a meaningful, coherent whole person . . . [this] was related to his identification with his father, to whom he felt somewhat inferior . . . he felt he had to emulate, live up to [him], and it was particularly harder to please somebody who is dead than someone who is alive . . ."

"Doctor," Schmidt continued, "underlying, and I think perhaps coinciding with this, were you also able to diagnose or detect any mental illness or disease in Mr. White, and if so, what would that be?"

"Yes, I think he was suffering from what in the new classification is called a unipolar depressive reaction, and that means he was subject to recurrent bouts of depression to a major degree. Unipolar means he just went down. . . . I don't believe he got too high."

"Doctor, turning to the forensic terms . . . have you arrived at an opinion as to whether or not on the date of those tragedies . . . Dan White was capable of premeditation and deliberation . . .?"

". . . He did not have a mental capacity to maturely and meaningfully premeditate and deliberate. My reasons are twofold . . . one is because of his depression. . . . The other reason is quite a different one, which has to do with his character structure, which I described, and his basic personality and his morals and his principles. To me it seems quite inconceivable that Mr. White, who really couldn't even tell off somebody who stepped on his toes in a line, so to speak, would be able to plan, even briefly, something heinous, and certainly what he did was most reprehensible, if you want to make a value judgment."

His harboring malice, too, the psychiatrist said, was improbable. Reasonable men could question whether Dr. Solmon or any other psychiatrist was able to evaluate a past state of mind but that was what he was being paid quite well to do and that was what he was doing.

"Thank you," Schmidt said, and turned the witness over to Norman, who fell into the remorse trap. For hours the prosecutor prodded and pulled and shook the testimony of the psychiatrist, like an angry terrier with his teeth sunk into an ankle, and the longer he went on the less attractive he became. He had his best moments when he began by asking, "Doctor, what do you understand the issue to be in this case?"

"My understanding of the issue?" Dr. Solmon mumbled. "The degree of responsibility in regard to first-degree or not first-degree. I do not understand the issue at this trial primarily being that of legal insanity. I understand it has to do with degree, whether it's a first-, a second-, or manslaughter issue, not whether he did it, which he did do, and not so much whether he was legally insane but rather whether he had the requisite states of mind to have a first- or second-degree murder."

It was an accurate and thought-provoking answer. Experts such as Dr. Solmon had seized control of the criminal justice system by having taken for themselves the right to define what the issues were. As things stood in 1979, lawyers in legislatures and courtrooms had defined degrees of criminal responsibility but psychiatrists defined normal and abnormal behavior. If their definitions sometimes seemed as commonsensical as medieval debates over how many angels could dance on the head of a pin, that proved little more than that they were contemporary men. And if their definitions ultimately subverted something necessary, not justice precisely—because who could say with certainty what justice is?—but at least the confidence of a community that life was coherent and subject to commonsensical regulation, well, that was not their problem.

"Doctor," Tommy Norman asked rather shrilly, "he certainly could express the emotion of anger, couldn't he?"

"No, not very well," Dr. Solmon said. ". . . You know, I think a more normal person, if you will, who felt treated unfairly or outraged, would tell someone off, which, I think, might have been the appropriate thing for him."

"Doctor, given all those circumstances that led up to the morning of the twenty-seventh of November last year, you are aware that he took a gun with him when he determined to see George Moscone?"

"Yes."

"It was a loaded gun. You are aware of that, aren't you?"

"Yes."

"Why did he take that gun, in your opinion, Dr. Solmon?"

"Well, there are conscious and unconscious possibilities. . . . I think a gun to him, and I have material to support this, it was a security blanket in certain ways. . . ."

"Doctor, did he tell you that he hadn't carried that gun for approximately a month prior to that occasion?"

"Yes . . . although of course he hadn't been going down, as I understand it, to City Hall too regularly in that period of time."

"Well," said Norman, looking into the distance, ". . . he was at City Hall on the tenth of November, which would be about seventeen days before, and there were a couple of meetings with the mayor . . . and then he was at City Hall on Friday the twenty-fourth. . . . And it wasn't reported to you that he carried a gun on any of those occasions, I take it?"

"No. I think that if you look at it as a security blanket you can see security blankets are clung to, in situations of great . . . anxiety, as one sees with children, of course, with the actual teddy bear, or the security blanket, which Winnicott refers to as—"

"Pardon me?" interjected the court reporter.

"He's a psychiatrist," Dr. Solmon explained, "who is—"

Judge Calcagno cut him off. "He doesn't want an explanation, he wants to get the spelling."

"In *this* case, Doctor," Norman pressed ahead, "when he went to City Hall and went up to see George Moscone, do you believe, Doctor, that he had the capacity at that time to want to hurt George Moscone?"

"I actually went into this. I said something about, you know. . . : 'Well, I suppose you could [have] give[n] him a punch in the nose?'

"He said: 'That would have been totally out of the question.' Particularly because he felt in terms of his youth and strength and experience in boxing and so on that it would have been a completely unequal match, and that it would be totally out of the question for him to punch Mr. Moscone . . ."

Norman rattled his change and flushed. "Dr. Solmon, after he fired his gun twice into the body of George Moscone, were you aware that he shot George Moscone twice in the head when he was on the floor?" Tommy was angry; these shrinks were like pigs rolling in their own shit. "Doctor, after he shot George Moscone, did you know whether he reloaded his weapon or not?"

"Yes, he told me he did."

"Why did he do that?"

"He told me that that was the sort of automatic reaction that he had always been taught . . ."

"Just an automatic reaction, is that right?"

"Yes."

"It wasn't just an automatic reaction, was it, Doctor, when he fired those last two shots into George Moscone's head, was it?"

"I think he was out of control and in an unreasonable state. And I think if the gun had held, you know, maybe more bullets, maybe he would have shot more bullets . . ."

"George Moscone was shot four times, doctor. The gun had five cartridges in it. Did that change your opinion in any way?"

"No," said the psychiatrist. "I think he just kept shooting for a while."

It was mid-afternoon.

Dr. Richard Delman, a clinical psychologist who had done about two hundred court-ordered examinations, had already testified at Doug Schmidt's bidding that Dan had, in all likelihood, been too depressed to deliberate, premeditate, or harbor malice. The bearded assistant professor had explained that to help him reach his conclusions he had administered the Wexler Adult Intelligence Scale, the Minnesota Multiphasic Personality Inventory Test, and the Rorschach test.

The psychological palaver had been going on for more than a day and Tommy Norman was questioning the interpretation of one of the inkblots. On the far side of the glass Dan's stepfather, Frank McHugh, had dozed off and was fast asleep.

When they got done with the inkblots, Norman asked: "Doctor, why didn't he just go in the front door of City Hall . . . rather than go around to the side and climb through a window?"

"Well, he told me that he walked up to the front entrance . . . and that it wasn't until he got to the very top landing that he looked at the metal detector and remembered the gun . . . he said that he didn't want to embarrass the officer . . ."

"Now, Dr. Delman, why wouldn't he want to embarrass the officer, or why would that be of concern to him?"

"I didn't ask him why."

"You have been able to give us an opinion as to what he was capable of thinking, and so, have you an opinion in that regard?"

"Do I have an opinion about why he didn't want to embarrass the officer at the metal detector?"

"Sure," Norman said. "What would be the difference?"

Judge Calcagno, who had been leaning back in his big chair, sat upright. "Hold it! Hold it! That's not a question, is it?"

"Yes," said the prosecutor. "What would be the difference?"

"Well," Dr. Delman answered, "he still thinks of himself as a policeman and a fireman . . . and that these are the people who have been behind him consistently for a long time . . . it seems to me he takes special considerations not to hurt their feelings."

"Why would it hurt the . . . officer's feelings if a police officer saw him and said, 'Look, you're carrying a gun'?"

"He just said he didn't want to embarrass him."

Crossly, Norman said: "I'm just asking you for your opinion."

The judge had had enough. "Let's move on to another question. It's completely irrelevant, Mr. Norman, what he believes the answer should be."

"Well, Your Honor, he has told us clearly here that the man—"

"Let's move *on.* You are just arguing with the witness now." Judge Calcagno's impatience put an end to the discussion of Dan's possible embarrassment when faced with the guard and the metal detector, and so other questions about the subject would never, as it turned out, be raised during the trial.

How would Dan's having a gun embarrass the guard? If the guard took the gun away from him, would that be embarrassing? If he allowed him to keep the gun and Dan eventually left City Hall without using it, would that be embarrassing? Or would it be embarrassing to the guard if he let a gun be brought into City Hall and it was used to kill a supervisor and the mayor?

When Dan walked into the courtroom on Thursday morning he advanced the dozen paces or so toward Mary Ann, as always, then turned and sat down. He rubbed his eyes with his fingertips and assumed his customary position. There was one more shrink to go, one more day of whatever mortifications were being inflicted by this public probing of his life and psyche, one last episode of this humiliation far greater than any George or Harvey had been responsible for, but which was necessary if he did not want to die in the gas chamber. He had betrayed his own code to save his skin.

Mary Ann leaned over to Dan's mother and whispered, "He said good luck to me."

Dr. Donald Lunde, whose name was probably the most highly respected in California in the field of forensic psychiatry, was taking the stand. A self-composed man in his mid-forties, Lunde had spent his entire career at Stanford University. The author of the authoritative study, *Murder and Madness,* it was his usual pleasure to be the last psychiatrist to testify; his clarity and eminence were such that lawyers had learned to trust him with tying up loose ends and making sure a psychiatric defense was completed as well as concluded. In fact, Dan White's case was already being called, by some lawyers and psychiatrists, a Lunde defense. There are psychiatrists who refuse to go into the courtroom because they find it compromises their professional ethics, but Donald Lunde was not among them.

Dr. Lunde had done far more, in the course of his consultations with Doug Schmidt, than merely interview Dan. He had listened to the tape, read the police reports, spent five hours with Mary Ann, and several more with Dan's sister Nancy. He had reviewed Dan's army, police and fire department records, read the preliminary hearing transcript, and studied the transcripts of the police interviews with ten others, from Dianne Feinstein to Cyr Copertini, from the engineer who had seen Dan climb through the basement window to the city attorneys Lazarus and Toomey, who had not been called to testify.

When Schmidt asked Dr. Lunde for his diagnosis, he replied:

"My opinion is that he was suffering from mental illness on and prior to November twenty-seven, 1978. The mental illness is depression of a fairly severe degree; secondarily, he also has, of longstanding duration, a very compulsive personality. . . . That is, someone who from a fairly early age is quite rigid, overly conscientious, overly upset, uptight as an adult, characterized as a workaholic, someone who finds it difficult to get much pleasure out of anything except work, and such people are prone to be, prone to depression . . .

"Anyhow, the reason for the diagnosis of depression is that for several years, off and on, Mr. White has had episodes during which he exhibited both the biological and psychological symptoms of depression.

"When I use the term I am using it in a psychiatric sense and not in the sense that people say: I feel depressed, I feel sad or blue or something like that . . . but I am . . . referring to a specific disorder, which is a fairly serious disorder, and has specific symptoms . . .

"Biological includes such things as sleep disturbance, inability to, difficulty falling asleep, waking up frequently at night, and some nights not sleeping at all. Biological symptoms also include change in appetite, and this was quite striking, these episodes, as to Mr. White, as to his appetite and eating habits, which were changed rather drastically. . . ." The Stanford man evidently could not bring himself to say Twinkies.

"Then, in the psychological sphere, some of the symptoms and feelings are hopelessness and worthlessness and despair, to the point of, in fact, feeling suicidal . . .

"Mr. White, in fact, was suffering from very severe depression. . . . It's contradictory and ironic, but the way it works is that for such a person the American Dream is a nightmare, for somebody like Dan White, because the notions of working hard and achieving and being independent, self-reliant, so forth, tend to play into the problems, and these problems lead to depression . . . and what happened to Mr. White is that the harder he works, and the more he achieved, the worse he felt . . .

"And the depression became longer and more intense, so that by November of 1978 he was really very seriously ill."

If, in the modern American courtroom, the psychiatric experts had seized a certain degree of control by having defined themselves as the arbiters of normalcy and abnormalcy, had captured that degree of power, the question still remained: to what use would they put this power?

In any criminal proceeding, as Dr. Solmon had said, once the act was acknowledged the crucial question was: how responsible was the defendant for his own actions? That was the question the jury had to decide. Some psychiatrists, like Dr. Blinder, argued that because people are subject to pressure and don't handle it very well, their actions may well be excusable. Dr. Lunde was made of sterner stuff, a man of science.

And men of science no longer inquired after the condition of the soul, but after the state of mind. Science had replaced God as the source of awe—medical research had conquered polio and men had walked on the moon—and psychiatrists had replaced priests in determining the razor-sharp issues of personal responsibility. Some compassion may have been gained but certainly something had been lost as well. What had been lost were fundamental, unflinching standards of right and wrong, those moral tensions carried forward through centuries of juris-prudence. Though psychiatrists claimed a scientific dispassion, their conclusions could hardly have been more subjective; and this seemed doubly true in a courtroom where their judgments reduced them to little more than opinion-mongering.

The law viewed murderous responsibility as having three aspects. Did the defendant premeditate? Did he deliberate? Did he harbor malice? Those terms had been defined and redefined, questioned and requestioned, during the trial. Now Dr. Lunde would define them once and for all, more incisively than they had yet been explained. And defining them, he would determine that they had been absent from Dan White on the day he killed George Moscone and Harvey Milk. He would conclude, in short, that the state of Dan White's mind had diminished his degree of responsibility, which it was within his power to do.

"Premeditation and deliberation are mental states which are required for first-degree murder," Dr. Lunde began.

"Premeditation refers to planning, actively planning out a murder beforehand.

"Deliberation refers to mature, meaningful reflection about a planned killing.

"Deliberation also includes the notion that someone has given careful consideration to the reasons for and against a particular course of action, that they have considered and thought about the consequences of an act of killing . . . consequences not only for the victim but consequences to the defendant as well, and that person has thought,

in other words, about all those things . . . in a mature, meaningful way
. . .

"And in Mr. White's case, he not only did not premeditate or deliberate these killings, but as a result of his mental condition, he was not capable of any kind of mature, meaningful reflection on the morning of November twenty-seventh of last year.

"His mental condition was such that even if he had tried—which he didn't—he would not have been capable of sitting down and maturely, meaningfully reflecting upon the act, weighing the pros and cons of doing it, of not doing it, of doing it a certain way versus another way, thinking about the possible consequences . . . that sort of thing, all of which is part of premeditation and deliberation, which is necessary for someone to have committed a first-degree murder."

"Doctor," Schmidt asked, "we also deal with the term malice, or malice aforethought, although that is ill defined in the law. Can you give us some understanding of the meaning of those terms? And then secondly, your conclusions . . . with regard to whether Dan White's capacity for harboring that state of mind on November twenty-seventh, 1978?"

"Malice," said Dr. Lunde, "is the mental state that distinguishes a murder from a manslaughter. Without malice you don't have murder, first- or second-degree.

"And malice can be either expressed malice or implied malice.

"Expressed malice is present when there is, among other things, an intent to kill, but it's important to point out that intent to kill, in itself, doesn't make it malice . . .

"In order to have expressed malice there must be, in addition to intent to kill, an ability at the time of the killing, an ability to be aware of the laws of society, duties imposed upon the person by society, and to obey the law, and [there] must also be an ability, mental and emotional ability, to conform your conduct to the requirements of the law.

"Now, as regards to . . . expressed malice, Mr. White was *not,* at the time of these killings, capable of thinking about his obligations to society, what the laws were and how they might affect him . . .

". . . And in regard to the other kind of malice, implied malice, that is present when someone commits a dangerous act, an act which is likely to result in serious injury or death to someone else. But again, that is not enough.

"The act itself isn't sufficient." The five words summed up the source of Dr. Lunde's power and his great confidence.

It was an hour before lunchtime when Tommy Norman approached the coolly poised witness, knowing full well that the Stanford doctor's background and manner had made him more believable than any of the other experts. Norman had called Lunde himself to examine Dan White on the day of the killings but had not reached him. If he had, the formidable man of science might well have seen Dan White within hours of the shootings and could well be testifying for the prosecutor instead. Norman had been watching the jury and could see that they were impressed. Dr. Lunde had not titillated them with stories of Dan and Mary Ann's sexual frequency, nor told them that the .38 special was really a teddy bear, nor bored them with inkblots in the shape of the defendant's father. Precise as a surgeon, the man of science had laid out a body of facts and cut away the parts that offended until what was left on the operating table was a human being very nearly devoid of responsibility for his acts. At fifty dollars an hour he was a real bargain.

Norman approached the witness slowly, his nose pointing down toward his small cherry lips and slightly recessive chin. You could see the bald spot in the back of his pomaded, curly hair. He was thinking that his best shot would be to attack not the credibility of the witness, but of his source of information, Dan White.

"Doctor, I take it that he explained [his] feelings to you upon which you are expounding now?"

"Yes. In response to questions of mine."

"Do you depend in large part upon what a person tells you and reports to you in making your psychiatric evaluation of him with respect to certain issues?"

"I depend on that, and to the extent I can any corroboration from any other people who might have observed him . . . or talked to him about those feelings . . . and so on."

"I take it," Norman said, "you favored yourself with his statement that he gave the police on that same day following the shootings?"

"Yes."

"In that statement, do you recall he said he hadn't carried the gun for some time previously to that?"

"Yes. I don't understand why he said that. But then . . . it's obvious that he was very emotionally distraught at that time he made that statement. . . . And so I think that's probably the reason why there is, I think, a mistaken statement because he has told me that in fact he carried the gun off and on many times . . . within those last months . . .

"Because for him it wasn't that big a deal in the sense that as a former police officer . . . and having also been in Vietnam . . . I suppose [carrying a gun] is as common an experience as wearing a suit and tie is for you or for me."

"I take it, Doctor, that you regard his statement . . . to be inaccurate to that extent?"

"I think . . . as regards [that] it had been several months, I think that that's mistaken. I have no way of proving that, but I think it's mistaken."

"Doctor, is he intelligent enough to be capable of telling a lie?"

"At some other time when he was not upset or suffering from his depression and so on, sure, he would be intelligent enough to do that if he wanted to. It's not generally in his character to make up or consciously fabricate, though."

"The emotion of self-preservation is a strong one, isn't it, Doctor?"

"Well, for most people," Lunde said, unruffled by Norman's acid insinuation. "For people who are depressed and suicidal, it's not so strong."

"The pain in his head and the difficulty in hearing is something which we have learned from him only, isn't it?"

"Well, yes."

"There is no way to corroborate that, is there?"

"Other than asking him, no. It's such an odd thing that I would have . . . no reason to think that he was fabricating it."

"Well, I'm just pointing out—"

Dr. Lunde interrupted. "I'm sure that we have to rely on his statement for that." The doctor was unflappable and unshakable. Try as he might, Norman could not budge him. And Dr. Lunde, true to his reputation, in the hours that Norman had at him, even found opportunity to tie off one, last loose end for the defense. When Norman asked about Dan's state of mind in the time after he left George Moscone's body and started out toward Harvey Milk, Dr. Lunde invoked the testimony of the private investigator, Harland Ansel Minshew.

"It would appear that since, as I understand it . . . even walking fast, [it's] forty seconds from the mayor's office to the supervisor's office . . . and he was running . . . you are talking about perhaps half that time, twenty seconds total . . . I really don't think he was generating anger [toward] . . . Harvey Milk during that matter of really a few seconds."

Before he released Dr. Lunde, Norman sought to remind the jury that even the most authoritative psychiatrists were, after all, not just impartial scientists volunteering their services when they testified in court, but rather hired witnesses.

"Doctor, may I ask you what your fee is going to be in this case . . .?"

"It's an hourly rate . . . it will be fifty dollars an hour."

"How many hours do you have in this case?"

"A total?"

"Yes."

"Honestly, I don't know. But I will give you an estimate if you would like."

"Please."

"It probably falls between thirty and thirty-five hours. . . ."

"Thank you, Doctor," said Tommy Norman, who was feeling rather badly; he had gotten nowhere trying to discredit the psychiatrist, who had so much power in the arena within the glass.

"Any questions?" Judge Calcagno asked Doug Schmidt. He sounded weary.

"Just a couple."

"Let's get the couple."

"It will be very brief, I promise," Schmidt said. "Doctor, does your opinion depend on how much money you are paid?"

"No. I am paid for my time and not for my opinion."

"Doctor, we have been confusing a lot of terms here, and I just want to ask you . . . is . . . a killing for revenge . . . consistent with his personality and character?"

"Not at all."

"Now, there are first degrees of premeditation and deliberation, and murders by psychopaths?"

"Yes, contract killers, so forth."

"People who kill somebody and damn well think about it, plan it out, and kill somebody, and that happens?"

"Yes."

Dr. Lunde was excused and the psychiatric testimony for the defense was complete. Mary Ann sat with her palm against her cheek and her thumb, beneath her hair, slowly rubbing her neck. If the psychiatrists had contributed one thing above all others to saving her husband's neck it was this: they had offered a legally sturdy peg to any juror who wanted someplace to hang his sympathy.

16
Heart of the Matter

Good luck, Dan had said silently to his wife, and with the hands of the wall clock at sixteen minutes before 4 P.M., it became clear what he had meant.

"Your Honor," said Doug Schmidt, "I will call Mary Ann White to the stand." She stood. A bailiff opened the door in the security glass and Mary Ann stepped inside and walked toward the bench crying and dabbing at her eyes with a tissue. The jurors were riveted. As she sat down a second bailiff placed a red plastic cup of water in front of her.

Schmidt was on his feet behind the defense table. "Mrs. White, you are married to this man who sits to my right, is that correct?"

"Yes." Dan's months in jail had turned him a sickly pale green. Mary Ann was ashen, the color of a death watch.

"When did you first meet him?"

"I, I met h-him . . ." She was sobbing. When she had stood her height had been striking, but in the witness box, her small chin trembling, she seemed almost toylike.

The judge said, "If you want to take any time out, just let us know."

"I met him in April 1976," she said. An iron moth, Father Tom Lacey had called her.

Schmidt approached her. Softly, he said, "Now, Mrs. White, after you met Dan White, did you ever notice him to act in an unusual way, and if so, when and what did you notice?"

"Well," she said, sighing, "when I first met Danny, I think the thing that I was, the thing that attracted me most to him was . . . the vitality, energy, and the fact that he always had the ability to kind of inspire in you something that made you want to do your best, like he always did, and he was just so energetic, got along well with people, and made you feel good all the time." Her hands rolled her recalled excitement.

Before long, though, she said, she noticed that he was sometimes moody. "Then, I . . . tried to make myself believe and think, okay, and then we went out just, it was always so good, he was always trying to do things for you, and just like little surprises for you, and . . . just to be thoughtful, wanted to make you feel good . . . but these days would kind of recur, and of course then I was still thinking: it must be something *I* said. And this is when you are getting to know somebody, and he would reassure me: no, no, it wasn't anything you did."

"You eventually were married, were you not?"

"Yes." She was worrying the tissue in her large hands.

"And you took a trip?"

"Yes, we went to Ireland on our honeymoon, because Danny had been to Ireland. . . . He just had this feeling that Ireland was like a place that was just peaceful. He just really likes, *loves* everything about Ireland and so we, so we went there. For about five weeks. I guess."

"During that five-week period did you notice anything unusual about his behavior?"

"Yes. I mean, you know, when we went I thought . . . it was going to be kind of romantic, really nice, and when we got there, it was all of a sudden, he went into almost like a two-week-long mood, like I had seen before, but I had never seen one, I guess, all the way through. . . . He was real aloof, kind of withdrawn. I mean, I just was newly married, and I thought: what did *I* do?"

"Now," Schmidt said. "You were teaching school at that time, and he was a fireman?"

"Yes, I was."

"Did you later quit your job teaching?"

"I did, in May, the following year, after we had wed."

"I take it that was because you had a child?"

"Right, I had a baby in June."

"Did these down moods that you described kind of continue on through this period?"

"They were, all the time, from the time we got married . . . it was when he ran for the Board of Supervisors, in June, and I noticed then that he would kind of go, it was at that point that I stopped feeling personally responsible, and I thought: well, it's not me."

"During these times, when he would be home, how would he act? Could you describe for me, when he was in those moods he had?"

"He was just, be very withdrawn, withdraw himself from me, and anyone else. It would be where maybe he would get up in the morning and seem okay, and then all of a sudden he would just go in his room, close the door, never come out, and if I happened to go into the room to get something, he would never speak, and if I spoke to him he wouldn't answer."

"Now, after he was on the Board, did you notice these became more frequent, or any change in him?"

"Yes . . . when he took office he seemed to be very enthusiastic about the job. He wanted to do the best job he could . . . and then, as he went down to the board meetings, they just seemed to drain him. He would not come back, on Monday, until two o'clock in the morning, three o'clock in the morning, and would come home from these board meetings just exhausted, and so about March, all of a sudden, he started going into these real kind of down periods, and they would last for maybe a week, and then he would seem to come out, and then say, 'Well, I'll be okay. I can pull myself together.' And then he would go out, one day, try and run, and I would think, well now, I'll get myself started again . . . I would want to cook him a decent meal, and he just wasn't interested, and it just got worse."

"Let me ask you this: did he sleep with you during this period of time, toward the end?"

"Well, not toward the end at all, no." Mary Ann hung her head, her Clairol-ad-perfect hair momentarily obscuring her pale, small face. "I mean, it just went from, you know, where we would be sleeping together, and pretty soon, gradually less and less, and pretty soon toward November not at all, and he would be gone."

Aparicio, the door rattler, and Darlene Benton were both leaning forward, rapt.

"And there came a time when he resigned from the Board, is that right?"

"Yes."

"In November. Did he consult with you beforehand?"

"Not about going down to resign. He had talked to me about how hard the job was on him . . . and different times, when, you know, we could . . ." She choked back a sob. "Obviously you can sense when you are not sleeping together, when you are just like two people living in a house, when you are not really growing together, and once in a while we would talk about it . . . And I said: it's just him, he's not satisfied with what I'm doing, and I don't like myself, and so I can't—" The tears overcame her again and she cried.

When she had regained her composure Schmidt had Mary Ann describe Dan's relief at quitting, the effort to regain his job, her departure for Omaha the day after Thanksgiving.

"When you returned on the twenty-sixth, how was Dan at that time?"

"Well, it was like he was just very, you know, just kind of blah. I came home and, of course, was ready to tell him about everything that had happened, and I just remember going up the stairs and, and I opened the door and he was in the living room, or standing there, and he just kind of, it was like, you know, like you usually hug each other and give each other a kiss, and he just kind of stood there . . .

"He just kind of walked through the house and went out, and went out to the bedroom and was lying on the bed then, watching television. So I went in. Tried to start to tell him about what, I could see he was very uninterested, so I just stopped."

"On the night of the twenty-sixth, did you sleep together?"

"No."

"Did you see him the next morning?"

"Yes, I did."

"And at that time did he indicate what he was going to do that day?"

"It was just, he was going to stay home. He wasn't leaving the house."

"You took the car?"

"I took the car."

"How many cars do you have?"

"One."

"Then did you go to your potato stand?"

"Yes."

"After that, did you receive a call from your husband?"

"Yes, I did."

"And did he ask you to meet him somewhere?"

"Yes, he did."

"Where did you meet him?"

"I took a cab and went to Saint Mary's Cathedral."

"And did he tell you what had happened?"

"Yes. He, when I went and I saw him and he walked over toward me, and I, and I could tell he was crying. Well, when I talked to him on the phone I knew he had been crying, and I could tell by his voice. Then when he walked over toward me I could see that he had been crying, and I, I just kind of looked at him and he just looked at me and he said, he said: 'I shot the mayor and Harvey.' "

"Now, after that time did you go with him down to Northern Station?"

"Yes, I did."

"And he turned himself in, is that right?"

"Yes."

"I have nothing further. Thanks," Schmidt said.

"I don't think I have any questions," said Norman.

"All right," said Judge Calcagno. "Are there any additional witnesses today?"

The defense, a Quaker funeral for a living corpse, was at its end. "No, Your Honor. In fact, we are prepared to rest at this time. . . ." Doug Schmidt's jaw was clenched, and as sometimes happened, his hair had fallen slightly over his forehead.

17
Moms

Thursday night, May 10, the moon was full and the city beneath its sway. The skyline was sharply etched in the pale light, and the road lamps gaily strung along the causeways made the bridges glitter like jeweled bracelets; it was as if the city itself were a gaudy piece of jewelry and the bridges its slender links to the dark rolling density of the continent hunkering to the north and east. Its beauty made San Francisco a dance hall belle, a place not so very distantly removed from the days of the Barbary Coast. Of course sailors were no longer shanghaied in dark waterfront alleys patrolled by constables with long knives under their Bobby's coats; they were rolled by thugs in the employ of certain North Beach and Tenderloin entrepreneurs. The city was still a bawdy place, in a raw, open Western way, from Eighteenth and Castro to the barkers outside the strip joints on Broadway, to the discreet and elegant brothels of Twin Peaks and Pacific Heights. It had been seventy-three years since the earth had shivered and cracked and the burst gas mains had sent the buildings up in flames. After that they had revised the building codes and ever since, the absence of decorations on tall buildings and the *give* engineered into the structural steel had made San Francisco a city with a built-in anticipation of disaster. And disasters, of course, still occurred.

There was a certain luminous frenzy on Thursday night. Doug Schmidt had said that society had nothing to do with what happened in that courtroom, but that was the lawyer speaking. The man, whose parents had come to town from Alpina in time to see the last few days of their son's big case, could not help but understand that there was more to it than that. Because the city was on trial. And not in the melodramatic sense that the newsweeklies or the Eastern dailies talked about, that sense in which if Chicago were synonymous with heft and New York with theft or deft, San Francisco was just another way of saying bizarre. Not that at all. The people who had lived there long enough or were thoughtful enough to understand what had happened to their town, the people who had witnessed the dislocations of the past decades and the bitterness, those who understood the passions of every kind represented by the electoral victories of George Moscone and Harvey Milk and Dan White, those who understood that the political struggle had for a time been a struggle over morality, those who saw that Dan White's crimes were as intrinsic to their hometown as was the cross on Mount Davidson being eclipsed by the communications tower, those were the people who understood the sense in which their city was on trial. *Vengeance is mine,* Dan's gun had said, or so it seemed to many San Franciscans. And now his act was being judged, not by whatever passion or reason any one person or the mob might think, but under the rule of law: *the act itself isn't sufficient.*

On Thursday afternoon, and Thursday night in the light of the full moon, and Friday morning, everywhere you went you heard bits and snatches of conversation about what was happening in the windowless courtroom with its artificially bright light and its fishbowl-green security glass. In restaurants and cafes, in office elevators and markets, on buses and in bars and taxicabs, everywhere people were talking about the trial of Dan White. What they knew of it they had learned from television news or the newspapers, and the limitations (of time and space and attitude) imposed upon those media being what they are, the people of the city knew only the tiniest portion of what was going on in the courtroom. Knew enough so that the big billboard near the junction of two midtown freeways that proclaimed HOME OF TWINKIES had already become an ironic landmark. Knew enough to suspect that the verses being written by the city's poets were frighteningly near to the truth:

> White Knight. White Hope.
> White Man's Burden.
> White Bread. White Sugar.
> Blue Collar. Red Blood.
> White Wash!

* * *

Tommy Norman was already in his office at 7:45 when his phone rang. The call was from Supervisor Carol Ruth Silver. She had read in the *Chronicle* that the trial was about to end, and from what she had been reading in the newspapers the whole thing sounded outrageous.

She suggested that Norman call some people from City Hall to testify that Dan hadn't exhibited any crazy behavior. Norman said that sounded like a good idea. Carol Ruth spent part of the day rounding up potential witnesses, and when she and the prosecutor talked again in the evening he asked if she would be willing to come down and testify herself when prosecution rebuttal continued on Monday.

"Sure," she said. "But I'm not the best person because I was so close to Harvey." But she agreed to the subpoena nonetheless.

"Doctor," Tommy Norman asked Roland Levy, who had a high dome and big dark-framed eyeglasses, "is there any opinion based upon your experience of many years, any value, or any significant value, of having a psychiatric examination or consultation of a subject near the time of the occurrence?"

"It would," said Levy. "In my opinion the closest you can get to the time of the occurrence the better you can make that particular assessment as to the mental status which existed at the time of the offense.

". . . it's rare that I have had the chance to make an assessment that close to the time, and usually it's a matter of weeks, if not months later, and when you see a person early the tendency is for a secondary type of fabrication not to develop, and that you have a chance to see a more pure form of what the individual's status is."

"Doctor, oftentimes, is it not a fact that some people tend to rationalize certain types of behavior, and as time goes by the accuracy of that type of behavior tends to diminish, doesn't it?"

"It's a normal state of events, yes."

"At that time, initially, what were your impressions of Mr. White? That is, did he appear to be alert, did he appear to be oriented to time and place, what he was there for?"

"Yes, he was completely oriented." Dr. Levy pulled the cuff of his shirt a little farther beyond the sleeve of his well-tailored suit. "His intellectual functions were quite intact."

"Doctor, up to that point, was there anything to suggest to you that the defendant was suffering from any mental disorder on the day of November twenty-seventh?"

"There was nothing in my interview which would suggest to me there was any mental disorder."

"Doctor, what does depression mean to a psychiatrist?"

"Depression means a number of things. Depression may be a symptom. It could be a normal reaction to a situation. It may be an abnormal reaction, in a form of neurosis where the individual is developing depression out of some type of internal conflict, or it may be a psychotic state. . . .

"I found him to be less depressed than I would have expected him to be," Dr. Levy said.

"Now, Doctor, can a person be depressed and not have mental illness?"

"Oh, yes."

"Well now, Doctor, in this particular case, having the concept of malice in mind, Doctor, did you feel that the defendant was precluded by anything including mental disease or disorder, from whatever source, from forming that quality of thought which we understand in our law as malice?"

"Well, in terms of the capacity to *form* malice I found nothing that would indicate a lack of such capacity."

"Doctor, did you feel or did you see anything which suggested that he could not premeditate, that is, to plan ahead . . .?"

"I felt that he had the capacity to premeditate."

"With respect to deliberate, do you feel that he was able to form or arrive at a course of conduct weighing considerations?"

"To that extent, I felt he had that capacity, yes."

"I think that will be all," Norman said.

Schmidt had not thought too highly, to say the least, of Tommy Norman's cross-examination of the psychiatric witnesses for the defense—he had not even elicited the psychiatric commonplace that depression is the turning inward of anger one has forbidden oneself to express—and as he rose now to take Dr. Levy to task he was prepared to give the older, more pompous attorney a lesson in how it was done.

As their son stepped forward, Doug's mom and his dad, who had operated a tractor franchise until his retirement, could not help but beam proudly.

From his first questions, Schmidt seemed driven by a ferocity he

had not displayed before. "You currently are a staff psychiatrist
. . . at Langley Porter Institute?" he asked Levy.

"Yes."

"Are you a full professor . . .?"

"No. I am an associate clinical professor."

"Uh huh. May I inquire of your age, sir?"

"I'm fifty-five."

Schmidt wrapped his arms around his chest and paused for a beat.
Rather old to be an *associate* professor.

"And, as I understand your testimony, that psychiatric evaluation
occurred on the evening of November twenty-seventh, about seven
o'clock?"

"Yes, about seven o'clock."

"Would you say that Mr. White's emotional state at about seven
o'clock was approximately what it would have been at about, say,
noon?"

"I can only say that it didn't seem much different than what I
could ascertain from the tape."

"From the tape *you* would ascertain that emotionally he was
thoroughly well together and appeared to be intact with his affect?"

"Yes."

"As I understand it, you saw Dan White just once?"

"Yes. It was just the one interview."

"That was about two hours?"

"A little beyond two hours."

"Did you ever contact me with regard to other information that
possibly could be provided with regard to this action?"

"No, I did not."

The questions were coming fast now, fast and flat.

"Did you ever make a request of me that you talk to Dan White
on any other occasion?"

"No."

"Now, Doctor," Schmidt said, looking at some papers in his hand,
"would you feel that 'information obtained from witnesses such as his
aide or people in the mayor's office might be useful in getting a more
complete picture with regard to his emotional state just prior to the
offenses'?"

"I think," said Levy, "any information that could be obtained
could be *potentially* useful."

"In fact," Schmidt said, "that's a quotation from your report?"

"Yes."

"And in fact you did not gather that information, did you?"

"I didn't get it myself."

"Did you ever talk to the aide?"

"No. I talked to no one related to Mr. White."

Schmidt's voice was shaking with anger. "You didn't talk to any of the family members?"

"No, I did not."

"You didn't talk to *anyone* that might have known him and known of his past history?"

"No."

". . . you indicated that you concluded that he was in the same basic mental condition at the time you saw him as when he made the taped statement to the police?"

"His mental condition substantially was the same, yes."

"And I believe you stated that he was calm while he talked to you? Relatively calm?"

"For the most part, yes."

"All right. He wasn't particularly upset?"

"Not during the time I saw him."

"Now, Doctor, if I suggested to you that police and other witnesses have testified that upon observing Dan White shortly after the shootings he was shattered, shocked, appeared to be a broken or shattered man, emotionally and physically, I think *you* would disagree with that, is that fair?"

"No, I wouldn't disagree with that."

"And yet you maintained he was calm and not upset at the time you saw him?"

"By the time I saw him he was calm, yes." At the moment the doctor did not seem entirely calm himself.

"I see," Schmidt said. "Huh. But I thought you also said that he was in the same state, mental condition, as he was at the time that the police officers had seen him?"

"You mean when he was first seen? No, what I am describing is the way I heard it on the tape."

"Your explanation of *that* is that he was calm and not upset?" Schmidt turned his broad back on Dr. Levy and faced the jury.

"He certainly was not as calm as when I saw him, but I wouldn't describe him as distraught and shattered, as he appeared on the tape."

"I *see.*" Schmidt folded his arms across his chest and turned back to the witness.

"I can only go by what I heard," Levy said. "I didn't see him."

"I understand. So would it be your suggestion now that he was not in the same mental state at the time he made the tape as when you saw him?"

"No, I would say he was in essentially the same mental state, but his *emotional* reaction was certainly more pronounced on the tape than when I saw him."

"Would you agree that emotions play some part in one's mental state?"

"Emotions are not part of mental state, but they are certainly close."

"Certainly," Schmidt said, "they affect mental state?"

"Each affects the other, yes," sighed the psychiatrist.

Every time Schmidt turned or paced he had been favoring a leg, and now Judge Calcagno took judicial notice. "If you desire to sit down, Mr. Schmidt, you may."

"Perhaps I should," Schmidt said. He had racked up the knee and not been able to run or lift weights in a while. "I am really not feeling too well."

"Okay," said the judge as Schmidt, limping slightly, sat down at the table with Dan and Steve Scherr and continued his questioning. Before long he asked, "Now, Doctor Levy, I believe you mentioned you read the testimony of the various doctors that testified . . . Doctor Delman . . . Doctor Lunde . . . Doctor Solmon and Doctor Blinder?"

"Yes."

"That testimony did not cause you to change any of your opinions, is that fair?"

"That's fair, yes."

"Do you disagree, then, with the testimony of those . . . doctors?"

"Objection," said Tom Norman. "In what regard? It's vague in its form." As Tom Norman's arch singsong registered his objection it seemed a reminder that not once during the trial had Schmidt objected. *I intend to present all the facts.*

"Sustained," said the judge.

"Do you agree—it *is* vague," Schmidt said. "Do you agree, or do you disagree, rather, with regard to their diagnosis of a mental illness suffered by Dan White?"

"Well, they didn't all diagnose a mental illness, or they didn't all diagnose the same mental illness," Levy said. "I am not sure what you're referring to."

"I think Doctor Lunde and Doctor Solmon . . . and Doctor Delman all suggested that Dan White was suffering from a major mental illness, depression . . ."

Levy said, "Well, you mean to assume that is true? Because that's not the way I recall reading it."

Schmidt explained, and Levy agreed, to distinguish between small *d* depression and the capital *D* mental illness, Depression.

"Now," said the lawyer, who was back on his feet, "turning to the morning of November twenty-seventh, which is of course the time that we are going to have to deal with here. What would be your estimate of the degree of depression Mr. White was laboring under?"

". . . I would call it moderate."

"If the other doctors suggested that it was severe, then your statement would be just, in difference to theirs, it would be just a matter of degree, is that accurate?"

". . . it would seem to be, yes."

"Now, Doctor, assuming that a patient came to you, anyone came to you—this is a hypothetical situation—and he suggested that he had suicidal thoughts, weight increase, change in diet, sleep difficulty, loss of energy, loss of interest in usual pleasures, decrease in sex drive, and indecisiveness, would you then suggest that person was mentally ill?"

"It would seem to me he was having symptoms which would suggest he was having mental illness, yes."

"And that mental illness would be depression?"

"It's one possibility, yes."

"Now, adding to that: if your patient was a man of ordinary good character and he had inexplicably killed two persons, would you assume he was mentally ill?"

"I would have to know much more about that than just that statement."

"Precisely," said the lawyer. "You would have to know whether or not he had suicidal thoughts, weight increase, changes in appetite, sleep difficulty and have a complete history, isn't that correct?"

Whatever Levy's answer was, it seemed to disappear under the masterful tone of Schmidt's question. Schmidt, obviously hot, didn't let up.

"Now, doctor, you testified to certain forensic conclusions and you did write a report which was provided to me?"

"Yes."

"Do you recall, it appears you wrote that report on November twenty-seventh, 1978. Is that accurate?"

"No. The dates on my reports are always the date that I see the individual, not the date that I wrote them."

Schmidt looked at the report he was holding. "Doctor, your report is dated November twenty-seventh, 1978, is it not?"

"Yes."

"And yet the report was not *written* on November twenty-seventh, 1978?"

"I am quite sure it wasn't."

"Well, when *was* it written?"

"I don't know. It would have been within several days of that time."

"And then it was *dated* November twenty-seventh, 1978?"

"Yes," said Levy, apparently relieved to be understood at last.

"Oh," said Schmidt. "Well, regardless of the *backdating,* or whatever, when did you come to your conclusions, your forensic conclusions?"

"I'd say the conclusions would have been on November twenty-seventh."

"And that was after a two-hour talk with Dan White?"

"Yes."

"Doctor, would it be fair to say you made some snap decisions?"

"*I* don't believe I did."

"Now, I don't mean to be facetious, but this *is* a fairly important case, is that fair?"

"I would certainly think so, yes."

". . . In the report itself, Doctor, you made a conclusion on November twenty-seventh, regardless of when you wrote your report. In the report itself it says, in fact I will read this: '. . . if you have any questions please get in touch with me. I am sure that there are aspects of this defendant's life that were not touched upon in the interview. And should those seem significant areas, I would be happy to talk with him further.' You didn't talk with him further?"

"No, I was not requested to."

Tommy Norman knew there would be questions from the press

about *that*, and he had answers all ready: he would say, what would be the point of sending Levy back in now? Schmidt, after all, had had months in which to coach his client, and he wouldn't be worth a damn if he hadn't. White had had months to learn how to answer questions. Levy's whole value, Norman would say, was that he had seen Dan White before that happened.

"Well, in fact," Schmidt continued, "you didn't do a complete assessment, is that fair?"

"I would say it's not as complete as I would have done. . . ."

"Well, this was an important case, was it not?"

"Yes, it was."

"And yet you didn't do a complete assessment?"

"I was not asked to do a complete assessment."

"Now, you've testified that you thought you did a fairly adequate job . . . is that fair?"

"For the purpose of the report."

"The purpose of the report was to determine whether or not this was some sort of diminished capacity defense?"

"Yes."

"Diminished capacity relates to deliberation, does it not? The ability to and capacity to deliberate?"

"That is one of the factors."

"You didn't address that issue at all, did you?"

"I didn't include it in the report."

"I see. Now, would it be fair to say that mental illness, depression, might have an effect on the capacity to deliberate?"

"Yes."

"In fact, you have indicated in your forensic opinion that he had the capacity to premeditate largely because there was no reason to conclude to the contrary. In other words, it's the absence of information, is that fair?"

"That's right. The assumption is that people have these capacities unless you can demonstrate some reason why it should be impaired."

"Mental illness, if it were true, would be a reason, would it not?"

"It could be a reason, yes."

"Emotional turmoil could be a reason?"

"It could be."

"In fact, you have indicated that he, at least, was in an emotional turmoil at the time of the crimes, is that fair?"

"Yes, he was."

". . . would you define him to be a moral person, truthful person?"

"Yes, I would say: truthful, moral, honest, industrious, hard-working."

"Would it be fair to say that acting out of malice or with malice, it would be out of character for him?"

"He would have to be quite angry to act with malice, yes."

"In other words, he would have to have an aroused heat of passion?"

"He would have to be quite angry," Levy said stubbornly.

Schmidt was just about through. "Heat of passion is a legal term, of course. And if it produces any killing, then that is voluntary manslaughter?"

"It's one of the considerations, yes."

"No further questions," the defense lawyer said and sat back down, his knee throbbing.

On his brief recross Norman continued the same line of questioning Schmidt had ended with, taking it a step further, so that it was back over on the prosecution side of the line. "You have said and testified here that he felt angry, he felt betrayed. Do you feel humiliation was another emotion which was entertained by Mr. White?"

"Yes, I think that is a very strong emotion with him."

"Asked about his character, you said something about his killing in justification, or feeling justified. In this case, Doctor, you feel that he felt he was justified?"

"At the time I saw him it seemed that he did feel that it was justified."

"Thank you, Doctor Levy," Norman said.

Schmidt stood. "This is going to be very brief.

"Is there anywhere in your report, the report that was drafted sometime after November twenty-seventh but dated November twenty-seventh, did you say that he felt he was justified?"

"I don't think it's in there."

"I don't think it is *either,*" Schmidt said.

On the Friday evening news a television reporter sat with a flowerbed behind her. Mother's Day weekend, she said. Was that what the Dan White case was all about? Three bereaved mothers? Gina Moscone. Mary Ann White. Eileen McHugh. From the Hall of Justice, she said. The flowerbed was in front of the coroner's office.

When somebody suggested to the newsperson on Monday morning that perhaps she had laid it on a bit thick, she pointed at the jury. "Six mothers," she said. "What do you think *they* were thinking about Sunday?"

18
Persuasion

Carol Ruth Silver brought with her into the courtroom a whiff of the burning cordite atmosphere of City Hall politics. She had been testifying for just a few moments when Norman asked her if there had been "loud and perhaps hostile" exchanges during board debates between Dan and Harvey.

"Not loud," she said, "but very hostile." On the last full day of the trial the jury had finally been told for the first time that everything was not simply peachy between Dan and Harvey.

Norman asked her to explain and she began to describe a debate over the closing of Polk Street for Halloween. "However—and ultimately Dan White voted for it—but in the course of the debate—"

"Your Honor—" Schmidt was on his feet. "I object. First off it's inaccurate, probably. I don't think he did vote for it. Also—"

"I checked the record," Carol Ruth interjected smugly.

"Please," the judge admonished her. She had not been in the courtroom all along and she simply didn't appreciate how her bristling adamance jarred. "All right. Sustained."

When Schmidt's turn came to cross-examine he asked: "Did Mr. Norman contact you last week, or did you contact him?"

"On Friday morning I called his office because I was reading the newspaper—"

"*Don't* tell us," the judge said quickly. "The jurors are told not to read the newspaper. . . ."

"I apologize," she said unapologetically.

"In any event," Schmidt continued, "you contacted Mr. Norman, did you not?"

"Yes, I did."

"But to use your words, after having read what was in the paper you said that the defense sounded like 'bullshit' to you?" How had Schmidt known that?

"That's correct."

"Miss Silver, you are part of the gay community also, are you?"

"Myself?"

"Yes."

She smiled. "You mean, am I gay?"

"Yes."

"No. I'm not."

It seemed that she had come and gone in a moment, a discordant note preferably forgotten. She had served only to demonstrate for the jurors the vituperation Dan had met at City Hall. And, perhaps, how desperately Tommy Norman was flailing on the eve of his final summation to the jury.

19
Adverting

"Both sides having rested in this case," Judge Calcagno said at nine o'clock on Tuesday morning, ". . . you may commence with your . . . argument, Mr. Norman."

The prosecutor stood, his notes and his transcripts spread before him on the table. "Argument, to me, ladies and gentlemen, seems to partake of a harangue, and I am certainly not going to visit that upon you. However, the signal purpose of a *summation* . . . is simply to indicate to you the reasons why it is believed by me that the charges in this particular case have been proved beyond a reasonable doubt and to a moral certainty, which is all that is required by the law."

His hip cocked, his left hand resting on the table while he held his half-frames in his right hand, Norman began to recapitulate the evidence. It took him fifty-five minutes to reach his first significant conclusion: that, in his estimation, Dan White had "executed, and I use the word advisedly," his victims. Fifty-five minutes during which he explained the legal elements of murder, pored over the testimonies of a medic and a criminologist and the coroner and the photographs to make the uncontested point that George Moscone and Harvey Milk had indeed been killed; fifty-five minutes during which he left not a detail unreviewed ("Cyr Copertini . . . explained her job, what she does, where her desk is located"), during which he again and again demonstrated that Dan White had been sentient enough to walk and talk and open doors on November twenty-seventh; fifty-five minutes that seemed to prove nothing so much as the pedestrian lengths of his step-by-step mind. And he was just beginning.

While he talked, his boss, District Attorney Joe Freitas, who had reappeared in the courtroom, glared at the jury in a display of bad form.

And having finally said that the victims had been executed, Norman hurried on and the fifty-five minutes became as but a moment. One by one he reviewed the testimony of nearly every witness. He was not delivering a harangue but a filibuster. On the far side of the glass the reporters and spectators were whispering and doodling.

Over the taped statement he paused. "It's a tearful, it's an emotional interview. I don't think, members of the jury, that there was a one of us who was not reasonably moved by it and its emotional impact. And we all feel, naturally, a certain sympathy for others who find themselves in a rather serious, unpleasant, unfortunate plight.

"However, members of the jury, be mindful of the fact that through the defendant's conscious, willful, deliberate act which he undertook himself, that he removed from George Moscone and from Harvey Milk irretrievably their most valuable possessions that they had in this world. Their respective lives. And he removed their lives and snatched it away from them in this very violent fashion when they were offering no threat to him. They weren't attacking him. They were unarmed. They were defenseless. And, members of the jury, he acted by giving each one of them the shots in the head, giving the coup de grace shots, as they are called."

And then he was off again; once again he was *adverting,* because Tommy Norman hardly ever *mentioned* anything, nor *referred,* nor *called attention,* he adverted. It was his verb of choice, and yet he misspoke himself, because when Norman adverted he did not in fact make glancing reference. He adverted to the testimony of a half dozen of Dan's character witnesses and all that adverting consumed another hour and in the end the point was always the same: these people were the friends and family of Dan White. Could they be trusted?

He did more than advert to Denise Apcar. He read the jury eleven pages of her testimony. Eleven pages.

Just before lunchtime, when he had been talking for close to three hours, he said: "It was Harvey Milk whom the defendant regarded as working against him . . . to prevent his appointment to the Board. It was George Moscone who had promised he would appoint him to the Board, and then George Moscone reneged on that promise, and that was not nice to do, that was no doubt bad to do. But, members of the jury, we don't redress those wrongs by going up to the mayor's office and going to the supervisor's office and dispatching them with a couple of body shots, and giving them the coup de grace to the head.

"That does little to separate us from the jungle."

After lunch the prosecutor began to consider the testimony of the psychiatrists. Their opinions, he said, were not chiseled in stone. "Doctor Lunde didn't feel the defendant was expressing a whole lot of anger. Of course, on the other hand, as you recall, Doctor Solmon substantially disagreed with him on that one point."

He noted that Dan White had brought on his own dilemma, that nobody had forced him to quit. It was a strong point and it led him toward his conclusions.

"Ladies and gentlemen, the facts here, as I have outlined them, and as the record appears to support, amply and clearly [compel] us to the conclusion that the defendant, while he was an intense man, while he was no doubt a good man, and while he wanted to do something for his constituents, something for society, he was well motivated; however, rather precipitously, for reasons best known to him, he submitted a resignation . . . then he changed his mind . . .

". . . it was he who brought the gun to City Hall. . . . It was he who brought the extra cartridges. . . . He went to City Hall . . . there was a metal detector . . . he knew that he was carrying a gun, he knew that he had extra cartridges for it. Instead of going through the door, being in the state of mind that he was in, he went around the corner. He was capable, at that time, of expressing anger. He was capable of, according to the doctor—well, parenthetically, members of the jury, I don't know how they can look in your head and tell you what you are able to say . . . he went through a window. . . . He appeared . . . to act calmly . . .

". . . in order to shoot the mayor twice in the head, he had to even lean down to do it. He reloaded the gun somewhere . . . wherever he reloaded the gun, he did reload it." Several of the jurors were looking at him with what seemed a mixture of disappointment and incredulity: was he not going to tell them where the reloading had taken place? Because that was crucial in determining whether Harvey Milk's death had been manslaughter or murder. If he had reloaded in the mayor's office then that seemed to support the defense theory that he had done so out of instinct. But if he had reloaded in his own office or any place else, before he called Harvey in, that seemed to indicate a plan, an intention to use the gun again.

"Members of the jury, it escapes me as to what you can ascribe to this other than a premeditated, deliberated murder . . . This amounts to two executions . . . you should find him guilty of murder in the first degree two times. For George Moscone. And for Harvey Milk.

"Thank you very much."

He had spoken and he had adverted for nearly four hours, and he had been unforgivably dull. He had bored the jury, you could see it in their faces, heavy with the effort of concentrating. Yet they took their responsibility seriously—how many people would not, with a man's life at stake?—and so there was a far more grievous fault in Norman's summation, in Norman's case. It lacked a motive. In his heart, Norman knew how patently untrue was the claim that the defendant's acts had been no more than momentary aberrations, quirks of a disturbed psyche. If ever a killer had acted in a personal and historical context it was Daniel James White, so Norman believed. It had been Norman's job to make clear that context for the jury. And without a context, without a believable motive, without a demonstration of malice, they could not find Dan White guilty of murder. Never once in four hours had Tommy Norman said: revenge.

20
Please, God

"Ladies and gentlemen," Doug Schmidt began, and his voice was trembling, "I want to start off by saying that I am nervous, very nervous, and I hope that I say all the right things. . . ." Wearing a brown three-piece suit, like the one Dan had worn on November 27, he stood at a lectern that had been brought into the courtroom and placed squarely in front of the jury.

"I think that on several occasions Mr. Norman has suggested something that I believe was misleading, and I will not use the word dishonest, but he suggested that because a man can walk, talk and isn't slobbering at the mouth, can use a key to open a door, that he can materially and meaningfully weigh and reflect upon the gravity of an act like killing somebody. And don't misunderstand me, I never want to make light of what happened at City Hall, because it was a terrible, terrible tragedy. No question about that."

His hands were outstretched, the long, suprisingly delicate fingers spread in a gesture of supplication. "I don't say to you to forgive Dan White, let Dan White walk out of this courtroom a free man. . . . He is guilty, and the degree of responsibility is the issue here . . . and the judge will instruct you fully and properly on the law."

Calcagno was, in fact, working over his instructions to the jury with a red pen as the lawyer spoke.

"I am conceding," Schmidt continued, in his appealing yet disingenuous way, "that I am not much of an arguer, because I can't marshal words together, talk the way Mr. Norman can talk . . . but I do believe very much in things. . . .

"The whole issue, the whole issue was the mental state. It's not as to who was killed—*why* were they killed? It's not who killed them, but why. And for that reason, because it's such an important case, I felt: my God, where can I turn to, what kind of information can I get?

"I know common sense tells me . . . one thing, that he is a good man, a man with a fine background, who doesn't cold-bloodedly and calculatingly go down and execute two people as Mr. Norman would have you believe. That just doesn't happen. There was something wrong with that man.

"Now, as to psychiatrists, they are not auto mechanics" —as indeed juror George Connor was— "who put spark plugs in a car, if that is the trouble. . . . It's not a perfect science. . . . But I said: something happened to this man . . . the doctors have got to give you some input . . .

"I said: well, we have got to have people look at him, got to have them tell me so that I can perhaps in some way stumble through it, and tell you what happened.

"I said: . . . just come in and look at him and tell me honestly what you think." Schmidt was making his appeal to the jury personal, as Dan had taken politics personally. But what had been a fatal weakness in the client was a strength in his lawyer because it gave him conviction. "That is the attitude I took with all these psychiatrists, because common sense again told me that there was something wrong here."

Dan had turned his head slightly to the right and was looking at his lawyer and nodding, ever so slightly. Schmidt was saying that the psychiatrists had all agreed, Dan suffered from a mental illness, depression. "These depressions, or these moods, which extend back for ten years. My God, they are there." The young lawyer's voice was hoarse with emotion.

"Not for a minute do I ever want you to think that we are saying this was justified or excusable homicide. . . . I want to differentiate where I feel this case lies . . . voluntary manslaughter is the killing that occurs unlawfully, intentionally . . . but the killing is not accompanied . . . with malice aforethought. Malice aforethought cannot be there for two reasons. One, that the person's capacity is diminished . . . or two, [he] acts under a heat of passion.

"There are a couple of things I have to mention in regards to heat of passion. First off, one has to be provoked to have his passion rise in him." Provocation such as would make an ordinarily reasonable man act irrationally, he explained.

"Taking that into account, you can consider the circumstances that Dan White was in at the time, his mental and emotional condition at the time. But Lord God, nobody can say that the things that happened to him days or weeks preceding wouldn't make a reasonable and ordinary man at least mad, angry in some way.

"Surely, surely, that had to have arisen. Not to kill. Not to *kill.* Just to be mad, to act irrationally. Because if you kill when you are angry or under the heat of passion, if you kill then the law will punish you. And you will be punished by God. God will punish you."

His voice wavering, Schmidt thrust his index finger skyward, presumably toward that white-bearded, benevolent figure whom Frank Falzon had identified as the Man Above. ". . . And my God, that is what happened, at the very least."

The lectern at which Schmidt was standing, that he had brought into the courtroom especially for his summation and placed in front of the jury so that he could address these good, conventional, God-fearing people, suddenly it wasn't a lectern at all. By some illusory magic it had become a pulpit. A pulpit from which Schmidt would invoke the name of God twenty-one times before he was finished. And never mind that he hadn't been to church himself since he was a boy; no juror knew that, it didn't signify.

"My God," he said, ". . . if there *is* an intent to kill, and I think there is a very grave doubt, [even then it's] got to be voluntary manslaughter . . . I say that to you honestly." Schmidt was rocking gently back and forth as he stood at his illusory pulpit, almost like a rabbi at prayer. Was it possible, was it conceivable that even this was planned, planned perhaps for Mintzer, the Jewish jury foreman? No, that degree of cunning is beyond belief, even for Schmidt. Yet so rigorously and minutely calculated was the defense that the question did occur. For the devout there was God, and for the tenderhearted there was Mary Ann. For the mechanic there were sparkplugs and for those who were unfamiliar with guns, or afraid of them:

"You would ask, why would he take the extra shells? Well—"—he looked around the courtroom—"Why do the bailiffs carry extra bullets? And all of them have extra bullets on all their belts, and bullets go in guns. It makes sense to me. I'm not much of a gun guy, but it makes sense to me."

Schmidt turned his attention to Dr. Levy. ". . . I don't want to become personal about this," he said. "He wasn't asked to do a complete job? My God, this was important . . . it shook this city. . . . It frightened all of us because we thought: my God, what could have happened to this guy?

"Doctor Levy says that he saw no signs or symptoms of depression. . . . One, he was having a chronic sleep problem . . . that's a symptom of depression. He wasn't sleeping with his wife. From that I think you can infer that his sex drive was down. That's a symptom of depression. Two."

You could as readily say, of course, that those were features of his condition. But it was the power of the psychiatrist in the courtroom to define terms.

"Now," Schmidt said in his earthy twang, "reasonable doubt is another concept, and I have to mention it to you. And this is another concept that sometimes I have a little trouble with. But I will make it as clear as I possibly can . . . if you have *some* doubt as to whether or not he was able to harbor malice either from heat of passion reasons or diminished capacity reasons, then you have a duty to resolve that doubt in favor of Dan White, giving him the benefit of that doubt and finding him guilty of that great crime of voluntary manslaughter . . . the reasonable doubt standard relates only to that. The degree. The degree of responsibility. . . . And in case you have any doubts on the higher degree, then our law says find him guilty of the lower degree."

Schmidt paused. He looked at the jurors. "Then we played those tapes. . . . My God, that was not a person that was calm and collected and cool and able to weigh things out. It just wasn't. That tape just— just totally fogged me up the first time I heard it. It was a man that was, as Frank Falzon said, broken, shattered. This was not the Dan White that everybody had known. Something happened to him and he snapped. . . . The pot boiled over here, and people that boil over in that fashion, they tell the truth. . . .

"Have the tape played again if you can't remember what was said. He said in no uncertain terms: my God, why did I do these things? What made me do this? How on earth could I have done this? I didn't intend to do this. I didn't intend to hurt anybody. My God, what happened to me? Why?" Dan, of course, had not asked those questions. He had done no more than wonder out loud about his motives.

". . . Now. I don't know what more I can say. And believe me, if I had words that could convince you of what I'm saying, I'd say them. I'd say them. I'd *beg* you." His voice shaking, Schmidt turned his outstretched palms up. "I would do anything at this point to try and convince you of what I am saying. . . . He's got to be punished and he will be punished. He's going to have to live with that for the rest of his life. His child will live with it and his family will live with it, and God will punish him, and the law will punish him, and they will punish him severely.

"But please. Please. Just justice. That's all. Just justice here."

Tommy Norman, sitting just a few feet away, heard the emotion throbbing in his adversary, and looked up from the notes he had been taking. Doug Schmidt was crying. And as Norman and the jury watched the tears welling and spilling, the prosecutor got the abiding feeling that Doug Schmidt believed in what he was saying. Believed it every bit as devoutly as five months earlier Dan had believed that George Moscone and Harvey Milk had ruined and killed everything he had to live for. In this, too, the defense lawyer and his client were alike: if they tried hard and were sincere, didn't that mean that they were *right?*

Schmidt bowed his head. "Thank you for listening to me," he said. It had been a magnificent performance, he had been every bit the advocate he possibly could be. And in the end he had given the jury something comforting to hold onto during their deliberations. In their sequestration, in the obsessive isolation of their lives since they had left everything else behind and become the conscience of their community, into whatever gloom this intimate immersion in the mind and the acts of Dan White had cast each of them, he had given them an excuse. A legally justified excuse. They did not have to submit themselves to the horror of confronting and judging cold and nameless passions. God willing, they could choose to believe.

It had taken him exactly one minute less than one hour.

21

Verdict

On Sunday morning, May 20, at the start of the fifth day of their deliberations, eight of the jurors went to church.

After early mass they returned to the jury room and just after lunch they sent a note to the judge telling him they wanted to rehear the testimony of Dr. Martin Blinder. Schmidt and Scherr considered that a good sign. Twice previously, on Thursday and then again on Saturday, the jury had asked to be reinstructed, and both times the foreman Mintzer had seemed to pay particular attention to the law covering irresistible impulse. Darlene Benton had wanted to know more about the question of provocation. Each time they filed back into the courtroom to have the instructions reread to them by the court clerk the jurors had looked wearier and more emotional, but Benton had looked the worst. There were dark circles under her puffy eyes, and she sat shielding them with a hand, as if the bright lights were intrusively irritating.

Every time the jurors reheard the instructions, the defense lawyers were encouraged, although Scherr admitted that they were so long and complex that after enough repetitions they began to sound contradictory even to the men who had drafted them. Charging the jury on Wednesday, Judge Calcagno had incorporated the key modifications requested by the defense. One of the most important of these was based in part on a case called *People* v. *Logan*. It read:

> The law does not undertake to limit or define the kinds of

passion which may cause a person to act rashly. Such passions as desperation, humiliation, resentment, anger, fear, or rage, or any other high wrought emotion . . . can be sufficient to reduce the killings to manslaughter so long as they are sufficient to obscure the reason and render the average man likely to act rashly.

In deciding *People* v. *Logan* the court had added a caveat which the defense lawyers did not include in their proposed modification:

For the fundamental of the inquiry is whether or not the defendant's reason was, at the time of his act, so disturbed or obscured by some passion—not necessarily fear and *never, of course, the passion for revenge. . . .*

It was up to the prosecutor to suggest the additional modification, and Tommy Norman had not done that. Nor had he asked Judge Calcagno to incorporate in his charge to the jury a "cooling off" provision, the usual language of which instructed:

The killing must be *upon* a sudden quarrel or heat of passion, i.e., suddenly as a response to the provocation and not belatedly as revenge or punishment.

So when on Sunday afternoon the jury asked to rehear Dr. Blinder's testimony, including his assertion that Dan had been in a heat of passion, they received it in the context of only a single theory of the law governing their decision—the defense theory.

The press room in the Hall of Justice was right beside the offices of the district attorney, and from time to time during the long wait for a verdict Norman would pop in and pick up the latest scuttlebutt, and, of course, subject himself to questions from the reporters, who themselves were consulting a ouija board.

"When did you prove beyond a reasonable doubt that it was murder in the first degree?" Norman was asked.

"That's a good question," he said. "The whole case."

"Okay. Did you prove beyond a reasonable doubt that Dan White strapped on that gun to kill them?"

"No," Norman said. "I don't think so."

The reporters kicked around a lot of ideas about the trial. A law-'n'-order type like Dan White, it was often pointed out, would have hollered for a death penalty in a case like this one if his own neck hadn't been on the chopping block. George and Harvey, as everybody knew, had been against capital punishment. A columnist for a weekly summed up the defense in one short line: "They had it coming, and besides, he couldn't help himself." The reporters said that if Dan had been a poor black man his defense would have been laughed out of the courtroom. And one idea that gained a lot of currency during the verdict wait was that prejudice against homosexuals being what it is, White would have stood a lot more chance of being convicted of first-degree murder if he had only killed Moscone. Although, of course, based on the circumstances the case for first degree was stronger on Milk: the gun had been loaded when White had strapped it on to go see George, this reasoning ran, and there may have been a quarrel, whereas he had had to reload before he got Harvey.

By Sunday the jury had reached a verdict in the killing of George Moscone, although it wasn't announced. They had decided that the act was voluntary manslaughter. That had been on Friday. Now they were considering Harvey Milk's death. The jurors, they would later say, never once gave serious thought to a first-degree verdict in either killing. They agreed with Tommy Norman's assessment of his own case.

Norman was having dinner with some friends and one of them teased him by saying that when he turned around in the courtroom he swished.

Somebody else asked him what was taking the jury so long.

"They're trying to decide if *I'm* gay," he said, and rolled his eyes. It got a good laugh.

Cleve Jones was a young man who had worked for Harvey Milk in the months before his death, and several times during the wait he came around to talk with whichever reporters would listen.

He had seen and heard, he said, a rising rage in the gay community. The Briggs amendment had been frightening, and Harvey's assassination horrifying, he said, but if Dan White was convicted of manslaughter, that would be enraging. There would be a riot. He didn't mention that the notion did not entirely displease him. He had been saying the same thing to the police brass, but they didn't heed him. Their attitude was; Be serious; pansies riot?

The reaction in the press room was for the most part similar.

The district attorney, Joe Freitas, whose political career was on the line and whose political considerations had colored the thinking of the prosecution, spent Sunday evening on Alcatraz Island, where, as the *Chronicle* reported on its society and women's pages (called "People" in deference to contemporary sensibilities), "the foreboding prison rang with laughter when S.F. law enforcement wiggled around to a disco beat."

The occasion was a benefit preview of fall fashions from designers such as Pierre Cardin and Ralph Lauren, with the proceeds going to the Police Athletic League. Freitas was something of a clothes horse himself. He was a foppish man who sometimes draped a white silk scarf around the shoulders of his suit. The D.A. did not serve as a model, though he was certainly handsome enough, but as a commentator on the fashions.

"I'll probably buy a few myself," he said toward the end of the evening.

The jurors, meanwhile, had asked the judge to release them from their deliberations at 4:45. But Calcagno had asked them to keep working. At six Mintzer sent a note to Judge Calcagno: "Judge: May we retire now? Seven people have headaches and we are extremely tired."

Sunday night, too, Doug Schmidt watched a televised rerun of the John Wayne classic, *Stagecoach*. Schmidt loved the old westerns in which a lone man stood up to the forces of evil and emerged triumphant. When it came right down to it, it was not the tragedy of which he had hinted in his opening statement that was his favorite dramatic form, but heroic melodrama.

Monday afternoon Scherr, Schmidt and a couple of reporters were in the basement cafeteria. Did it bother him ever, Schmidt was asked, when he had helped a client get away with something?

"I'm not talking about this case, of course," he said, "but I've defended people who've gotten away with murder." His blue eyes twinkled behind their rimless glasses and he laughed at his own little joke.

About an hour later the jury sent word to Judge Calcagno that it had reached its verdicts. Almost at once the courtroom began to fill up. Freitas, Norman and Falzon were together when they were told a verdict was coming. Relations between Norman and Falzon were still testy. It was cocktail hour when the phone call came. They stood up, Freitas popped a couple of mints into his mouth, and they went down to Department 21.

Just behind the courtroom was a holding cell. Dan had been brought down from the jail and was waiting there for his lawyers to join him before he went to hear what would be done with him. He had sat in court day after day listening to himself be described by people who had known him all his life and by people who hardly knew him at all; to his lawyers and the psychiatrists they had hired he was a moral man undone by mental illness and overcome by a heat of passion. To the prosecutor and his psychiatrist he was an executioner who had felt justified in killing. That was the nature of the adversary system of deciding what was just: both sides presented not a portrait of a man but a case. And the two cases were not in fact incompatible, except inside the glass.

And then, too, as Dan had said to Ray Sloan and Denise Apcar in the Irish Embassy: "Nobody knows what goes on inside me."

In his opening statement to the jury, Doug Schmidt had described his client as a man without much insight about himself, and it was certainly true that nobody would ever know just what exactly Dan had been thinking when he strapped on his gun and took his extra bullets and went down to City Hall. Perhaps even he didn't know any longer. He was a man accustomed to hiding his feelings—his effort of will in sitting virtually motionless and expressionless at his trial was the most extraordinary example of this—and it was a good bet that he had hidden his truest feelings from himself, as well as from everybody else. If he had ever consciously wanted to murder George and Harvey, he no longer knew that; the thought had gone far away, beyond where conscious knowledge exists. All that his lawyers or the psychiatrists really knew of Dan White was what he had told them. In a sense his defense had been his own creation (that novel he had always wanted to write?) and it was as precisely truthful as he was able to be with himself. In the gray concrete holding cell was a smudged mirror in which he could study himself, if he wished to. Did he see a martyr? Or a man who had hidden his self-justification in order to save his neck, a coward who had murdered two unarmed men?

When the lawyers came into the cell he thanked them for all they had done. Just before they walked into the courtroom to face the jury, Dan—the team captain—cautioned them not to show any emotion if the verdict was good, not to slap each other on the back, or smile, or anything like that, in effect to maintain those poses which had seemed to work so far.

The jury filed in looking drained, depleted. All except for Aparicio, the door rattler who had been the last juror empaneled. Aparicio had the face of an overgrown boy, one of those men who never matures, just grows older. In contrast to the other jurors at this climactic moment, he was ruddy, vibrant. As he walked past the defense table he smiled broadly and rapped on it with his knuckles. Seeing that triumphant gesture, Tommy Norman felt that maybe something was wrong.

Mary Ann was taking deep, hyperventilated breaths.

"Mister Foreman," asked the judge, "has the jury reached verdicts in this case?"

Mintzer stood. "Yes, it has, Your Honor." He handed the written verdicts to a bailiff who gave them to Calcagno. The judge read them silently, showing no reaction, then handed them to the clerk to be read aloud.

"We, the jury," began the clerk, ". . . find the defendant guilty of the crime of voluntary manslaughter in the death of George Moscone. . . ." Schmidt released his breath in a sudden, relieved but silent whistle. Dan looked down, blinking. By the time the clerk had read the second verdict, voluntary manslaughter for Harvey Milk, there were tears in Schmidt's eyes. Dan didn't stir but Mary Ann was sobbing and hugging his mother. Darlene Benton and Grayce Jackson were crying too. Grayce gave a timid little wave in the direction of Mary Ann. The judge was saying, "The people of San Francisco owe you a debt of gratitude," and telling the jurors they could go home. They began to file out. Aparicio crossed the room and pumped Schmidt's hand.

In the corridor outside the courtroom there was a crush of reporters and cameramen and technicians holding their lights aloft waiting to question the lawyers. Tommy Norman said very little. He looked ill. White faced a maximum sentence of seven and two-thirds years; with time already served and time off for good behavior he would be free in less than five years. Freitas did most of the talking. His office had blown the case, and with it perhaps his future in politics, and he put the blame on the jurors. With the glare of the television lights on him he stared off above the heads of his inquisitors. "I think the jury was taken in by the whole emotional aspect of this trial."

Tommy Norman went back to his office and had a few drinks and then a few more. He felt sick with the nausea of failure and disappointment. It did not seem to him then that he would ever recover. He was told that some of the press was suggesting that he had lost the case because he had been oversure, arrogant.

"I don't think I've ever been arrogant in my life," he said. "I was deferential to all the witnesses. I was even deferential to the defendant." In the end it was the things he hadn't said which told the most. "I could have referred to him"—and he growled with emotion— "as this animal, this scum. But I never did."

22

The Glass Shatters

The explosive splintering report of the first window in City Hall to be destroyed by a rock hurled from within the seething crowd sent shivers along the spine.

"Ooooooh," the crowd sighed. "Oooooh," as a second window shattered. It was dark, there was no moon. The grand green dome was awash in it own arc lights, a reassuring symbol of stability and order and justice.

"Ooooooh."

The brightly lit trial had been a nightmare in which reality never ran fast enough to keep its desperate appointment within the glass. Here at City Hall dark had cloaked the anguished, furious, frightened crowd, restlessly shifting and surging, and made of it a mob. Another window shattered. Dan's demons were at large again.

"Ooooooh." Like a beast with a single voice.

Radio and television stations interrupted their regular programming beginning at 5:30 for bulletins about the verdict. On a live radio hookup, Cleve Jones said: "This means that in America it's all right to kill faggots." The police band radio also announced the verdicts and somebody began to sing:

> Oh Danny boy
> The pipes, the pipes are calling

> 'Tis you, 'tis you must go
> And I must bide . . .

The meaning of the verdict was like a text, subject to interpretation. To some cops at least it said: it's okay to kick candyass. To most gays it said: man's laughter. Harry Britt, who had been chosen to fill Harvey's seat on the Board, called the verdict "obscene" and the jury "insane." Mayor Feinstein spoke at a press conference: "As far as I'm concerned these were two murders. . . . I think it's important that this town pull itself together again. We've gone through a physical bloodbath and now we are going through a mental one."

A crowd was just beginning to gather at Market and Castro when the mayor left City Hall and drove home. She ate lambchops for supper. At six, the supervisors recessed their regular Monday-night meeting to take their dinner break. Nobody was really worried about what would happen if the homosexuals and lesbians marched on City Hall. The night of the assassinations perhaps thirty thousand people had walked solemnly down Market Street to City Hall in a candlelight parade. Joan Baez had sung "Swing Low, Sweet Chariot" a cappella. It had been peaceful, cathartic. If it happened again, all the better. Police Chief Gain had not issued any alert, the day shift had gone home, mostly to the suburbs. Nobody had heeded Cleve Jones's warnings. Sissies didn't riot.

At 6:30, Jones—slight, handsome, livid—was standing on Castro Street speaking through a bullhorn. "He was convicted of manslaughter, what you get for hit and run. It wasn't manslaughter. I was there that day at City Hall. I saw what the violence did. It was murder. I suggest," he shouted, "we get our gay brothers and sisters out of the bars and into the streets."

> Out of the bars and into the streets
> Out of the bars and into the streets

The chant was taken up. The crowd, perhaps five hundred people, began to march.

> Dan White was a cop
> Dan White was a cop

and

> Join us!
> Join us!

Out of the bars and into the streets

As it marched the crowd swelled. The evening erupted with the shrill call of hundreds of silverplated police whistles. A drummer marched at the head of the parade playing a solitary dirge.

About eight o'clock, when there was still a dusky light, hundreds and then thousands of people reached the Polk Street steps of City Hall. While they were unfurling a long red-on-white banner that read STOP ATTACKS ON LESBIANS AND GAY MEN, a lone baby-blue police car hurried up to the curb and a single cop emerged and ran into the building. The supervisors were just returning from dinner. At his office in the Hall of Justice Chief Gain was mobilizing men from the station houses and dispatching them to City Hall. Damn few were available. Finally Gain went down there himself to set up a command post on the corner of McAllister Street, between the plaza and City Hall.

A new chant was taken up:

> *Dan White*
> *Hit man for the New Right*

The whistles screamed their angry terror-stricken warning.

Norman and Freitas were at a restaurant in North Beach. Tommy was drinking vodka on the rocks. He had the awful certainty that the verdict was destined to be his albatross. Freitas was trying to console him.

Dianne Feinstein was heading back to City Hall with her fiancé, Richard Blum, driven in her limo by Gary Wommack.

Doug Schmidt and Steve Scherr were watching the news on television, their jobs done. Much later, when Scherr went to sleep, he put a gun beside his bed. It was the first time in his life he had ever done that.

As soon as it was dark the first rocks began to fly.

"Ooooooh." The shattering glass set loose the beast that crowds harbor. Men began to pry and twist parking meters until they were uprooted. News vending boxes were overturned, trash cans seized. A thin line of policemen, perhaps a dozen in all, had taken up stations in front of the doors. Several steps below them a line of gay men and women joined arms and faced the mob, placing themselves between its simmering ferocity and the triple glass doors of City Hall, with their ornate metal grillwork. The mob kept surging forward. The policemen, their backs to the glass, were frightened. Rocks and bottles were lofted toward them, landing all around. The middle doors opened and cops brandishing nightsticks wedged out and covered the retreat of their fellow officers into the building. The whistles trilled and trilled.

A man in bluejeans and a denim jacket broke through the linked arms of the peacekeepers and seized hold of a length of grillwork, yanking at it frenziedly. Suddenly it broke loose and he stumbled, a spear in his hands. Other men ran forward and began to pry other stanchions loose. One of the peacekeepers tried to restrain the man with the spear, shouting at him. There was a momentary, swirling dispute until, in a fury, the man with the spear attacked the door. The sound of glass breaking triggered a huge roar. Again and again the man, now joined by others, attacked City Hall.

Inside, the police fell back. Behind the jagged edges of broken glass in the dimly lit interior you could see the metal detector.

> *Dan White was a cop*
> *Dan White was a cop*

and

> *Avenge Harvey Milk*
> *Avenge Harvey Milk*

A new chant was taken up. It began with a few voices, voices that were very nearly ironic, but swiftly turned deep, slow, murderous:

> *Kill Dan White*
> *Kill Dan White*

The police were itchy. City Hall was under attack. It was their duty to stop it. But Chief Gain wouldn't let them move. In uniform, his jaw like stone and his eyes blazing, he left the command post and went up to Dianne Feinstein's office on the second floor to consult with her. The mayor and the chief talked in the ceremonial office, where several windows had been broken and the carpet was dusted with shards of glass.

His overall objective, Gain explained, was to protect life and to minimize injuries to police officers, to the rioters, and to the many people outside who were deploring the violence, who had come to City Hall to bear witness. The chief told the mayor that he did not yet have the men available to disperse the crowd. From the window they could see that there were now as many as five thousand people roiling in the streets and the plaza. More police were being called in, he explained, but if they took on the mob now and failed to disperse it, the rioters might overrun City Hall.

The mayor urged him to take action, but left the tactical decisions in his control. It had crossed her mind that the verdict could be construed by madmen as a license to kill public officials.

The Board, meanwhile, had adjourned its meeting and Carol Ruth Silver had come to the mayor's outer office and wanted to go out on a balcony above the front door and the plaza. She was trying unsuccessfully to find a candle to hold aloft. A policeman handed her his Bic lighter and she went out on the balcony and tried to speak over the roar of the mob and the trill of the whistles. There was no bullhorn available but somebody finally found a little megaphone. When she held the lighter aloft there was a dull roar from below her. She began to say that it had been a sad day for all of them but that nothing should be done in the names of Harvey and George which would dishonor their memories. The crowd took up a chant:

> *Come down!*
> *Come down!*

"Is it safe?" she shouted down to the peacekeepers below her, their arms linked. The flame was burning her fingers.

"Yeah, you'll be okay," somebody said.

She went downstairs and tried to speak from the steps, but very few people heard her or cared to. The din was unremitting. After a while she went back upstairs and talked with the mayor. She tried to keep her tone formal, as befitted the circumstances.

"Madame Mayor," she said. "You should go out and talk to the crowd." She nodded toward the balcony.

Dianne said she wouldn't do that. "I would be a lightning rod," she said. She explained that she had sent to the army base at the Presidio and was waiting for the arrival of a loud hailer. The mayor was immobilized. She lacked the moral authority or perhaps the physical courage to expose herself. She knew she would not be heeded. There were only two San Francisco politicians who might have had a chance at restoring order, but George Moscone and Harvey Milk were not available.

At 9:30 a tree on the lawn north of the front doors was set on fire. The orange blaze cast flickering shadows on the facade of City Hall. Chief Gain was still holding back the men under his command, but he allowed a single wedge of cops, in riot helmets, their faces distorted by hard plastic shields, to drive toward the front steps from his command post on the corner. As they moved into the edge of the mob, rhythmically beating their riot sticks on their open palms as they tried to clear a path, they were met by a determined resistance. Men holding grillwork spears and parking meters and beer bottles faced off with the advancing police wedge. In the no-man's-land between the two forces a rangy, rawboned cop, his visor down, was half crouched with a club in his hand. With his other hand he was coaxing closer a giant of a man with a full beard and a burly chest. They circled each other in the glow of the burning tree.

"Oh, c'mon candyass," the cop was pleading, taunting, beckoning. "C'mon, c'mon, c'mon, candyass."

The big man's eyes were popping with rage. "Motherfuck, I'm gonna break your pig ass. Motherfuck. Motherfuck pig." Behind him the mob was chanting:

> *Dan White was a cop*
> *Dan White was a cop*

and surging toward the police wedge. The cops, badly outnumbered and finding that the mob would not back down, retreated toward the command post. Whistles howled. The mob jeered and taunted. Only something had shifted, it was no longer a mob exactly. What was happening was no longer a riot. It was a brawl. And for the moment the stronger force was the men from Eighteenth and Castro. And the women. Four women fell upon a female cop and beat her to the ground. She was screaming for help into her walkie-talkie. Finally she shrieked in pain. Her leg was broken.

Before the night was over 120 people would sustain injuries, about equal numbers of police and civilians. That was four times the number of people who would be arrested. A brawl, not a riot, not a police action, was in progress.

At the corner of Grove and Polk, across from the southeastern edge of City Hall, a police squad was surrounded by a howling circle of men closing in on them. One officer disobeyed his orders and in panic began to toss tear gas canisters. As soon as he did, men ran forward toward the smashed doors and windows of City Hall and began to lob canisters of their own into the building, as if softening it up for an assault. The canisters had been stolen from the long line of baby-blues lined up across from the McAllister Street side of the plaza. Neither the cops nor the rioters had gas masks. The riot squad, bunched up inside the building behind the metal detector, fell back to the open area beneath the rotunda. As the acrid, stinging gas spread, men in and out of uniform began to choke and gag. People leapt into the reflecting fountain, trying to wash their burning eyes.

> *Kill Dan White*
> *Kill Dan White*

The whistles shrieked. You could hear, too, the dangerous trill of frenzied, mad voices, like the cries in *Battle of Algiers.* Supervisor Harry Britt was talking with a reporter on the steps, where bottles and rocks were still landing. "Society," he said, "is going to have to deal with us not as nice little fairies who have hairdressing salons, but as people capable of this violence."

> *Hnugh!*
> *Hnugh!*
> *Hnugh!*

The sound was like a deep, bestial exhalation. The TAC squad had been unleashed and they were advancing on the front steps in a kind of crippled goosestep, dragging one foot behind, their batons held diagonally across their chests. And every lurching step, as broken glass crunched beneath their heels, they made that noise.

> *Hnugh!*
> *Hnugh!*
> *Hnugh!*

They started up the shallow steps, clearing everybody from their path. The peacekeepers, sitting on the steps with their arms linked, began to scream and shout as the batons fell on them with deep, sickening thuds. They ran and the police held the steps. They formed a line and faced the enraged, seething mass. But though the advance had been a tactical success, it was a strategic disaster. The cops on the steps were an easy target. Rocks and bottles and garbage can lids crashed at their feet and off their helmets.

> *Ooooooh!*

Their commanders would let them neither retreat into the building nor advance. Policemen were nearly crying with rage and frustration. Cops were shouting, "Let us go! Let us fucking go!" But Chief Gain was not ready. He was waiting for more men and an opening at the center of the mob. And the longer he held his men back, the more certain you could be of their viciousness when they were eventually turned loose.

Carol Ruth Silver was on the steps, too, talking with Chief Gain, when a rock caught her in the mouth and sent her sprawling to the ground, bleeding. She was carried upstairs to a couch in the anteroom of the Board Offices. The mayor, Richard Blum, and Gary Wommack were already sitting there; they had been driven away from the east side of City Hall by the tear gas streaming in through the broken windows. The mayor was on a couch, her head hanging, saying almost nothing, doing almost nothing. "This is awful," she said. "This is terrible. Something has to be done." Her face was drawn and there were deep, dark circles under her eyes.

After a while Carol Ruth was taken to a hospital to have her lip sewn up, and the entire party of officials returned to the mayor's office. One young woman with dark hair started out toward the balcony to get a better look. Alarmed, Dianne took her hand and pulled her back.

"Don't go out there," she said. "They'll think you're me."

But the young woman had seen something she could hardly believe. A police car, left in front of the building hours earlier by the first cop to arrive at City Hall, was on fire. A man in heavy Frye boots had kicked in a rear window, and then somebody had lifted a garbage can overhead and smashed the front windshield. There were warwhoops of delight from the swirling mass of men around the prowl car. A man ran up with a burning newspaper and tossed it through the shattered window. Thick plumes of gray smoke began to pour out of the wounded car and then a few tentative licks of oily orange flame and then a bright ball of heat and light. There was a wartime odor of burning rubber. As the car burned there were cries of "oink, oink," and the battle trill and the piercing whistles and then, starting with a low moan, the siren mechanism began to wail and keen like an ox at slaughter.

A moment later there came the urgent wail of a different siren, and a hook-and-ladder appeared on McAllister and tried to turn into Polk. But hundreds of men blocked its way, refusing to move. They were chanting:

Dan White was a fireman
Dan White was a fireman
Kill Dan White
Kill Dan White

Unable to pass or to turn, the firetruck began to back up past the command post, pursued by men heaving bottles and screaming, "We won. We won." The advance took the command post by surprise and it was overrun, the cops falling back under attack from rocks and chunks of concrete torn loose from benches in the plaza. Windows were now being smashed everywhere among the public buildings ringing the plaza. The cops regrouped and moved forward and retook the corner, but the cars they had left behind when they were driven back had all their windows smashed.

The streetfight was now ebbing and surging on many small battle-fronts, like amoebas beneath a microscope. City Hall was no longer under sustained attack. A big debris bin was set afire. Police radios on motorcycles spoke in an urgent voice: "Out of control! Out of control!"

Appearing like surreal visions came men and women in evening dress, in gowns and white silk scarves. They seemed like hallucinations drifting around the small, ferocious battles as the whistles screamed and the sirens keened. The PDQ Bach concert at the Opera House had ended and the audience was trying to make its way to their cars parked in the garage beneath the plaza. As the operagoers picked their way through the chaos, the police cars that had been lined up along McAllister Street and left unguarded fell under attack. Their windows were systematically kicked in and bashed with stanchions and each time a window shattered somebody ran up with a flaming torch and threw it through the jagged glass into the interior. One after another they went up until the entire line was lurid with flames, and as the heat reached a certain intensity, the sirens were set off, bleating their own death notices, until they, too were consumed.

In the ghastly light of the burning cars two slender young men stood kissing each other softly on the lips.

Chief Gain was with Mayor Feinstein in her office. The mayor again opportuned him to disperse the crowd. He stood in the shadows on the balcony. As the crowd surged toward the burning cars he saw his opening and issued his orders. Two hours after the first rock had shattered a window in City Hall, he directed his men to advance on all sides and disperse the crowd, to sweep the streets and the plaza.

Hnugh! Hnugh!
Hnugh! Hnugh!

Their goosestepping boots lifting and falling in double time, they crunched over broken glass. Released at long last, some cops stayed in formation but others, maddened with frustration and hurt and impotence, broke loose, clubbing and kicking everybody in their path. The sound of the trilling whistles became more distant as hundreds of men turned and ran until, finally, just before midnight, the plaza was quiet except for the intermittent crackling of police radios and the crunch of glass underfoot every time somebody moved.

Eleven police cars stood black and charred, silent witnesses to the exorcism of some demons. But not all.

The baby-blues descended on Castro Street with four cops in every car. Word of what was happening brought gays spilling out of the crowded bars to line the sidewalks. *"Go Home!* they chanted. *"Go Home!"* and *"Our Street! Our Street!"* A blue line began to sweep down the broad thoroughfare, ducking bottles lobbed from rooftops. A cop went berserk and charged into the chanting homosexuals on the sidewalk.

"Motherfucking faggots," he was screaming, as he thrashed and spun, laying waste. "Sick cocksuckers," he was wailing. Other policemen ran to back him up. In their wake men lay on the sidewalk beaten and bloody.

"We lost the battle of City Hall," said a tight-lipped police captain, "but we're not going to lose this one."

A couple of squads of cops hollering "Banzai!" rammed their way into one of the most crowded bars, panicking and stampeding the patrons who tried to squirm their way to safety as the cops beat and kicked them with a savagery bred of humiliation. Every cracked skull redeemed and asserted manhood.

It was after 2 A.M. when Chief Gain and Supervisor Britt met in the street and negotiated a withdrawal.

His face dripping sweat and distorted into a mask of mocking rage, a young man on the sidewalk screamed at Britt:

"Harvey wouldn't let this happen, Haaarry. If you got clout, Haaarry, let's see you use it!"

When Gain, pale and rockfaced, insisted his men pull back beyond Castro Street, a cop shouted at his back, "Coward fuck!"

By 3 A.M. the city was empty and exhausted. The Doggie Diner near City Hall, where Dan had called Mary Ann, stayed open all night, an oasis of light. Homeless men and insomniacs and a lone black streetwalker sat nursing cups of coffee. The enormous plaster dachshund with its frozen loonytunes smile surveyed the wreckage. On the whitewashed wall of the diner somebody had spray-painted a message in red that had dripped and run and dried.

It said: HE GOT AWAY WITH MURDER.

Dan was alone in his cell.

Riflemen were stationed on the roof of the Hall of Justice. Inmates on the tiers had been watching the riot reports on television, and the swollen din of the anchormen turned up to full volume was interrupted by shouts.

"You motherfucker, White!"

"You got away with it, you prick bastard!"

"Somebody gawn get you, white boy!"

The taunting was taken up by the crazies just around the corner from Dan's cell. Inmates were beating on their cell bars with anything they could find. It had kept up like that for hours when sometime around eleven o'clock Jane Halstead, the nurse, walked by Dan's cell. She looked in.

Dan was stretched out on his cot with the thin jail blanket pulled up so only his eyes and his pale, knotted forehead could be seen. The eyes were wide, frightened. My God, Jane thought, he looks like a terrified child. She stopped and stared at him.

Slowly Dan sat up, letting the blanket fall to his waist. He reached up and removed a pair of earplugs. Had he been using them at the trial?

"Jane," Dan said, "what is going *on* out there?"

You dead meat, pig, a prisoner howled.

Jane thought: what the hell is going on with *you?* You know. You know so much more than you say. It's time for someone to talk straight to this guy.

"People are taking to the streets," she said. "They're smashing windows and burning cop cars in front of City Hall. It's a riot."

Dan looked baffled. "Why?" he asked.

Jane wondered if he knew she was a lesbian. She didn't broadcast it but her hair was cropped short and she wore no makeup and carried herself in a way that was not exactly feminine. "Because they're really angry. They're angry about what they feel is the unjust verdict you got." She didn't hate him and she didn't say it harshly. She had decided that in a funny way he was really a softie.

"But," Dan said, "they had to see what happened at the trial. If they had listened, I mean, don't they understand all the pressure I was under? Didn't they listen to the trial?"

"You know, Dan, everyone in this jail is under pressure. Some of them, pressure you'll never know. You had privilege, you could have gotten help they never could. That's why they're so angry."

"Didn't it come out at, at the trial?" He was stammering. "I mean, it *did* come out. The pressure, you know . . ."

"Apparently it didn't."

Dan's eyes went blank. She watched him withdraw into himself, retreating from her words. Slowly he put the earplugs back in and lay down. Beside his bunk were books of Irish history and newspapers from Dublin. *A terrible beauty is born.* He pulled the blanket up under his eyes. He saw nothing, least of all that he was no martyr for a just cause. Charlie White had been a brave man but his son was a coward.

Author's Note

It was while covering Dan White's murder trial (for *Rolling Stone* and *Time* magazines, as well as writing opinion pieces for the *Los Angeles Times*) that I began to consider writing a book about the incident at San Francisco's City Hall on November 27, 1978. The trial became my obsession, a sharply etched recurring nightmare. So much that could and should have been said was not. The courtroom, for all that it was starkly lit, was a dark and awful place. Political and psychological passions were being suppressed, for reasons that were themselves political and psychological. i understood that passion had no place at a trial, which after all is a kind of societal prophylactic protecting us from vengeance. And yet the absence of passion, when it is so deeply felt in the blood of the acts, creates a pornographic atmosphere. The less we know, the more circumscribed our emotions, the more lurid things seem.

At first my guiding feeling was that Dan White was a reactionary punk, a man whose own much-invoked moral code should have prohibited him from hiding behind psychiatric doubletalk and his wife's heartbreaking tears. One moment it was easy to despise White's lawyer, Doug Schmidt, for being so cunning in such an unworthy cause, but the next it was impossible not to admire his cleverness in behalf of his client. I wanted the prosecutor to prove the case for first-degree murder and was dismayed by the ponderous ineptitude of Thomas Norman and contemptuous of the selfish, politically motivated trial strategy endorsed by his boss, District Attorney Joseph Freitas. In the final analysis, Dan White's light sentence was their failure. But as the trial proceeded, my anger, which had been severe enough to make me physically ill, gave way to a grudging acknowledgment of what a trial is and what it isn't. What I slowly came to see was that both lawyers' cases were partially valid and yet neither was entire of itself. Whatever had happened on November 27, 1978, was more subtle and more complex than would be revealed by the trial. Lawyers are paid to employ only as much of the truth as benefits their clients.

The trial ended. The law had triumphed over justice. I felt cheated, my curiosity wasn't satisfied. The city's leaders, and most of the rest of us, consigned the events at City Hall to a limbo of partially absorbed forgetfulness. Life went on. When what had happened was mentioned, it was usually with a murderous bitterness (in 1982 Supervisor Carol Ruth Silver told me that if she ever bumped into Dan White on a street corner, "I would kill him"), or else with a mocking glee by people who had hated Moscone and Milk as viscerally as White had ("Gina Moscone's better off with him dead," said an anonymous caller to a radio talk show). But most San Franciscans kept their own counsel. Mention White's name and a shamed, angry silence descends. No other single event of our time more acutely reflects the terrible divisions in our city, those divisions which the Chamber of Commerce and most of the politicians would paper over with civic-minded Babbittries.

White was sentenced to seven years, eight months in Soledad Prison for his two manslaughter convictions and related gun charges. With time off for good behavior (he has been a model prisoner and has received no psychiatric or psychological treatment), plus the time he served in city jail before and during his trial, he was due to be released on January 6, 1984. It is his hope to emigrate to Ireland. When he regained his freedom he was thirty-seven years old.

As the time for his release drew nearer there were several attempts to keep Dan White in prison. The Governor was asked to revoke White's parole; the U.S. Department of Justice was asked to prosecute him for violating the civil rights of Milk and Moscone. The newspapers speculated that he would be killed if he returned here. There was a steady drumbeat of stories. The fury provoked by his most perverse acts and his lenient sentence has in no way diminished. It lies just below the surface. Still and all, most people here in San Francisco choose to turn away from the memory. I could not. Understanding is no panacea, but it can be a bridge over which we can move forward. This book is my bridge.

I didn't begin to work on *Double Play* at once; other things kept me from it. As time went on there were occasional stories in the newspapers that brought back the pain of loss. George Moscone's widow Gina was awarded a pension and the story itemized the various benefits that had come to her and her children. The total was more than $700,000. It was a grim irony that because her husband had been slain she was financially secure for the first time in her life. Another story reported that a child had been born to Mary Ann White after a conjugal visit with her husband at Soledad. The newborn child was afflicted with Down's syndrome. Could bad karma be transmitted through the chromosomes?

I finally decided to write this book after being interviewed by Randy Shilts, who was researching a biography of Harvey Milk. As I answered his questions a beehive of thoughts and memories came swarming back and could no longer be avoided. As luck would have it, just a few days later I was called by Dianna Waggoner, who at that time was an editor for Addison-Wesley Publishing Company. She asked if I wanted to do a book for them. I did. I hope she feels that her dime was well spent.

In the course of conducting more than two hundred interviews, and while examining tens of thousands of pages of public and private documents (trial and hearing transcripts, psychiatric reports, minutes of Board of Supervisors meetings, newspaper coverage, personal diaries, police reports, and the like—many of which had not been available to any other investigator), I began to piece together the facts about the two dead men and their killer. White turned down my request for an interview, as he did all other interview requests. Once the trial was over his wife also stopped talking with me. Doug Schmidt cut off our conversations after he learned that I was writing a book. I was left with very little choice in my method. Because the principal characters in the drama were not available to be interviewed, I would have to work more like an historian than a reporter, interpreting rather than merely recording. I have taken every care to recreate events as faithfully and accurately as possible.

Gathering, checking, confirming, organizing and filing facts and recollections was a necessary first step. But making them add up to a story which revealed the truth about these three men and their city was, and had to be, a labor of informed inquiry.

Allow me your indulgence to describe my method in writing a single scene. On Thanksgiving morning, 1978—four days before he assassinated Mayor Moscone and Supervisor Milk—Dan White is to be found alone in his den, brooding, poring over some newspaper clippings. How, it might legitimately be asked, could I have known about what he did that morning, and how, in addition, could I have gauged his state of mind?

The explanation begins on the evening of the killings, when a search warrant for the White home at 150 Shawnee Avenue was issued by Municipal Court Judge Raymond Williamson to Homicide Inspector Frank Falzon. Several other detectives and representatives of the district attorney's office accompanied Falzon to the house. In the course of their search they took possession of some newspaper clippings piled on a little desk in White's basement den. Four years later, in the winter of 1982, I was granted permission to look at them.

One quiet Sunday morning Detective Earl Sanders, who had been along on the search, accompanied me to the property room in the basement of the Hall of Justice. He used a pocket knife to slit the official seals on the cardboard boxes of evidence, which had not been opened since they were sealed a few days after the killings. Inside were three lumpy packages done up with brown wrapping paper and tied off with twine. One held the clothes that George Moscone had been wearing when he was gunned down; a second, Harvey Milk's. Even after four years the odor of life—or was it death?—was still upon the stiff, blood-caked garments, a meaty, musty smell. The last package contained Dan White's suit and tie, his shirt and socks and belt and shoes. Everything except for the black leather belt was color-coordinated in shades of brown. The suit was a polyester-wool blend, poorly tailored, the best suit you can buy from a cheap department store. Miraculously, considering all the blood White had spilled, not one speck of it had touched him.

In one carton was the large manila envelope in which the clippings had been stored. Inspector Sanders slit open the envelope and we sat down to look through them. As I read each one and passed it to Earl Sanders I began to see a pattern in the news items that White had chosen to save: they were a running record of his losses and defeats at City Hall and of the triumphs of the two men he blamed for beating and humiliating him, Milk and Moscone. In the pile, as well, were a number of old, yellowed clips recording the moment of heroism in the life of Charlie White, Dan's father. Not a single item among the dozens in the envelope, however, recorded one of his own many victories or accomplishments.

As he was resealing and initialing the evidence cartons, Earl Sanders, who had been an ally and a personal friend of George Moscone, said out loud what I had been thinking: "That was one unhappy man."

What I had seen in the clippings (the last of them was from the morning paper on the day the scene is set) was augmented by police photographs of the basement den, by what I knew from my years of investigation and dozens of interviews regarding Dan White's relationship to his father and to some of the events depicted in the newspaper stories he had chosen to save, by his having told a psychiatrist that he had spent that morning puttering around his house, and by his wife's court testimony about White's mood on Thanksgiving Day. I talked with several people who had seen or spoken to him that day and asked each of them to assess his mood. Four different people described the room for me. Out of that evidence the scene was made. A similar method was employed throughout. The results speak for themselves.

At the courthouse I had spent a lot of time in the company of three other reporters, each of whom understood the trial differently. The trial was a dead-earnest drama, subject to as many interpretations as there are perspectives. To one reporter it was an acting out of the subtle interplay between psychiatry and the law. Another was watching a simulacrum of California mores: fast foods and instant gratifications. To the third it was a tale of discredited codes and failed machismo. I would like to thank them for the help their ideas have been: Nora Gallagher, Paul Krassner, and most especially Francis Moriarty, who has been a good friend to this book and its author.

Many, many people have helped and encouraged me. I can't possibly thank them all by name, but they know who they are and I want them to know as well how much I value what they have offered to me, even when it caused them personal difficulty and, in some cases, put them in jeopardy. Three of them who appear in the narrative have asked me not to use their names: the nurse "Jane Halstead," George Moscone's lover "Maisie Bright," and Alma de LaPantera. Some details surrounding all of them have been arranged to disguise their identities. I would also like to thank Larry Adelman, Maxine Brown, Darryl Cox, Frank Falzon, Goldie Judge, Jeffrey Klein, Arnie Pachter, Amy Rennert, Ray Sloan, Kevin Starr and Phil Tracy. The generosity of my parents was more than a son has a right to hope for. My own children,

Josh and Bessie, have been a source of pride and encouragement. Ashley Dunn and Jim Morgan assisted me with careful, diligent research. The Fund for Investigative Journalism provided me with a grant. Carole Rafferty gave more of herself to this book and its author than I can say, everything good in it is informed by her intelligence and concern.

Randy Shilts, whose book *The Mayor of Castro Street* is an indispensable tool for anyone wanting to know about the life and times of Harvey Milk, has shared his knowledge with me. Walter Bean's *Boss Ruef's San Francisco* and Chester Hartman's *Yerba Buena* are other books from which I have drawn.

Of course, no one mentioned here is in any way to blame for errors I may have inadvertently committed.

A while ago, at a wake in Dan White's old neighborhood, I met a man who had been visiting White in prison. He told me a story White had told him. The story was ominous, suggestive, a bit of bragging White had done to a friend that ultimately came to symbolize to me the impossibility of knowing just what White's intentions were when he strapped on his gun and went down to City Hall.

The inmates in the protective housing unit where White has been incarcerated are allowed into the exercise yard each afternoon when the other prisoners are kept away. Every day Dan White runs on the track. During his first few weeks at Soledad, only one other prisoner ran at the same time. White didn't know the other man's name but he admired his muscular physique. Day after day the two hard, silent men circled the lonely track in the late afternoon sunshine all by themselves. Finally, White introduced himself. The other runner was Sirhan Sirhan. They have become good friends.

Mike Weiss
San Francisco, 1983